ENTROPY ANALYSIS

An Introduction to Chemical Thermodynamics

ENTROPY ANALYSIS

An Introduction to Chemical Thermodynamics

Norman C. Craig

Oberlin College

Norman C. Craig
Department of Chemistry
Oberlin College
Kettering Hall
130 W. Lorain Street
Oberlin, OH 44074-1083

Library of Congress Cataloging-in-Publication Data

Craig, Norman C., 1931-
    Entropy analysis: an introduction to chemical thermodynamics/
 Norman C. Craig
        p.   cm.
    Includes bibliographical references and index.
    ISBN 1-56081-539-6 (hardcover). -- ISBN 1-56081-599-X (softcover)
    1. Entropy. 2. Thermodynamics. I. Title
 QC318.E57C73 1992
    541.3'69--dc20   92-2584
                                                                   CIP

Printed in the United States of America.
ISBN 1-56081-599-X VCH Publishers

Printing History:
10 9 8 7 6 5

Published jointly by:

VCH Publishers, Inc.	VCH Verlagsgesellschaft mbH	VCH Publishers (UK) Ltd
220 East 23rd Street	P.O. Box 10 11 61	8 Wellington Court
Suite 909	D-6940 Weinheim	Cambridge CB1 1HW
New York, NY 10010	Federal Republic of Germany	United Kingdom

Dedicated to

Ann, David, Mary, Julia and Mark

PREFACE

Although chemistry students may receive several exposures to the subject of thermodynamics during their undergraduate years, few of them become confident users of thermodynamic arguments to the same degree that they are users of orbital, spectroscopic, and structural arguments. Many students learn that, with the exception of a few standard formulas, thermodynamics is a subtle and complex subject that is best left to the experts. Students learn little about how to use approximations and about how to apply semiquantitative thermodynamic reasoning. Often, the mathematical apparatus of calculus obscures simple thermodynamic truths. Students learn the buzz words, especially *entropy*, but they do not understand the concepts behind them. Excessive reliance on the Gibbs energy function causes students to overlook the centrality of the entropy function as the index of chemical change. They do not learn how to recognize all of the entropy terms that contribute to the total entropy change; instead, they learn that enthalpy changes and entropy changes compete, despite the difference in their units.

The introduction to chemical thermodynamics presented in this text gives first and second year college students access to the fundamental concepts of thermodynamics and equips them to apply thermodynamic reasoning to many chemical systems. Most calculations are done at a level of reasonable approximation. An extensive table of thermodynamic data in Appendix D facilitates a wide range of applications. The laws of themodynamics are expressed in a universe-level ("global") point of view instead of the standard, system-level ("local") point of view. (See Appendix A for a reconciliation of the global and local formulations.) In the global formulation, the change in the energy *content* of each contributing system is monitored. This formulation avoids the subtle problems of heat and work being energy *transfer* terms rather than energy content terms.

The change in the total entropy is a natural expression in the global formulation. *Entropy analyses*, showing all the contributions to the total entropy change, are exemplified. The entropy function is investigated at the microscopic level through the use of the simple harmonic oscillator model and the cell model, initially with systems that are so small that the number of microstates can be counted. These are so-called "countable systems." Entropy as a measure of the dispersal of energy is emphasized. A useful distinction between *ordered* and *disordered* energy is developed in this context. Patterns in molar entropies are also explored at the macroscopic level. Through the global formulation of thermodynamics the entropy function comes naturally to the foreground. By contrast, in the standard, local formulation energy functions are in the foreground and entropy is in the background.

The treatment of thermodynamics in this text is experimentally robust as well as logically complete. The experimental basis for thermodynamic quantities is emphasized throughout. Thus, a laboratory program in thermodynamic measurements and applications is a desirable and natural accompaniment.

While developing this presentation of the global formulation of thermodynamics, the author has written many problems keyed to it. To illustrate and encourage the use of this method, many of these problems are included in the text. As a further encouragement to students, brief answers to most of the problems are given.

The chapters are organized to permit use of an abbreviated version of this text. Likely candidates for omission are Chapter 5 on the classical statements of the second law with applications to refrigerators and heat engines, Chapter 9 on electrochemistry, and Chapter 10 on energy conversions. The section in Chapter 7 illustrating a number of $\Delta_r H° - \Delta_r S°$ analyses is another candidate.

Although the author had studied thermodynamics at the graduate level, taught it, and used it in research, he did not get a satisfying grasp of the fundamentals until he encountered the global formulation and the emphasis on the centrality of the entropy function in Henry A. Bent's *The Second Law* (Oxford, 1965). The author knows from his own experience that adapting to the global formulation and entropy-rich treatment of thermodynamics takes a retraining effort by an instructor. The rewards, however, are great for the instructor and especially for the students. The goal is to give students the confidence to analyze processes thermodynamically and not merely to be manipulators of equations.

The author is indebted not only to *The Second Law* but also to Henry Bent himself for many fruitful exchanges. He is also indebted to his chemistry colleagues Martin Ackermann, Terry Carlton, Richard Schoonmaker, and Harry Spencer, and to his chemistry students at Oberlin for stimulating the development of the material in this text for use as an introduction to thermodynamics. He is grateful to Martha Lermond, who has played a crucial role in producing the camera-ready manuscript. Timothy Bean and Alice Smith were of great assistance in preparing the table of thermodynamic data. The material has also been used in a AAAS Chautauqua course for college teachers, in a Woodrow Wilson-Dreyfus summer course for high school teachers, and in a series of lectures in China.

Oberlin, OH 44074 Norman C. Craig

CONTENTS

1. · INTRODUCTION

Thermodynamics, the science of energy transactions, provides the means to evaluate chemical change. In doing so, thermodynamics is concerned with the *quality* of the energy gained or lost as well as with the *quantity* of energy transferred between the parts of an overall system. Thus, the thermal energy associated with a water bath is qualitatively different, in the sense of usefulness, from the energy supplied by an electrical battery. All of the energy supplied by a battery can be used to run an electric motor. Only a fraction of the energy supplied by the water bath can be used to do so and, then, only if a second water bath at a lower temperature also receives some energy.

In thermodynamics an important function, called the *entropy* function and symbolized with S, characterizes the quality of energy in a system. The name "entropy" comes from the Greek meaning "change in." The entropy function, which tells about change, clearly applies to chemistry, the science of the transformation of matter. Entropy tells whether or not a proposed process, such as a chemical reaction, is possible and where the process comes to equilibrium. Thus, we shall develop the entropy function fully and make extensive use of it.

The outcome of a chemical reaction is commonly summarized by an equilibrium constant expression. For example, for the dissociation of acetic acid in water, the chemical equation is

$$HOAc(aq) \rightleftharpoons H^+(aq) + OAc^-(aq)$$

and the corresponding equilibrium constant expression is

$$K = \frac{[H^+][OAc^-]}{[HOAc]} \tag{1.1}$$

Thermodynamic relationships provide the justification for the general algebraic formulation of all equilibrium constant expressions. Thermodynamics also provides the means for calculating the numerical value of an equilibrium constant without a direct investigation of the particular reaction. Developing such relationships with the aid of the entropy function is a major objective of our presentation.

Usually, the numerical data for thermodynamic relationships come from tabulations such as the one in Appendix D. A glance at this appendix reveals that the functions $Hf°$, $Gf°$, and $S°$ are tabulated for various chemical species, where H is an energy function called *enthalpy* and G is called the *Gibbs energy*. If we can show from thermodynamic reasoning that $\Delta_r G° = \Delta_r H° - T\Delta_r S°$ and $\Delta_r G° = -RT \ln K$, then we have the means of obtaining a numerical value for an equilibrium constant, K, as described in the previous paragraph. We can obtain K from $\Delta_r G°$ or from $\Delta_r H° - T\Delta_r S°$. Furthermore, we can find how K varies with temperature.

To provide an understanding of the entropy function and ways of using it, we shall investigate its connection to the microscopic world of atoms and molecules. Often, it is said that "entropy measures disorder." The disorder that entropy measures is the extent to which energy has been dispersed over the various motions of atoms and molecules. Dispersed energy is less useful than is energy concentrated in a single form. The concept is analogous to the difference in usefulness of two forms of money. An amount of money in a bank account is a concentrated, ordered, highly useful form of money for a big project. This money has low entropy. The same amount of money dispersed to many people as dollar bills and coins is a dilute, disordered, less useful form of money for a big project. This money has high entropy. When a community decides to buy a big ticket item like a fire truck, the money in the bank account is much more useful. The odds of gathering the dispersed, high-entropy money from the populace for such a purchase are very low. Similarly, the odds of gathering a quantity of energy from the dispersed form in a water bath are low compared to receiving energy in a concentrated form from an electrical system.

In our development of thermodynamics, we shall include a consideration of electrochemical cells, which are important energy convertors. Under optimal conditions an electrochemical cell converts chemical energy efficiently into electrical energy at constant temperature. Conversely, in electrolysis, electrical energy is converted into chemical energy for storage in a cell. We shall also find that the voltage of an electrochemical cell is a direct measure of the Gibbs free energy, $-\Delta_r G°$, which appeared in the preceding equations. Also, we shall see that the voltage of a cell may be a useful and specific measure of the concentration of a chemical species, such as the hydronium ion (expressed as pH), even at very low concentrations.

Although we shall derive the important thermodynamic relationships, we shall stress applications. In doing so, we will not hesitate to use approximations that make it possible to understand various types of change and to predict qualitatively outcomes of particular chemical reactions. For more precise analyses of chemical change we will employ the comprehensive table of thermodynamic data in Appendix D. By stressing applications to actual chemical systems, we intend to demonstrate the simple and widespread applicability of thermodynamics to chemistry.

We close this introduction with two pieces of advice to you, the student. One concerns restraint in learning equations; the other concerns diligence in drawing diagrams of thermodynamic systems. Essential algebraic expressions are placed in boxes in this text. You should become thoroughly familiar with these expressions and any limitations on their uses. Other expressions, which can be derived from these fundamental ones, need not—indeed should not—be learned. Rather, you should develop the skill of deriving these more specific expressions from the fundamental ones as needed.

The text contains many diagrams of the essentials of overall thermodynamic systems. A set of symbols is introduced to identify each type of system that contributes to the overall system. Using such diagrams and symbols is a great aid to doing thermodynamic analyses. You are urged to become proficient at sketching such diagrams.

2. ENERGY PRINCIPLE: THE FIRST LAW

We begin by presenting the first law of thermodynamics and developing some of its immediate consequences. The first law is an energy conservation principle for the transformations of energy. To use the first law, we must have concrete, experimentally based expressions for evaluating some energy changes. Such expressions are developed in this chapter for the change in energy with height of a mass in a gravitational field and for the change in energy with temperature of a water bath or similar body. A direct application of these two expressions is made to the analysis of the Joule experiment, in which mechanical energy is transformed completely into thermal energy. For the important case of constant pressure of the atmosphere applied to a chemical system, a common occurrence in chemistry, the energy change for the weight system is reexpressed in pressure–volume variables.

The First Law (Energy Principle)

The first law asserts that the total energy of an *overall system* or *universe* does not change even though changes may occur in the different forms of energy in the distinct parts of the overall system. The first law is often summarized by saying energy is conserved. Energy may be in the form of thermal energy (heat-like), mechanical energy, chemical energy, electrical energy, or light energy, to name the most important types. Familiar transformations between these forms of energy are

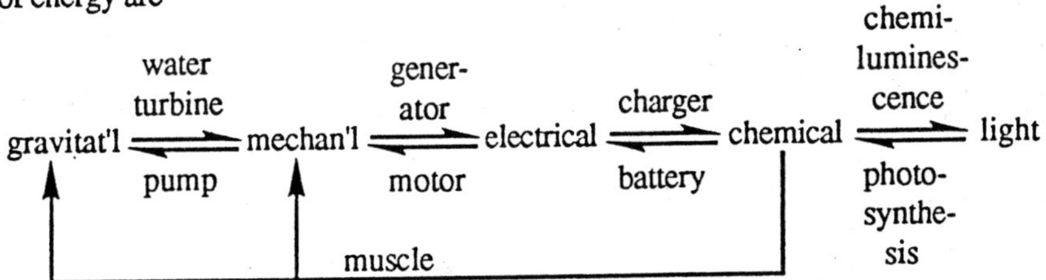

Gravitational energy is a special form of mechanical energy. In principle, all of the energy conversions shown in the scheme may occur in either direction with high efficiency.

When thermal energy is involved, however, we find a one-wayness in energy conversions. Electrical and mechanical energies can be transformed completely into thermal energy, but the inverse transformations are not possible from thermal energy at a single temperature.

$$\text{electrical} \xrightarrow{\text{resistor}} \begin{array}{c} \text{thermal energy} \\ \text{(single temperature)} \end{array} \xleftarrow{\text{friction}} \text{mechanical}$$

The limitations on the conversion of thermal energy into other forms of energy are central to the second law of thermodynamics.

To analyze energy transformations we divide an overall system into its energy-distinct parts. For many applications in chemistry it is sufficient to recognize three parts:

> *Reactive system*, σ — that part upon which we focus our attention, usually the chemical reaction. σ is sigma, the Greek letter corresponding to s.
>
> *Thermal reservoir*, θ — a large reservoir, such as a water bath, that is in good contact with σ and that exchanges energy with σ by conduction; often called a *heat bath*. θ is theta, the Greek letter corresponding to th.
>
> *A weight (mass in a gravitational field)*, wt — the weight is mechanically linked to the reactive system and may be supplemented with or replaced by other *potential energy reservoirs*.

Figure 2.1 is a schematic diagram of such an overall system. Typically the thermal reservoir is a large water bath that surrounds the reactive system, which can be the contents of an open beaker. The weight is usually the weight of the column of the atmosphere in the earth's gravitational field. This column of the atmosphere is the one that rests on the surface of the reactive system. When we speak of the "universe of an event" or simply the "universe," we mean all of the parts in which energy changes take place.

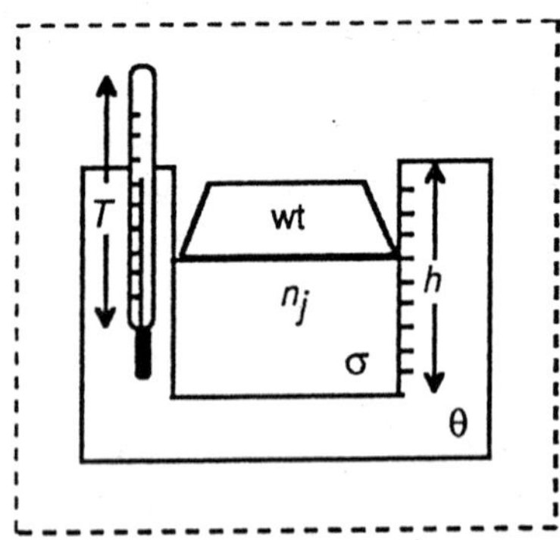

Figure 2.1. Prototype thermodynamic system. σ, reactive system; θ, thermal reservoir; wt, weight system. n_j is the number of moles of a reactant or product, T is the temperature of θ, and h is the height of the wt. The dashed line surrounds the overall system.

When we give equal attention to all the parts of the overall system or universe, as we do in Fig. 2.1 and throughout this text, we call this the *global point of view*.

The first law is expressed by an equation and by the properties of various energy functions. U is the symbol for energy. Thus,

First Law of Thermodynamics

$$\Delta U_{\text{total}} = \Delta U_\sigma + \Delta U_\theta + \Delta U_{\text{wt}} + \dots = 0$$
where $U_\sigma, U_\theta, U_{\text{wt}}$ are independently
state functions, and U_σ is an extensive function

(2.1)

ΔU means a finite change in the function U or $\Delta U = U_f - U_i$, where U_f is the energy of the *final* state and U_i is the energy of the *initial* state. The "..." allow for possible energy changes in addition to those in a reactive system (σ), a thermal reservoir (θ), and a weight (wt). In some applications related to the second law of thermodynamics we shall include terms for two thermal reservoirs. For electrochemical systems we shall need a term for the change in energy in an electrical system. The equation summarizes much experience that energy can neither be created nor destroyed but may be changed from one form to another. A given change in energy in the reactive system may be exactly compensated by many different combinations of changes in energy in the thermal reservoir and in the weight system. We shall often refer to the first law as the "energy conservation principle" or briefly, as the "energy principle."

An *extensive function* is one that is proportional to the amount of material. For example, if the amount of given chemical material in a reactive system is doubled, then U_σ is doubled. If the amount of reactants consumed is tripled in a reaction under given experimental conditions, then ΔU_σ is tripled. The extensive function property also means that, if two systems are combined without reaction or any changes in temperature, pressure, and composition, the overall energy is the sum of the energies of the two separate parts. *Intensive variables*, such as temperature and pressure, do not have the additive property of extensive ones.

State functions have the property of undergoing the same numerical change regardless of the details of the process in going from a given initial state to a given final state. The *state* of a system is defined by measurable properties such as temperature, pressure, and composition. Systems in the same state have the same temperature, pressure, and composition. If the reactive system undergoes a change from one well-defined state to another well-defined state, then ΔU_σ is the same if the process is done in one reaction step or in a series of steps involving isolatable reaction intermediates. For example, sulfur trioxide may be made from crystalline sulfur in a two-step process in which the intermediate, gaseous sulfur dioxide, is isolated and then allowed to react with more oxygen to form gaseous sulfur trioxide,

$$S(c) + O_2(g) \;\rightleftharpoons\; SO_2(g)$$

$$SO_2(g) + 1/2 O_2(g) \;\rightleftharpoons\; SO_3(g)$$

or in a single-step process

$$S(c) + 3/2 O_2(g) \;\rightleftharpoons\; SO_3(g)$$

These chemical equations include specifications for physical states, "g" for gas and "c" for crystalline. The overall ΔU_σ is the same for the two-step and one-step preparations of sulfur trioxide from 1 mol of sulfur at the same temperature and pressure. U_θ and U_{wt} are also state functions in that changes in these functions depend only on the net changes in temperature and height, respectively. For example, a person may walk to the top of Mount Washington or arrive there by helicopter from the same point of departure. Then, ΔU_{wt} for that person is the same for the two different paths. The state function property of the various U's is not derivable from energy conservation. Rather, the state function property is another important property of the energy function that emerges from observations. As a consequence of the state function property of the energy function and of other thermodynamic functions to be introduced later, we are often more concerned with "ends" than "means" in thermodynamics.

In our statement of the first law we have said that the U's for the various systems that make up the overall system are *independently* state functions. By this we mean that the change in each U is well defined by the variables within each system. Thus, ΔU_{wt} is defined by properties of the weight, and ΔU_θ is defined by properties of the thermal reservoir. Were this not true it would not be possible to measure ΔU_{wt} and ΔU_θ experimentally. ΔU_σ is defined by the properties of the reactive system even though its value is usually found indirectly in experiments with the aid of the first law through the relationship

$$\Delta U_\sigma = -\Delta U_\theta - \Delta U_{wt} \tag{2.2}$$

We emphasize that the first law is expressed in terms of energy *changes*. Absolute energies cannot be known within the framework of thermodynamics.

As the unit of energy we use the "joule." A joule is related to more fundamental quantities through the expression

1 joule = (1 kilogram)(1 meter/second^2)(1 meter) = (1 newton)(1 meter)
1 J = 1 kg m^2/s^2 = 1 N m

A joule is also related to the calorie energy unit by 1 cal = 4.184 J.

ΔU_{wt} and ΔU_θ: Directly Accessible Quantities

To use the first law we must have experimentally well-defined ways of obtaining all but one of the energy changes. Figure 2.1 shows the prime measurables for ΔU_{wt} and ΔU_θ. For the weight system the prime measurable is its height, h, in the earth's gravitational field. For the thermal reservoir the prime measurable is its temperature, T.

ΔU_{wt} is expressed in terms of the change in height, Δh, and other familiar quantities, the mass, m, of the weight and the acceleration due to gravity, g, which is 9.81 m/s^2 at mean sea level. The expression for ΔU_{wt} is

$$\boxed{\Delta U_{wt} = mg\Delta h} \tag{2.3}$$

ΔU_0 is expressed in terms of the change in temperature, ΔT_θ; the mass, m_θ; and the specific heat (thermal energy) capacity, c_θ, of the thermal reservoir. A *specific* quantity is a per-mass quantity, usually per gram. For most of our applications the thermal reservoir consists largely of water for which c_θ = (1.00 cal/K·g)(4.184 J/cal) = 4.184 J/K·g. Often the volume of water is known and, since the density of water is 1.00 g/mL = 1.00 kg/L near room temperature, the mass of the thermal reservoir is numerically equal to its volume. The expression for ΔU_θ is

$$\boxed{\Delta U_\theta = m_\theta c_\theta \Delta T_\theta} \tag{2.4}$$

In a practical application the thermal reservoir may be a composite of water, container, thermometer, etc., in which case the overall heat capacity includes contributions from each part. For a two-part, composite thermal reservoir eq. (2.4) becomes

$$\Delta U_\theta = m_1 c_1 \Delta T_\theta + m_2 c_2 \Delta T_\theta = (m_1 c_1 + m_2 c_2)\Delta T_\theta = C_\theta \Delta T_\theta \tag{2.5}$$

As a symbol for an *overall* heat capacity, we use *capital C_θ*.

For our purposes, when we speak of *thermal energy*, we mean an experimentally well-defined energy change that occurs in a thermal reservoir according to eq. (2.4) or its modifications. Taken together the thermal reservoir and the weight system are often called the *surroundings* of a chemical reaction system.

The Joule Experiment

The famous energy conversion experiment of James Joule is a direct and simple application of eqs. (2.1), (2.3), and (2.4) . In this experiment he used the change in height of a weight to turn a paddle in a water bath. The temperature increase of the water bath was observed with a very sensitive thermometer.

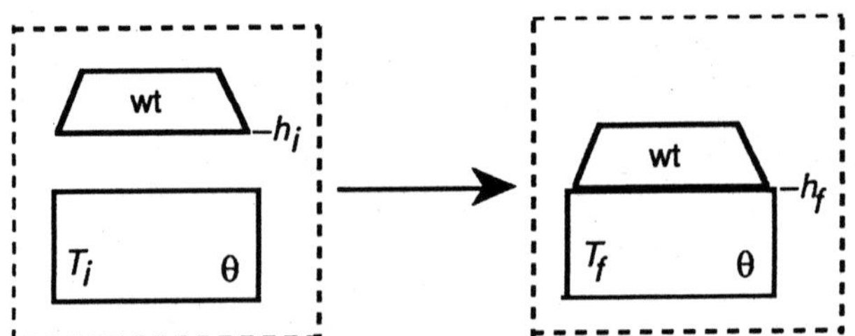

Fig. 2.2. **Essentials of the Joule experiment.** **A weight falls ($h_f <$ h_i), and a thermal reservoir warms ($T_f > T_i$)**

Figure 2.2 is a diagram of the essentials of this process in which the energy lost by the weight system is used to warm a thermal reservoir. We shall often use such sketches. Being able to make sketches of the essential parts of an overall system is a useful skill for thermodynamic analyses.

The Joule process involves no energy change in a reactive system. Thus, $\Delta U_\sigma = 0$, and the first-law expression reduces to

$$\Delta U_\theta + \Delta U_{wt} = 0 \tag{2.6}$$

Using measurements of $\Delta T = (T_f - T_i)$ and $\Delta h = (h_f - h_i)$ and expressions equivalent to eqs. (2.3) and (2.4), Joule obtained the so-called mechanical equivalent of heat. With modern accuracy this result is 4.184 J = 4.184 N m = 1.000 cal. As before, we have used f for final and i for initial.

As an example of a Joulean process, we calculate the temperature change when a penny falls into a beaker of water.

Worked Example

What is ΔT when a penny weighing 3.0 g falls 25 cm into 100 mL of water in a beaker?

Figure 2.2 shows the overall system for this problem. As reasonable simplifications, we neglect the temperature change in the penny, and we disregard the heat capacity of the glass beaker. Thus,

$$\Delta U_\theta + \Delta U_{wt} = m_\theta c_\theta \Delta T_\theta + m_{wt} g \Delta h = 0$$

Since all the quantities are known except ΔT_θ, we solve for ΔT_θ and have

$$\Delta T_\theta = -\frac{m_{wt} g \Delta h}{m_\theta c_\theta}$$

After inserting all quantities in SI (_Système International_) units except where mL and g cancel in the denominator, we have

$$\Delta T_\theta = -\frac{(0.0030 \text{ kg})(9.8 \text{ m/s}^2)(-0.25 \text{ m})}{(100 \text{ mL})(1 \text{ g/mL})(4.184 \text{ J/K g})}$$

$$= \frac{7.35 \times 10^{-3} \text{ J}}{4.18 \times 10^2 \text{ J/K}} = 1.8 \times 10^{-5} \text{ K} .$$

The temperature rise is $1.8 \times 10^{-5} \text{ K} = 1.8 \times 10^{-5}\,^\circ\text{C}$.

In addition to providing a numerical example of a simple thermodynamic analysis, this worked example reveals a truth about the relative ease of observing mechanical and thermal effects. In the example, the mechanical effect of the penny dropping is obvious, but the equivalent thermal effect gives an immeasurably small temperature rise. We need not worry about fountains boiling when coins are thrown in them. Thus, we also see why thermal effects may be overlooked in energy transactions and why brakes do not immediately burn up when stopping automobiles.

If a noticeable mechanical effect produces a negligible thermal effect, then a noticeable thermal effect must produce a large mechanical effect. Thus, the amount of gasoline needed to run an automobile is surprisingly small, and the chemical content of a tiny firecracker can produce a big bang. (Chemical energy can be converted into thermal energy or largely into mechanical energy.)

ΔU_σ, the Change in Energy in a Chemical Reaction System

In contrast to ΔU_θ and ΔU_{wt}, the energy change in a chemical reaction system, ΔU_σ, is usually not available by direct observation. We obtain ΔU_σ indirectly by setting up an overall system like that shown in Fig. 2.1, monitoring the energy changes in the thermal reservoir ΔU_θ and in the weight ΔU_{wt} as processes occur, and then applying the first law. Thus,

$$(U_{\sigma,f} - U_{\sigma,i}) = \Delta U_\sigma = -\Delta U_\theta - \Delta U_{wt} = -C_\theta \Delta T_\theta - mg\Delta h \qquad (2.7)$$

We shall illustrate the application of this relationship after we have developed the more widely used energy function for reactive systems, the enthalpy function, in the next chapter.

Here, we have illustrated the very important indirect strategy of thermodynamics. We learn about processes of interest, which may be complicated ones, such as chemical reactions or physiological processes, by making simple measurements in energy-coupled systems, such as thermal reservoirs and weight systems, and by applying thermodynamic laws.

ΔU_σ is often called the *internal energy function* since it is the energy of the chemical or reactive system upon which one customarily focuses attention.

Characteristics of ΔU_σ. The prime measurables for chemical reaction systems are the moles of reactants and products, which tell how much chemical change has occurred. In Fig. 2.1 the moles of reactants and moles of products are collectively symbolized with n_j, where the subscript j identifies a particular species. As we have said, U_σ is an extensive function. Thus, ΔU_σ for a reaction is proportional to the moles that react. In an experiment one measures ΔU_σ and then Δn_j for the limiting reagent in a reaction, e.g., consumption of hydronium ion in an acid–base reaction. Then, the observed energy change ΔU_σ is put on a per-mole basis by dividing it by Δn_j. We shall symbolize per mole quantities for changes in thermodynamic functions by putting a subscript "r" between the Δ and the symbol for the function. Thus,

$$\Delta_r U = \frac{\Delta U}{\Delta n_j} \tag{2.8}$$

Once an *extensive* function such as ΔU has been divided by Δn_j, the result, in this case $\Delta_r U$, is an *intensive* function. This transformation is developed in greater depth in Chapter 3.

U_σ, U_θ, and U_{wt} are separately *state functions*. One should not suppose, however, that fixing the value of ΔU_σ uniquely determines the values of ΔU_θ and ΔU_{wt}. Thus, ΔU_σ may have the same numerical value for a variety of transformations (paths) between given initial and final states of the reactive system, but ΔU_θ and ΔU_{wt} may differ widely and be consistent with the energy conservation principle because only the sum $(\Delta U_\theta + \Delta U_{wt})$ is fixed by a given ΔU_σ. For example, if 1 mol of hydrogen gas is burned in an open flame, ΔU_{wt} is small and $\Delta U_\theta \approx -\Delta U_\sigma$. If the same amount of hydrogen gas is burned in the cylinder of an internal combustion engine, however, ΔU_σ is the same and ΔU_{wt} is appreciable. Since $\Delta U_\theta = -\Delta U_\sigma - \Delta U_{wt}$, ΔU_θ is now much smaller.

Before the first law of thermodynamics was formulated around 1850, and in the following years when it was not widely understood, many inventors attempted to build "perpetual motion machines of the first kind." Such machines were supposed to make energy, not merely transform it. They were, of course, in violation of the energy conservation principle.

Expressing ΔU_{wt} in Terms of Pressure and Volume Variables

Many chemical investigations are carried out under conditions of constant external pressure, because the weight, which in practice is usually a column of the earth's atmosphere, is constant. In this case it is possible and convenient to express ΔU_{wt} in terms of the variables, P_{wt} and V_σ. P_{wt} is the pressure that the weight system exerts on the reactive system; V_σ is the volume of the reactive system. The result is

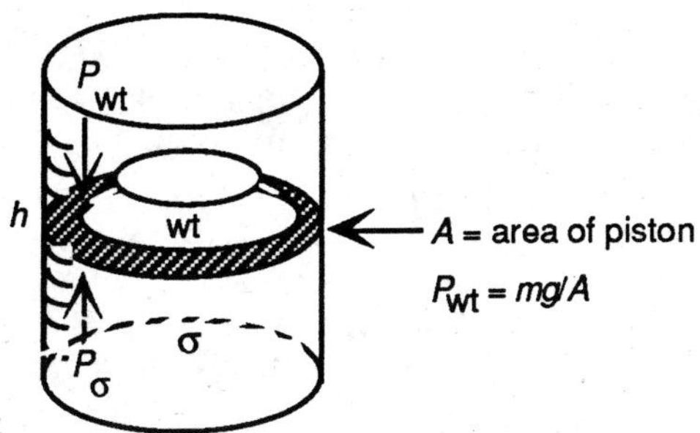

Figure 2.3   A reactive system which is a gas confined in a cylinder by a piston. The weight system exerts pressure P_{wt} on the piston, and the reactive system exerts pressure P_σ on the piston.

$$\boxed{\Delta U_{wt} = P_{wt}\Delta V_\sigma \text{ for constant } P_{wt}} \tag{2.9}$$

We shall now derive this expression and a very important special case. Pressure is defined as force per unit area. For a mass, m, in a gravitational field the force exerted downward is mg. Figure 2.3 shows the system of interest, a reactive system which is a gas confined in a cylinder by a piston of area A bearing a mass m. As a consequence, $P_{wt} = mg/A$. Were the gas in the reactive system to expand as a consequence of a gas-producing chemical reaction, the weight (the column of air) would rise in the gravitational field by Δh. The original expression for ΔU_{wt} may be transformed as follows:

$$\Delta U_{wt} = \underset{\text{force}}{mg} \cdot \underset{\text{distance}}{\Delta h} \cdot A/A$$

$$= \left(\frac{mg}{A}\right)(A\Delta h) = P_{wt}\Delta V_\sigma$$

where A is the area of the piston.

Using the new P–V expression for ΔU_{wt}, we can compute ΔU_{wt} without reference to mass, acceleration due to gravity, or the change in height.

Worked Example

If a volume of gas expands from 2 L to 8 L under a constant pressure of 1 bar, what is ΔU_{wt} ?

$$\Delta U_{wt} = P_{wt}\Delta V_\sigma = (1 \text{ bar})(8 \text{ L} - 2 \text{ L}) = 6 \text{ L bar}$$

$$= (6 \text{ L bar})\frac{(8.314 \text{ J/K mol})}{(0.08314 \text{ L bar/K mol})} = 600 \text{ J}$$

We have used the gas constant R expressed in both joules and in L bar to construct a conversion factor. In joules, R = 8.314 J/K mol. In L bar, R = 0.08314 L bar/K mol. 1 bar = 0.9869 atm = 10^5 Pa, where Pa stands for pascals. 1 Pa = 1N/m^2 = $(1 \text{ kg m/s}^2)/\text{m}^2$ = 1 kg/m s^2.

In thermodynamics, calculations of ΔU_{wt}–equivalent energy changes are commonly expressed this way rather than in terms of $mg\Delta h$. $P_{\text{wt}}\Delta V_\sigma$ is often called "pressure-volume work" or simply "$P\text{–}V$ work." Whenever the product $P\Delta V$ appears in a thermodynamic expression, it is an energy change.

In the process of reexpressing ΔU_{wt} in terms of P_{wt} and V_σ we have used another strategy that is common in thermodynamics. We have changed our point of view. Initially, ΔU_{wt} was expressed in terms of properties of the weight system. Our point of view was that of the weight system, and we used m, g, and Δh. Then, through changes in variables we expressed ΔU_{wt} in terms of pressure and volume variables which are compatible with the reactive system. Our point of view became essentially that of the reactive system. This important strategy, which we shall use again, we call the "change-of-view strategy."

Not only is the external pressure constant due to the weight of the column of the atmosphere for many chemical reactions, but it equals the initial and final pressure of the reactive system. Here, $P_\sigma = P_{\text{wt}} = P_{\text{atm}}$ = constant. As a consequence, ΔU_{wt} can be expressed entirely in terms of the variables of the reactive system. Thus,

$$\boxed{\Delta U_{\text{wt}} = P_\sigma \Delta V_\sigma \text{ when } P_\sigma = P_{\text{atm}} = \text{constant}} \qquad (2.11)$$

The change in point of view to that of the reactive system is complete, since both P_σ and V_σ are reactive system variables.

Experimental Basis of the First Law

At the time of its formulation in the middle of the nineteenth century, the first law summarized limited observations on heat engines, on chemical reactions, and on paddle wheel experiments. These observations were consistent with conservation of energy. Since that time, the validity of this important generalization has been tested repeatedly through applications of the law to the analysis of physical and chemical processes.

Summary

The first law of thermodynamics is an energy conservation principle. The sum of all the energy changes in an overall system is zero. For many overall systems of chemical interest, as shown in Fig. 2.1, the reactive chemical system

(σ) exchanges energy with a mass in a gravitational field (wt) and with a thermal reservoir (θ). A change in energy of the weight system is reflected in a measurable change in its height as $\Delta U_{wt} = mg\Delta h$. A change in energy in the thermal reservoir is reflected in a measurable change in its temperature as $\Delta U_\theta = m_\theta c_\theta \Delta T_\theta$. Typically in chemical applications, the first law is used to compute the change in energy of the reactive chemical system, ΔU_σ, from the observable changes in energy of the weight system and of the thermal reservoir.

When the air in the atmosphere acts as a weight system at constant pressure, the most common situation for chemical reactions, ΔU_{wt} can be reexpressed as $P_{wt}\Delta V_\sigma = P_{atm}\Delta V_\sigma$. When $P_\sigma = P_{atm}$ at the beginning and the end of a process, ΔU_{wt} can be expressed entirely in reactive system variables as $P_\sigma \Delta V_\sigma$.

Several concepts of general importance in thermodynamics are the state function, the extensive function, and the intensive function. U_σ is an example of a state function and an extensive function. T is an example of a state function and an intensive function.

Problems

1. To bookkeep changes in energy fully, what objects ought to be considered part of the universe of the following events? Make *simple* sketches which contain the standard labels (σ, wt, θ).
   (a) A solution of hydrochloric acid is mixed with a solution of sodium hydroxide in a well–insulated container open to the atmosphere. (The water containing the products of the reaction acts as the thermal reservoir.)
   (b) Hydrogen and oxygen explode in a closed, strong-walled metal chamber called a bomb; the bomb is immersed in an insulated water bath. (This is the experimental setup for bomb calorimetry.)

2. Designate with a sketch all the parts of the thermodynamic universe for each of the following processes:
   (a) A lead–acid automobile battery is used to run the starter motor of a car, which turns over the engine. Use el to designate an electrical system. Use KE to designate a system containing simple kinetic energy.
   (b) A gasoline-fired automobile engine is linked to an alternator that charges the lead–acid battery. Indicate any substantial one-wayness in the various processes in this part in comparison with part (a).
   (c) Photosynthesis in a green leaf. Use *light* for a light-energy source.

3. Indicate what types of nonthermal energy can be readily stored.

4. Estimate the maximum temperature rise in the rotors of the *two* disk brakes when a motorcycle stops. At a speed of 40 km/hr (25 mi/h) a 200 kg (440 lb) motorcycle has 1.2×10^4 J of kinetic energy, as can be computed from

$KE = 1/2mv^2$. Each rotor is made of stainless steel (heat capacity 0.444 kJ/K kg) and weighs about 4 kg. Ans: $\Delta T = 3.4$ K. (Of course, the instantaneous local temperature rise where the pad contacts the rotor is much greater.)

5. A block of aluminum metal weighing 50.0 g was heated to 100.00°C. Then it was immersed in 200 g of water, which was initially at 25.00°C. The final temperature of the overall system was 28.86°C. What is the heat (thermal energy) capacity of aluminum per gram and per mole? Treat the aluminum block as one thermal energy reservoir and the water bath as another. Make a sketch of the essentials of the overall system. One ans: heat capacity = 24.5 J/K mol.

6. Calculate the change in gravitational energy of the atmosphere (ΔU_{wt}) in liter bars and in joules when a gas expands (as a consequence of a chemical reaction) from 10 L to 20 L against a constant pressure of 1 bar at 25°C. Make a sketch of the essentials of the overall system. One ans: $\Delta U_{wt} = 10$ L bar.

3. THE ENTHALPY FUNCTION

Central to many applications of the first law of thermodynamics in chemistry is the enthalpy function. This function is a form of the energy function adapted to constant pressure conditions. The energy changes for chemical reactions that are commonly measured and tabulated are changes in enthalpy.

In this chapter we introduce the enthalpy function and show how to measure its change for chemical reactions in the laboratory. We illustrate the exact computation of the enthalpy of reaction from tabulated data and consider its approximate computation from average bond dissociation enthalpies. We shall also investigate how the enthalpy change in chemical reactions relates to the internal energies due to electronic and nuclear motions of reactant and product molecules.

Enthalpy Function

At the end of the last chapter we found that ΔU_{wt} could be reexpressed in reactive system variables when $P_\sigma = P_{atm}$ at the beginning and at the end of a process. Thus, under this condition of constant pressure, $\Delta U_{wt} = P_\sigma \Delta V_\sigma$, and the first law becomes

$$\Delta U_\sigma + P_\sigma \Delta V_\sigma + \Delta U_\theta = 0 \tag{3.1}$$

or

$$\Delta U_\sigma + P_\sigma \Delta V_\sigma = -\Delta U_\theta \tag{3.2}$$

This grouping of reactive system variables on the left occurs so commonly in chemical applications that a new function is introduced. This function, called the *enthalpy function* and symbolized with H, is defined such that

$$\boxed{\Delta H_\sigma = -\Delta U_\theta \text{ at constant } P_\sigma = P_{atm}} \tag{3.3}$$

The enthalpy function, named from the Greek meaning "heat in," has the formal definition

$$\boxed{H \equiv U + PV} \tag{3.4}$$

We have used the identity sign, $\equiv$, as a symbol for definition. Under the constraint of constant P_σ, eq. (3.4) gives

$$\Delta H_\sigma = \Delta U_\sigma + \Delta(P_\sigma V_\sigma) = \Delta U_\sigma + P_\sigma \Delta V_\sigma \tag{3.5}$$

which is, of course, the relationship that was the impetus for introducing the enthalpy function. The enthalpy function is an *extensive* function, one that is proportional to the amount of chemical material, since it is a linear function of the extensive variables, U_σ and V_σ. Thus, if the amount of material is doubled, U_σ and V_σ are doubled and consequently H_σ is doubled. It must be stressed that the enthalpy function is a useful function for the reactive system whenever $P_\sigma = P_{atm}$ = constant and whenever there are no additional potential energy reservoirs, such as an electrical one.

Let us consider the other properties of the enthalpy function. It is an energy function because the product, PV, has units of energy as does the U function itself. Second, the enthalpy function must be a state function since it is a function of state functions. The first law specifies this state function property for U. P and V define the state of a system without regard to the history of the system. Thus, changes in the enthalpy function depend only on the initial and final states of the system. Third, for chemical reactions occurring under conditions of constant pressure, the common constraint in chemistry, the enthalpy function automatically takes into account the pesky ΔU_{wt} term. For reactions involving only liquids and solids this term is quite small, a few tenths of joule per mole of reaction. Even for reactions involving gases the ΔU_{wt} term is not large. Whatever the case, ΔU_{wt} is absorbed into ΔH_σ. The ΔU_{wt} term is like dust swept under a rug. It is out of sight and need not concern us. We can think of ΔH_σ as the "change in energy of a chemical system" without apology. The only use for the enthalpy function is for reactive systems. Thus, for most applications we shall omit the subscript σ.

For many applications in chemistry the working form of the first law is eq. (3.3), $\Delta H_\sigma = -\Delta U_\theta$ under the constraint of $P_\sigma = P_{atm}$ = constant. Because H is a state function, the constant-pressure constraint applies only to the *beginning* and the *end* of the reaction. In the midst of a chemical reaction, such as an explosion, P_σ can vary wildly.

Relationship of the Enthalpy Change to a Chemical Reaction

Although the first law and its related function, the enthalpy function, provide no unique way to secure absolute enthalpies, we may formally associate enthalpies with individual species in a chemical reaction. We understand that the enthalpy change for a reaction is

$$\boxed{\Delta_r H = \Sigma v_P H(\text{prod}) - \Sigma v_R H(\text{react})} \qquad (3.6)$$

where the capital sigmas indicate summation, "prod" refers to products of the reactions, and "react" refers to reactants. In this expression we are using the "chemists' delta" which includes the stoichiometric coefficients—v_P for products and v_R for reactants—and subtracts reactants from products. The Greek letter v, "nu," is used for stoichiometric coefficients. Often $\Delta_r H$ is called the *enthalpy of reaction*. For example, for the acid–base reaction in aqueous (aq) solution,

$$H_3O^+(aq) + OH^-(aq) \rightleftharpoons 2H_2O(l)$$

we have

$$\Delta_r H = \nu_{HOH} H(H_2O) - \nu_{H_3O^+} H(H_3O^+) - \nu_{OH^-} H(OH^-) \tag{3.7}$$

From experiment we find $\Delta_r H_\sigma = -\Delta U_\theta / \Delta n(H_3O^+) = -55.8$ kJ/mol for this reaction as written. In this last expression we have used the σ subscript on $\Delta_r H$ for clarity. $\Delta n(H_3O^+)$ is moles of H_3O^+ reacting. Because $\Delta_r H$ is a per-mole quantity, it is an *intensive* function. [In more advanced treatments eq. (3.6) would be written as $\Delta_r H = \Sigma_i \nu_i H_i$, in which the stoichiometric coefficients, ν_i, of the reactants are understood to have negative signs.]

The reaction between hydronium ion and hydroxide ion is *exothermic*. In such processes energy leaves ("exo" = "out") the reactive system and enters the thermal reservoir. ΔH is negative; ΔU_θ is positive. For *endothermic* processes ("endo" = "in") energy enters the reactive system from the thermal reservoir, and opposite signs apply. The sign relationships among the energy terms are

	ΔH	ΔU_θ	ΔU_{total}	ΔU_{wt}
exothermic	–	+	0	± small
endothermic	+	–	0	± small

Depending on the sign of ΔU_{wt} energy may leave or enter the weight system. Whatever its sign, the enthalpy function absorbs this small term, as $\Delta H_\sigma = \Delta U_\sigma + \Delta U_{wt}$.

The enthalpy function is the energy function that is found in standard tables of thermodynamic data, such as in Appendix D. We also anticipate that the enthalpy function is of great importance in the application of the entropy principle (the second law). Direct applications of the enthalpy function are developed next.

Energy Changes from Calorimetric Experiments

Constant-Pressure Calorimetry. Calorimetry is the measurement of an energy change that occurs in a thermal reservoir, ΔU_θ, as a consequence of chemical reaction in a reactive system or exchange of energy with another thermal reservoir. In simplest terms, Fig. 2.1 shows the three-part overall system encountered in constant pressure calorimetry. Since reactive systems are normally open to the atmosphere, the atmosphere is the weight system. For such constant-pressure processes the enthalpy change is directly related to the experimental quantity, ΔU_θ. Thus, the applicable expression is

$$\Delta H_\sigma = -\Delta U_\theta = -C_\theta \Delta T_\theta \quad \text{for } P_\sigma = P_{atm} = \text{constant} \tag{3.8}$$

The overall heat capacity for the thermal reservoir is C_θ. The σ on ΔH_σ is retained in this expression for clarity. Provided the thermal reservoir is very large compared to the reactive system, little error is made in assuming none of the thermal energy remains with the products in the reactive system. For more accuracy the products of the reaction may be included as part of the thermal reservoir.

For constant-pressure calorimetry an overall system that is physically different from that depicted in Fig. 2.1 but conceptually the same is customarily used. These experiments are conducted in well-insulated vessels of the Dewar (Thermos-bottle) type. Nested Styrofoam drinking cups are an inexpensive approximation to such vessels. Figure 3.1 shows the essentials of such an experiment with Styrofoam cups. In perfect calorimetry of this type no thermal energy is exchanged with the surroundings. Instead of the arrangement depicted in Fig. 2.1, the products of the reaction serve as the thermal energy reservoir. As shown in Fig. 3.1 the reactive system usually consists of two parts, designated 1 and 2, at different initial temperatures. As before, the subscripts "i" and "f" mean initial and final, respectively.

Consider the reaction of the components of two aqueous solutions. In a simple experimental design the temperature of solution 2 would be measured in a separate container before being mixed with solution 1. When the two parts are mixed, chemical reaction occurs. Conceptually, what was a reactive system becomes a thermal reservoir. ΔH is given by

$$\boxed{\Delta H = -\Delta U_\theta = -(C_1\Delta T_1 + C_2\Delta T_2)} \qquad (3.9)$$

where C_1 is the heat capacity of solution 1 and C_2 is the heat capacity of solution 2. ΔT_1 and ΔT_2 are the respective temperature changes. If these are aqueous solutions, then, for example, $C_1 = m_1 c_1$, where m_1 is the mass (or volume $\times$ density) of one aqueous solution and c_1 is the specific heat capacity of water (4.184 J/K g).

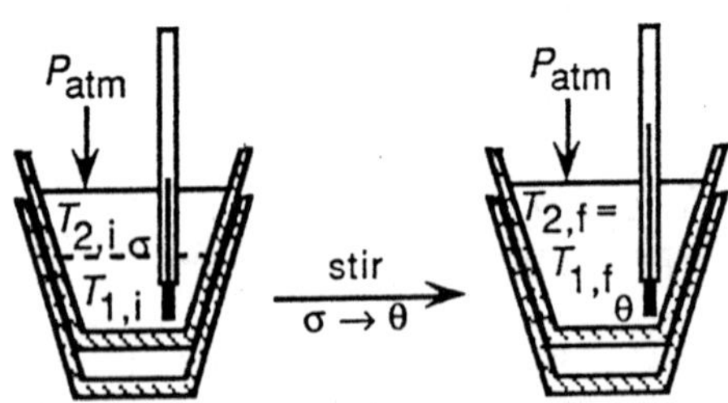

Figure 3.1.   An experiment in constant-pressure calorimetry performed in nested Styrofoam cups.

Worked Example

50.0 mL of 0.400 M aqueous hydrochloric acid at 22.75°C and 100.0 mL of 0.250 M aqueous sodium hydroxide at 23.05°C are mixed in nested Styrofoam cups. The maximum temperature of the mixture is 24.65°C.

What is $\Delta_r H$ for the reaction as written above?

$$H_3O^+(aq) + OH^-(aq) \rightleftharpoons 2H_2O(l)$$

Since we have $(50.0 \text{ mL})(0.400 \text{ mmol/mL}) = 20.0$ mmol H_3O^+ and $(100.0 \text{ mL})(0.250 \text{ mmol/mL}) = 25.0$ mmol of OH^-, the acid is the limiting reagent. $C_1 = (50.0 \text{ mL})(1.00 \text{ g/mL})(4.18 \text{ J/K g}) = 209$ J/K. Similarly, $C_2 = 418$ J/K. Thus,

$$\begin{aligned}
\Delta U_\theta &= C_1\Delta T_1 + C_2\Delta T_2 \\
&= (209 \text{ J/K})(24.65 - 22.75)°C + (418 \text{ J/K})(24.65 - 23.05)°C \\
&= 1066 \text{ J} \\
\Delta H \text{ per mole } H_3O^+ &= -\Delta U_\theta/\text{mol } H_3O^+ \\
&= -(1066 \text{ J})/(20.0 \times 10^{-3} \text{ mol } H_3O^+) \\
&= -53.3 \text{ kJ/mol } H_3O^+ \\
\Delta_r H &= -53.3 \text{ kJ/mol } H_3O^+
\end{aligned}$$

We have used the relationship, °C = K, for temperature changes. The value for $\Delta_r H$ is not exact. It includes some realistic experimental error.

Constant–Volume or "Bomb" Calorimetry. Reactions involving gases may be carried out under constant pressure conditions with the aid of catalysts. Commonly, however, reactions involving gases, such as the combustion with gaseous oxygen of many organic compounds, are carried out in heavy-walled reaction vessels called bombs. The reaction of benzene with oxygen is an example of this type of reaction

$$C_6H_6(l) + 15/2O_2(g) \rightleftharpoons 6CO_2(g) + 3H_2O(l).$$

In constant-volume calorimetry, $\Delta U_{wt} = 0$ since $\Delta V_\sigma = 0$. The energy change observed in the thermal reservoir is equal to the internal energy change itself, ΔU_σ, in the reactive system. Thus,

$$\Delta U_{wt} = P_{wt}\Delta V_\sigma = P_{wt} \cdot 0 = 0 \tag{3.10}$$

and

$$\Delta U_\sigma = -\Delta U_\theta = -C_\theta\Delta T_\theta \tag{3.11}$$

With the aid of the ideal gas law one can convert such ΔU_σ values into ΔH_σ values for use in constructing tables. We shall not bother to illustrate this conversion of ΔU_σ values into ΔH_σ values.

Applications of the Enthalpy Function

Hess' Law.   Hess' "law" of constant energy summation states that *the energy change (usually enthalpy change) accompanying a chemical reaction is equal to the algebraic sum of the energy changes accompanying a set of reactions that together are equivalent to the overall reaction.* The first law of thermodynamics including in particular the state function (path-independent) property of the energy and enthalpy functions justifies Hess' "law." (Today, Hess' law should be called Hess' corollary, since it is a consequence of the first law. In the development of thermodynamics Hess' law was established from experiments before the first law was codified. Indeed, Hess' law was important experimental evidence for the state function property of the energy function.)

As an example of Hess' law consider the indirect, two-step process of making sulfur trioxide from sulfur and oxygen in comparison with the direct one-step process. For the two-step process we have

$$S(c) + O_2(g) \rightleftharpoons SO_2(g) \qquad\qquad \Delta_r H_1 = -296.8 \text{ kJ/mol}$$
$$SO_2(g) + 1/2 O_2(g) \rightleftharpoons SO_3(g) \qquad\qquad \Delta_r H_2 = -98.9 \text{ kJ/mol}$$

where $\Delta_r H_1 + \Delta_r H_2 = -395.7$ kJ/mol. For the direct, one-step process we have

$$S(c) + 3/2 O_2(g) \rightleftharpoons SO_3(g) \qquad\qquad \Delta_r H_3 = -395.7 \text{ kJ/mol}$$

We see that $\Delta_r H_3 = \Delta_r H_1 + \Delta_r H_2$. Thus, $\Delta_r H$ is the same for two different reaction paths, as required by Hess' law.

It is also helpful to think of Hess' law in terms of a *thermodynamic cycle* which may be diagrammed as

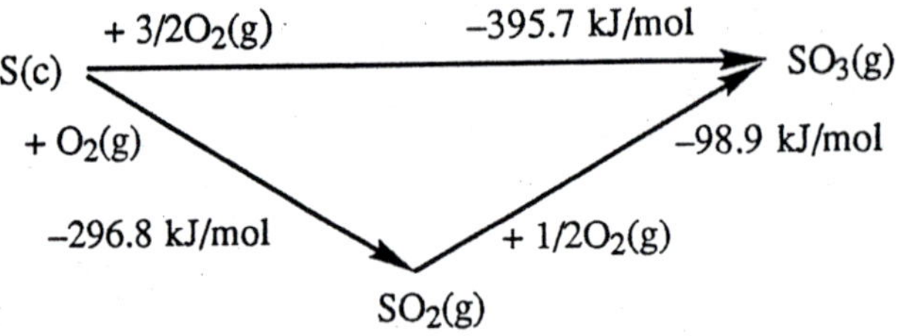

Because thermodynamic functions are state functions, the concept of thermodynamic cycles, which include processes run by two paths to reach the same outcome, is a useful construction.

Enthalpies of Formation.   Although the first law only provides a formalism for measuring *changes* in enthalpies, it is useful to define conventional but arbitrary "absolute" enthalpy values for chemical species. Such *enthalpies of formation*, symbolized by *Hf*, are useful for tabulating enthalpies and for calculating reaction enthalpies from tabulated values. This device depends on choosing some convenient *reference form* of each element and arbitrarily setting the enthalpy of formation of this form equal to zero. Pure elements in their most stable forms at 25°C and at 1 bar pressure are chosen for these reference forms. Many elements have more than one form. Ozone is O_3, whereas the stable form of oxygen is O_2. For carbon, graphite is more stable than diamond or any fullerene, such as C_{60}, at room temperature and atmospheric pressure. For the stable form of each element at 25°C, $Hf° \equiv 0$. The superscript zero or "super zero," °, denotes the *standard state*, which is 1 bar pressure for pure gases, liquids, and solids. For species in solution the standard state will be described later.

For a compound, $Hf°$ can be obtained from the enthalpy change accompanying its formation from the elements. For standard state enthalpies of formation, eq. (3.6) becomes

$$\boxed{\Delta_r H° = \sum v_P Hf°(\text{prod}) - \sum v_R Hf°(\text{react})} \qquad (3.12)$$

The full units of enthalpies of reaction are kJ/mol rxn where rxn = reaction (see below). The stoichiometric coefficients have units of mol i/mol rxn, and the $Hf°$'s for the individual compounds have units of kJ/mol i. The i stands for a particular species. For example, from the reaction

$$S(c, \text{rhombic}) + 3/2 O_2(g) \rightleftharpoons SO_3(g)$$

we have

$$\begin{aligned}
\Delta_r H° &= v_{SO_3} Hf°(SO_3) - v_S Hf°(S) - v_{O_2} Hf°(O_2) \\
&= -395.7 \text{ kJ/mol rxn}
\end{aligned} \qquad (3.13)$$

Since $Hf°(S) \equiv 0$ and $Hf°(O_2) \equiv 0$, we have

$$\begin{aligned}
Hf°(SO_3) &= \Delta_r H°/(1 \text{ mol } SO_3/\text{mol rxn}) \\
&= (-395.7 \text{ kJ/mol rxn})/(1 \text{ mol } SO_3/\text{mol rxn}) = -395.7 \text{ kJ/mol } SO_3 \quad (3.14)
\end{aligned}$$

$\Delta_r H°$ is a value obtained from calorimetric experiments as described above. Enthalpies of formation of compounds are expressed on a molar basis.

The unit "mol rxn" stands for a single multiplier of the stoichiometric coefficients of reactants *and* products that tells how far a reaction has advanced in consumption of reactants and in formation of products. A related way of thinking about "mol rxn" is as the extent to which a reaction has occurred "as written" in the chemical equation. For "1 mol rxn," the reaction has occurred to the extent of one round of the stoichiometric coefficients.

Although mol rxn is a universal quantity that applies to all equations for chemical reactions, a $\Delta_r H$ depends on a particular set of stoichiometric coefficients. For the reaction given above, but written with twice the stoichiometric coefficients,

$$2S(c) + 3O_2(g) \rightleftharpoons 2SO_3(g) \qquad\qquad \Delta_r H° = -791.4 \text{ kJ/mol rxn}$$

Thus, before eq. (3.12) can be applied to a chemical reaction, a balanced equation must be written for the reaction. In addition, the physical state of each reactant and each product species must be specified. *Since a value of $\Delta_r H$ depends on the stoichiometric coefficients and the states of reactants and products, the fully specified chemical equation must remain associated with a value of $\Delta_r H$.*

In most cases in this text, we shall simplify "mol rxn" to "mol" in giving units for reaction quantities such as $\Delta_r H°$. Remember, however, that this usage is a simplification, and this "mol" may not refer to any of the reactants or products. In the example just considered, none of the stoichiometric coefficients is unity.

In principle, the enthalpy of formation of any compound can be found from the enthalpy of the reaction that forms the compound from the elements of which it consists. Such enthalpies of formation are assembled in tables. Unless otherwise indicated we shall be using these enthalpies of formation under standard state conditions ($Hf°$) in our calculations. Many compounds cannot be formed directly from the elements. A compound may be unstable with respect to its elements, the reaction of the elements may be too slow for calorimetry, or a different reaction may occur. These practical problems, however, do not prevent finding the enthalpy of formation of such compounds. A Hess' law argument can be applied to find the desired $\Delta_r H$ of formation. Enthalpies of formation of many hydrocarbons have been found by this method as illustrated in the following example. Often, enthalpies of combustion are used for this purpose.

Worked Example

Show how to compute the enthalpy of formation of gaseous ethylene, C_2H_4, from the enthalpy of combustion for ethylene, hydrogen, and carbon.

The desired formation reaction is $2C(c) + 2H_2(g) \rightleftharpoons C_2H_4(g)$ and the enthalpy of formation of ethylene is given by $Hf°[C_2H_4(g)] \equiv \Delta_r H°$.

The available information is

$$C_2H_4(g) + 3O_2(g) \rightleftharpoons 2CO_2(g) + 2H_2O(l) \qquad\qquad \Delta_r H°_1$$

$$C(c) + O_2(g) \rightleftharpoons CO_2(g) \qquad\qquad \Delta_r H°_2$$

$$H_2(g) + 1/2O_2(g) \rightleftharpoons H_2O(l) \qquad\qquad \Delta_r H°_3$$

By Hess' law $Hf°[C_2H_4(g)] = \Delta_r H° = 2\Delta_r H°_2 + 2\Delta_r H°_3 - \Delta_r H°_1$.
Try drawing a thermodynamic cycle to show this relationship.

The table of thermodynamic data in Appendix D is organized in accordance with the positions of the elements in the periodic table. A chart showing the arrangement is at the beginning of the table. In this arrangement elements are generally in the order nonmetals to metals. The scheme starts with oxygen, goes to hydrogen, and then generally down each column from right to left in the periodic table. As each element is added to the table of data, compounds of the current element with all of the preceding elements are introduced. Thus, compounds consisting of nonmetals alone are found early in the table. Compounds containing alkaline earth and alkali metals are near the end of the table. Only formulas, not names, are needed to find a substance in a table. A compound is listed under the element in the compound that is last in the standard order according to place of the element in the periodic table. For many substances data are given for more than one physical state. It is essential to select the correct state.

Systematic Calculation of Enthalpies of Reaction from Tabulated Enthalpies of Formation. Enthalpies of reaction can be readily computed from tabulated enthalpies of formation. As in all thermodynamic treatments one must begin by writing the chemical equation, including specifications of the states of each reactant and each product. States are designated with "g" for gas, "l" for liquid, "c" for crystal, and "aq" for aqueous, i.e., water solution. Occasionally, more specialized state designations are used. Of course, temperatures and pressures must also be known. Standard state values (1 bar pressure) at 25°C (298 K) are what are usually given in simplified tables. As an example of a systematic calculation for 25°C data, we have for the combustion of methyl alcohol

$$CH_3OH(l) + 3/2 O_2(g) \rightleftharpoons CO_2(g) + 2H_2O(l)$$

$Hf°$ (kJ/mol): -238.7 0 -393.5 $2(-285.8)$

$$\Delta_r H° = 2Hf°(H_2O) + Hf°(CO_2) - Hf°(CH_3OH) - 3/2 Hf°(O_2)$$
$$= -726.4 \text{ kJ/mol} \tag{3.15}$$

The enthalpy of formation of each species is placed under the species in the chemical equation along with the stoichiometric coefficient if the coefficient is other than unity. Then, the enthalpies of reactants are summed and subtracted from the total enthalpies of products according to eq. (3.12). *In calculating enthalpies of reaction you are strongly urged to use this systematic procedure,* which always starts with a balanced chemical equation in which the states of all reactants and products are specified.

Hess' law helps explain the use of enthalpies of formation based on the arbitrary zero values for the elements in their reference forms. All reactions, such as the combustion of methanol, can be expressed by an indirect, two-step path involving the constituent elements as well as by the direct reaction. Thus,

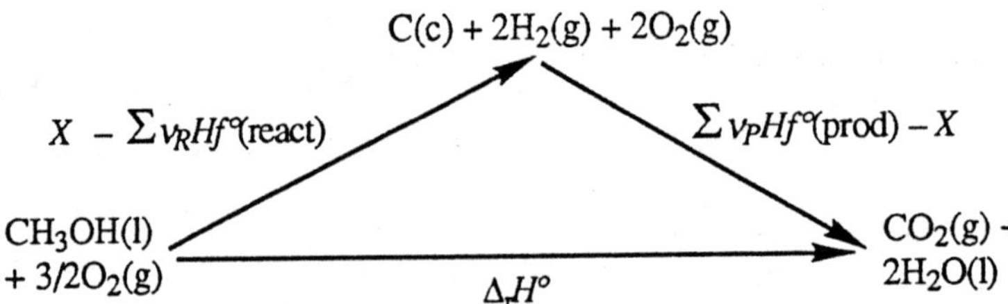

In the two-step, indirect path reactants decompose into the constituent elements
and then these elements recombine into products. As a consequence, enthalpies
of formation of *the elements*, whatever X value they may have, simply cancel
out for the overall process. They contribute X to the products in the first step,
and they contribute X to the reactants in the second step.

Thermochemical Equations. For some applications *thermochemical
equations* are useful. Such equations express conservation of energy, usually
enthalpy, as well as conservation of elements (chemical symbols) for chemical
reactions. Thus,

$$S(c,\text{rhombic}) + 3/2O_2(g) \rightleftharpoons SO_3(g) + 395.7 \text{ kJ}$$

Weak Temperature Dependence of the Enthalpy of Reaction

Handy tables of thermodynamic data give values only at the reference temperature
of 25°C. For many applications we shall want to know the enthalpy of reaction
$\Delta_r H°_T$ at other temperatures. Fortunately, the temperature dependence of $\Delta_r H°$
for reactions is generally so weak that we can approximate $\Delta_r H°_T$ with $\Delta_r H°_{298}$
over a wide range of temperature. To justify this generalization we shall
calculate the temperature dependence of $\Delta H°$ for one reaction and cite results for
several others.

Expressed in finite differences, the constant pressure heat capacity for
chemical substances is

$$C_P \equiv \left. \frac{\Delta H_\sigma}{\Delta T} \right)_P \tag{3.16}$$

where the subscript P designates constant pressure. Values for $C_P°$ are given in
standard tables as in Appendix D. For example, for the chemical reaction

$$S(c, \text{rhombic}) + 3/2O_2(g) \rightleftharpoons SO_3(g)$$

we can calculate $\Delta_r H°_T$ from $\Delta_r H°_{298}$ and $\Delta_r C_P°$. $\Delta_r C_P°$ is defined with the
"chemists' delta" in the same manner as $\Delta_r H°$. Thus,

$$\Delta_r C_P° = v_{SO_3} C_P°(SO_3) - v_S C_P°(S) - v_{O_2} C_P°(O_2)$$
$$= (1)50.67 \text{ J/K mol} - (1)22.64 \text{ J/K mol} - (3/2)29.36 \text{ J/K mol}$$
$$= -16.01 \text{ J/K mol} \tag{3.17}$$

To a reasonable degree of approximation,

$$\Delta_r H^{\circ}_T \approx \Delta_r H^{\circ}_{298} + \Delta_r C_P^{\circ} \Delta T \tag{3.18}$$

Thus, we have for our example at 100°C

$$\Delta_r H^{\circ}_{373} \approx -395.7 \text{ kJ/mol} + \frac{(-16.01 \text{ J/K mol})(75 \text{ K})}{1000 \text{ J/kJ}}$$

$$= -395.7 \text{ kJ/mol} - 1.20 \text{ kJ/mol} = -396.9 \text{ kJ/mol} \tag{3.19}$$

We find that $\Delta_r H^{\circ}$ has changed by only 0.3% in 75°C. Table 3.1 shows the modest changes in the $\Delta_r H^{\circ}$'s that occur in a 300-degree interval for several other reactions. Thus, we have much evidence that $\Delta_r H^{\circ}$ is a weak function of temperature for most reactions.

Frequently, we shall approximate $\Delta_r H^{\circ}$ as a constant. One warning must be issued, however, regarding this generalization. *No reactant or product may change state in the temperature interval under consideration.* For example, if water is shown as a liquid in a reaction at room temperature, water must also be shown as a liquid above 100°C. This approximation fails also for reactions involving ions in water.

Of course, heat capacities for individual substances are substantial and give a substantial temperature dependence to the enthalpies for these individual substances. For the *enthalpy of reaction*, however, the heat capacity contributions of reactants and products tend to cancel. In general, $\Delta_r C_P^{\circ}$ is not large, and the temperature dependence of $\Delta_r H^{\circ}_T$ is weak. These relationships are seen in the contributions to $\Delta_r C_P^{\circ}$ in the example of the oxidation of sulfur developed above.

Table 3.1. Temperature Dependence of $\Delta_r H^{\circ}$

	$\Delta_r H^{\circ}_{298}$ kJ/mol	$\Delta_r H^{\circ}_{598}$ kJ/mol	Percentage Change
Reactions Involving Gases			
$NO(g) + 1/2 O_2(g) \rightleftharpoons NO_2(g)$	−56.5	−58.6	3.5
$CO(g) + 1/2 O_2(g) \rightleftharpoons CO_2(g)$	−282.8	−284.9	0.7
$C_2H_4(g) + H_2(g) \rightleftharpoons C_2H_6(g)$	−136.8	−142.3	3.8
Reactions Involving Solids and Gases			
$CaCO_3(c) \rightleftharpoons CaO(c) + CO_2(g)$	178.2	176.1	1.1
$C(c) + 1/2 O_2(g) \rightleftharpoons CO(g)$	−110.5	−108.8	1.6

Adapted from G. C. Pimentel and R. D. Spratley, *Understanding Chemistry*, Holden-Day, San Francisco, 1971, p. 389.

Estimates of Enthalpies of Reaction from Bond Dissociation Enthalpies

Sometimes we want enthalpy changes for reactions involving species that are not listed in handy tables. Sometimes species are missing because of the limited scope of a table. Species may be absent because they are not known or because they are highly reactive molecular fragments that are difficult to study. Under these circumstances estimates of $\Delta_r H°$'s for reactions can be made from *bond dissociation enthalpies (DH°)*.

The bond dissociation enthalpy is the energy required to break a mole of a particular chemical bond, such as C—C single bonds. Thus,

$$H_3C\text{—}CH_3(g) \rightleftharpoons 2CH_3(g) \quad DH°(C\text{—}C) \equiv \Delta_r H° = 376 \text{ kJ/mol}$$

The $DH°$, which is the measure of the strength of a chemical bond, is often simply called the *bond energy*. It is a useful property because the strength of a chemical bond is, to a good approximation, independent of the other bonds in which the participating atoms are engaged. Of course, account must be taken of the substantial difference in strength between single bonds and multiple bonds. Also, bond dissociation enthalpies apply only to reactions that occur in the gas phase, where energy effects due to intermolecular interactions are negligible. $DH°$'s are always positive. The stronger the bond the larger the $DH°$.

Table 3.2 contains a list of *average* bond dissociation enthalpies for many common bonds that can be used to estimate $\Delta_r H°$'s for a number of reactions. The value of $DH°$ given above for the C—C bond is not an average value. More elaborate schemes of $DH°$'s, which take account of finer effects such as electron delocalization (resonance), the orbital hybridization of participating atoms, and the degree of branching of carbon atoms, have been developed. Such refined schemes yield rather good enthalpies of reaction.

An examination of the data in Table 3.2 reveals some patterns worth noting. Of course, triple bonds are stronger than double bonds, which are in turn stronger than single bonds. Among single bonds we find three exceptionally strong bonds in the highly polar H—F, O—H, and C—F bonds. Exceptionally weak single bonds occur when both of the participating atoms are highly electronegative or at least one atom is quite large, as in F—F, Cl—Cl, Br—Br, I—I, O—O, N—N, Si—Si, and C—I. Among double bonds, the ones involving two highly electronegative atoms are also weak. These weaker double bonds are found for O=O, N=N, S=O, and S=S.

Table 3.2. Average Bond Dissociation Enthalpies $DH°$ (kJ/mol)

				Single Bonds							
C—H	413	N—H	391	O—H	463			F—F	159		
C—C	348	N—N	163	O—O	146						
C—N	293	N—O	201	O—F	190			Cl—F	253		
C—O	358	N—F	272	O—Cl	203			Cl—Cl	242		
C—F	485	N—Cl	200	O—I	234						
C—Cl	328	N—Br	243					Br—F	237		
C—Br	276			S—H	339			Br—Cl	218		
C—I	240	H—H	436	S—F	327			Br—Br	193		
C—S	259	H—F	567	S—Cl	253						
		H—Cl	431	S—Br	218			I—Cl	208		
Si—H	323	H—Br	366	S—S	266			I—Br	175		
Si—Si	226	H—I	299					I—I	151		
Si—C	301										
Si—O	368										

			Multiple Bonds		
C=C	614	N=N	418	O=O	498
C≡C	839	N≡N	945		
C=N	615			S=O	323
C≡N	891			S=S	418
C=O	804*				
C≡O	1076				

*The value for CO_2.
Adapted from J. W. Moore, W. G. Davies, and R. W. Collins, *Chemistry*, McGraw-Hill, New York, 1978.

We shall now illustrate a systematic procedure for estimating enthalpies of reaction from the bond dissociation enthalpies in Table 3.2. For the conversion of methane into methyl chloride we have

$$H_3C—H(g) + Cl—Cl(g) \rightleftharpoons H_3C—Cl(g) + H—Cl(g)$$

$DH°$ (kJ/mol):   413   242   328   431

$$\Delta_r H° \approx DH°(C—H) + DH°(Cl—Cl) - DH°(C—Cl) - DH°(H—Cl)$$
$$\approx 413 + 242 - 328 - 431 = -104 \text{ kJ/mol} \tag{3.20}$$

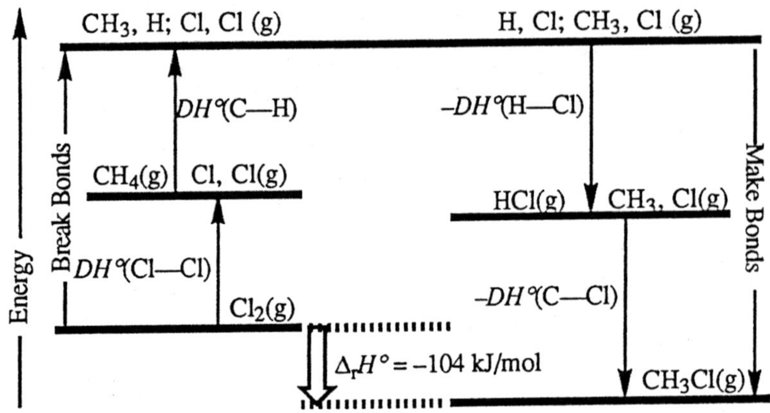

Figure 3.2.   Energy diagram showing enthalpies invested in bond breaking and recovered from bond making in the conversion of CH_4 and Cl_2 to CH_3Cl and HCl.

Note that we have only considered the bonds that have broken and the new ones that have formed. The accurate $\Delta_rH°$ computed from standard enthalpies of formation is −98.2 kJ/mol. In this calculation energy has been supplied to the reactive system to break bonds of the reactants and obtained from the reactive system when the new bonds in the products are formed. These relationships are shown in Fig. 3.2. The upward arrows show the investment of bond dissociation enthalpies. The downward arrows show the release of bond dissociation enthalpies. The broad arrow shows the net energy change.

The general expression for estimating enthalpies of reaction from bond dissociation enthalpies is

$$\Delta_rH° \approx \Sigma v_R DH°(\text{react}) - \Sigma v_P DH°(\text{prod}) \qquad (3.21)$$

It is essential to recognize that this use of $DH°$'s has the opposite sign sense to the use of $Hf°$'s in eq. (3.12). We shall return below to a consideration of this difference. The approximate sign, $\approx$, is used in eq. (3.21) to emphasize that such $DH°$ calculations are always approximate. Returning to the chemical equation, we see that the bonds that are broken in reactants and formed in the products have been identified with strokes. Bonds that do not change in the reaction, the CH_3 set in this case, are disregarded in the $DH°$ calculation.

As a second example consider the reaction in which the reactive intermediate, CH_2, which is called methylene, combines with hydrogen chloride to form methyl chloride. Thus, we have

$$CH_2(g) + H\text{—}Cl(g) \;\rightleftharpoons\; H\text{—}CH_2\text{—}Cl$$

$$DH^\circ \text{ (kJ/mol):} \qquad\qquad 431 \qquad\qquad 413 \quad 328$$

$$\Delta_r H^\circ \approx 431 - 413 - 328 = -310 \text{ kJ/mol} \qquad\qquad (3.22)$$

In order to see more clearly the difference between the role of bond dissociation enthalpies and enthalpies of formation in the calculation of enthalpies of reaction we consider a double Hess' law analysis. For the methane-to-methyl chloride reaction we may write

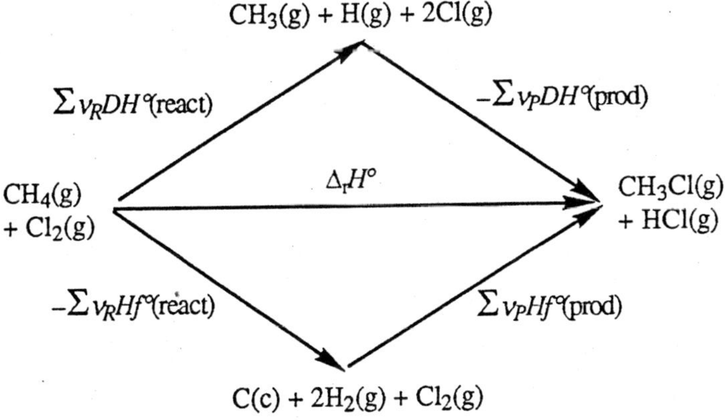

In the upper half cycle, we see the roles of the two $\Sigma v DH^\circ$ terms, which give,

$$\Delta_r H^\circ \approx \Sigma v_R DH^\circ(\text{react}) - \Sigma v_P DH^\circ(\text{prod}) \qquad\qquad (3.23)$$

Compare Fig. 3.2 again. In the lower half-cycle, elements are products of the first step, which is opposite in sense to that understood in defining enthalpies of formation. As a consequence, a negative sign is needed in $-\Sigma v_R Hf^\circ(\text{react})$. The second step in the lower half is the natural sense of a formation reaction. Thus,

$$\Delta_r H^\circ = -\Sigma v_R Hf^\circ(\text{react}) + \Sigma v_P Hf^\circ(\text{prod}) = \Sigma v_P Hf^\circ(\text{prod}) - \Sigma v_R Hf^\circ(\text{react}) \quad (3.24)$$

To make this comparison one other way, we note that the reference species for DH°'s are high-energy, unstable atoms and molecular fragments *as products*. In contrast, the reference species for Hf°'s are stable elements *as reactants*.

The Molecular Basis of the Enthalpy of Reaction

Up to this point in our presentation of chemical thermodynamics, we have been concerned with how to obtain energy changes for chemical reactions directly from experiments or from tables of enthalpies of formation or bond dissociation enthalpies. Energy changes have been related experimentally to temperature changes in thermal reservoirs and to height changes in weight systems, and the energy conservation principle has been used to calculate energy changes in chemical reaction systems. In none of this development was it necessary to refer to the atomic–molecular model of matter. However, just as we have seen this model used to advantage in other areas of chemistry, we can expect this model to help us understand the observed energy effects.

For simplicity we shall consider gas molecules for which the intermolecular interactions are negligible. The energy of a gaseous molecule is a composite of energies due to electronic, vibrational, rotational, and translational motions. For the latter three contributions, the sketch depicts three of the motions for a ball-and-spring model of a diatomic molecule. These motions

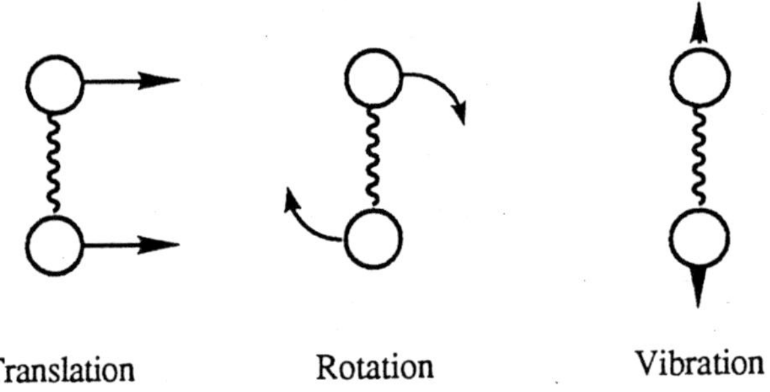

Translation   Rotation   Vibration

result from movements of the nuclei. Electronic energy changes, however, are caused by electron–nucleus and electron–electron interactions that occur when molecules with nuclei at rest are made from separated atoms at rest. By applying physical principles and advanced mathematical reasoning to the overall model, one can assess the relative contributions of the various energy terms at room temperature. In most cases, the temperature-independent electronic energy contribution is the dominant part. The other three energy contributions are small and temperature dependent. These three contributions constitute the thermal energy, i.e., the energy accumulation associated with temperature change.

Table 3.3 gives an analysis of the energy contributions to the reaction of carbon monoxide and oxygen to form carbon dioxide,

$$CO(g) + 1/2 O_2(g) \rightleftharpoons CO_2(g)$$

We find that more than 98% of $\Delta_r H°_{298}$ is due to the difference in ground-state electronic and zero-point vibrational energies between reactants and products. The zero-point vibrational energy is an amount of vibrational energy that must remain in molecules at absolute zero. The remainder is due in part to the small $P_\sigma \Delta V_\sigma$ term in $\Delta_r H_\sigma$ and in part to the small difference in thermal energies between reactants and products associated with translational, rotational, and vibrational motion. Because the electronic energy part, due to the difference in bond strengths of reactants and products, dominates the enthalpy of reaction at room temperature, *we regard $\Delta_r H°$ as essentially a direct measure of the electronic contribution*. In doing so, we disregard the small thermal and $P_\sigma \Delta V_\sigma$ contributions.

Table 3.3. Contributions to the Energies (kJ/mol) at 298 K of Participants in the Reaction: $CO(g) + 1/2O_2(g) \rightleftharpoons CO_2(g)$

	CO(g)	O_2(g)	CO_2(g)
$U°_0$ = Electronic, incl. zero-point vibrational	−1073	−491	−1597
Thermal energies			
Translational (298 K)	4	4	4
Rotational (298 K)	2	2	2
Vibrational (298 K)	~0	~0	0.4
$U°_{298}$ = Total	−1067	−485	−1591
$P\Delta V = \Delta nRT = -1$ kJ/mol			

Electronic energies are referenced to the separated, constituent atoms at rest. Zero-point vibrational energies, which are included in $\Delta_r U°_0$, are a small contribution.

$\Delta_r H°_0 = \Delta_r U°_0$(electronic, zero-pt. vib.)

$$= (1)(-1597 \text{ kJ/mol}) - (1)(-1073 \text{ kJ/mol}) - (0.5)(-491 \text{ kJ/mol})$$

$$= -278 \text{ kJ/mol}$$

$\Delta_r H°_{298} = \Delta_r U°_{298} + P\Delta V$

$$= \Delta U°_0(\text{electronic, zero-pt. vib.}) + \Delta U°_{298}(\text{thermal}) + \Delta nRT$$

$$= -278 \text{ kJ/mol} - 2.6 \text{ kJ/mol} - 1 \text{ kJ/mol} = -282 \text{ kJ/mol}$$

Summary

The enthalpy function is an energy function that is adapted to processes occurring at constant pressure, the most common constraint on chemical reactions. An enthalpy change takes account of the small ΔU_{wt} term without our bothering with it. The enthalpy change is what is measured in standard calorimetric experiments, for which $\Delta H_\sigma = -\Delta U_\theta$ at constant pressure.

Hess' law plays a significant role in the uses of the enthalpy function. Reflecting the state function property of enthalpy, this "law" holds that the net enthalpy change for a multistep process is the same as the enthalpy of reaction for a single-step conversion of reactants into products. Standard enthalpies of formation, $Hf°$, of compounds are an outcome of setting to zero the enthalpies of formation of elements in their most stable forms in the standard state of 1 bar. Once tabulated, enthalpies of formation at 298 K of elements and compounds may be used to compute enthalpies of reaction, $\Delta_r H°_{298}$, for many conceivable chemical transformations. $\Delta_r H°_{298}$ is an intensive, per-mol-rxn quantity given by $\Sigma \nu_P Hf°(\text{prod}) - \Sigma \nu_R Hf°(\text{react})$.

To a good approximation $\Delta_r H°$ does not change with temperature. Consequently, $\Delta_r H°_T \approx \Delta_r H°_{298}$ over reasonable temperature ranges provided physical states of reactants and products remain unchanged, and aqueous ions are not involved.

A chemical bond of a given type between two atoms in various molecules is fairly well characterized by a single, average bond dissociation enthalpy, $DH°$. For reactions in the gas phase good estimates of enthalpies of reaction can be made from bond dissociation enthalpies with the relationship, $\Sigma \nu_R DH°(\text{react}) - \Sigma \nu_P DH°(\text{prod})$. This relationship has the opposite sign sense to the one involving $Hf°$ values.

Four types of energy contribute to the overall energies of atoms and molecules. These four types are electronic, translational, rotational, and vibrational energies. At room temperature the contribution of the electronic part due to the difference in bond strengths between reactants and products dominates $\Delta_r H°$.

Problems

1. 50 mL of 0.20 M copper nitrate and 100 mL of 3.00 M ammonia water at the same temperature were mixed in a Styrofoam cup and the temperature rose 1.45°C. What is $\Delta_r H$ for this reaction per mole of tetraamminecopper(II) complex $[Cu(NH_3)_4{}^{2+}]$ formed? For comparison calculate $\Delta_r H°_{298}$ for this reaction from tabulated enthalpies. One ans: $\Delta_r H = -91.0$ kJ/mol *for the experiment.*

2. 100 mL of 0.30 M aqueous potassium iodide and 100 mL of 0.15 M aqueous lead nitrate at the same temperature were mixed in a Styrofoam cup, and the

temperature rose 1.10°C. What is $\Delta_r H$ for this reaction per mole of lead iodide (PbI_2) formed? For comparison, calculate $\Delta_r H°_{298}$ for this reaction from tabulated enthalpies.   One ans: $\Delta_r H$ = –61.3 kJ/mol *for the experiment.*

3.   In the precipitation reaction in the previous problem, suppose that the reaction is accompanied by a decrease in volume of 0.5 mL under a pressure of 1 bar. What would ΔU_{wt} be for this process? Does air rise or fall in the earth's gravitational field when this reaction occurs? What percent of $\Delta_r H$ would this ΔU_{wt} be? One ans: ΔU_{wt} is 0.005% of $\Delta_r H$. Note that the data are for the specific reaction in the previous question, not for a mole's worth.

4.   500 mL of gaseous hydrogen chloride at 1 atm pressure was dissolved in 200 mL of water in a well-insulated container at room temperature. (One mole of gas at 1 bar pressure occupies 25 L at room temperature.) Compute $\Delta_r H_{298}$ for this dissolution process from tabulated data and predict the temperature change that occurs. One ans: $\Delta T = 1.79$°C.

5.   2.5 L of ethylene (C_2H_4) gas at 1 bar pressure and 5.0 L of hydrogen gas at 1 bar pressure were mixed together and passed through a catalyst surrounded by a 1.0 L water bath at room temperature. The temperature of the bath rose 3.10°C (One mole of gas occupies 25 L at 1 bar pressure at room temperature). What is $\Delta_r H$ for this reaction per mole of ethane (C_2H_6) formed?   For comparison calculate $\Delta_r H°$ for this reaction from tabulated enthalpies. One ans: $\Delta_r H = -130$ kJ/mol *for the experiment.*

6.   For the reaction $1/2 N_2(g) + O_2(g) \rightleftharpoons NO_2(g)$, $\Delta_r H°_{298} = 33.2$ kJ/mol. By considering the two-step process of first making nitric oxide (NO) and then converting the nitric oxide to nitrogen dioxide (NO_2) show that Hess' Law is satisfied for this chemistry.

7.   Use a Hess' law argument to compute the enthalpy of formation of benzene, $Hf°[C_6H_6(l)]$, from the enthalpies of combustion of benzene, graphite, and hydrogen.
$C_6H_6(l) + 15/2 O_2(g) \rightleftharpoons 6CO_2(g) + 3H_2O(l) \quad \Delta_r H° = -3267.6$ kJ/mol
$C(c,graph) + O_2(g) \rightleftharpoons CO_2(g) \qquad\qquad\qquad \Delta_r H° = -393.5$ kJ/mol
$H_2(g) + 1/2 O_2(g) \rightleftharpoons H_2O(l) \qquad\qquad\qquad \Delta_r H° = -285.8$ kJ/mol
Ans: See the value for benzene in Appendix D.

8.   (a) From tabulated data calculate $\Delta_r H°_{298}$ for the dissolution of solid ammonium chloride in water. The solution contains aqueous ammonium ions and aqueous chloride ions. Is this process endothermic or exothermic? Ans: $\Delta_r H° = 13.8$ kJ/mol, endothermic.
     (b) If 10 g of ammonium chloride are dissolved in 100 mL of water at 25.0 °C in a well-insulated, low thermal energy capacity container so that no

thermal energy is exchanged with the surroundings, what is the final temperature of the solution? Assume $\Delta_r H°_{298}$ is independent of concentration of the solution and that the heat capacity of the solution is the value for water, 4.18 J/K. Ans: $T = 18.9°C$.

9. Some substances do not undergo clean combustion with oxygen but do with fluorine. From measurements of their enthalpies of combustion with fluorine their enthalpies may be computed. The enthalpy of fluorine combustion of gaseous 1,1-difluoroethylene to gaseous HF and gaseous CF_4 is −2059.8 kJ/mol. Using this value and tabulated data compute $Hf°$ of gaseous 1,1-difluoroethylene. Ans: $Hf°(C_2H_2F_2) = -332.4$ kJ/mol.

10. Using the relationship $\Delta_r H°_T \approx \Delta_r H°_{298} + \Delta_r Cp°(T - 298\ K)$, find $\Delta_r H°_{600}$ for the reaction, $C(c) + 1/2 O_2(g) \rightleftharpoons CO(g)$. By what percent does $\Delta_r H°$ change in going from 298 to 600 K? Ans: $\Delta_r H°_{600} = -108.7$ kJ/mol; 1.6% change.

11. From tabulated bond-dissociation enthalpies estimate $\Delta_r H°_{298}$ for the following reactions, *after first making a qualitative judgment about each reaction being endothermic or exothermic.*

Addition reaction

$$Cl_2(g) + H_2C{=}CH_2(g) \rightleftharpoons ClH_2C{-}CH_2Cl(g)$$

Partial oxidation

$$CH_4(g) + O_2(g) \rightleftharpoons H_2C{=}O(g) + H_2O(g)$$

Formation of CF_2 as a reactive intermediate in making $CF_2{=}CF_2$, which is readily polymerized into Teflon,

$$CHF_2Cl(g) \rightleftharpoons CF_2(g) + HCl(g)$$

One ans: $\Delta_r H° \approx -406$ kJ/mol.

12. Using bond dissociation enthalpies, calculate $\Delta_r H°$ for the reaction

$$HC{\equiv}CH(g) + F_2(g) \rightleftharpoons HFC{=}CFH(g)$$

This reaction cannot be studied directly. CF_4 and HF are the products of reaction of F_2 with acetylene. Ans: $\Delta_r H° \approx -586$ kJ/mol.

13. The human body "burns as fuel" the food we eat, but uses the energy released much more efficiently than as an equivalent amount of thermal energy.

Different types of food differ substantially in their fuel value, and fats generally have a higher caloric value than proteins. As a model fat consider 1-monostearin (M.W. = 358.6 g/mol)

$$\underset{H_2C}{\overset{OH}{|}}-\underset{CHCH_2O}{\overset{OH}{|}}-\overset{O}{\overset{||}{C}}(CH_2)_{16}CH_3 \qquad \text{with } Hf^\circ = -1337 \text{ kJ/mol}$$

and, as a model protein, the amino acid glycine

$$H_2NCH_2COOH \qquad \text{with } Hf^\circ = -528 \text{ kJ/mol}$$

Calculate $\Delta_r H^\circ{}_{298}$ for combustion of 1 mol of each of these compounds assuming the products to be only $CO_2(g)$, $H_2O(l)$, and $N_2(g)$. Which has the greater fuel value on a per-gram basis? (It is interesting to note that the "calories" counted in your diet are actually kilocalories, possibly for psychological reasons.) One ans: $\Delta H^\circ{}_{298} = -12{,}928$ kJ/mol monostearin $= -36.1$ kJ/g monostearin.

4. ENTROPY PRINCIPLE: THE SECOND LAW

The first law of thermodynamics places no limits on energy exchanges provided energy is conserved. Experience teaches us that the weight-lifted energy of a raised book can be completely converted into thermal energy of a table top and the book when the dropped book lands on the table. The reverse process in which energy is also conserved is, however, impossible. Similarly, there are limitations on the transfer of thermal energy from a cold body to a hot body. A chemical reaction has a favored direction even though energy is conserved in both directions. Thus, where thermal energy is involved, we find a one-wayness in first-law possible energy transactions.

This chapter introduces the second law of thermodynamics and the entropy function that is the heart of this law. The entropy function is the index of change for all processes. It confirms the one-wayness of dropped books interacting with table tops. The entropy function tells whether a chemical reaction can occur as written and when a reaction has reached equilibrium. This chapter concentrates on chemical applications of the entropy function. The next chapter applies this function to the everyday energy convertors, heat engines and refrigerators.

Because the entropy function is a state function, tabulated molar entropies give the entropy of reaction in a simple way. Through the third law of thermodynamics, which is also introduced in this chapter, molar entropies have natural zero values at absolute zero (zero kelvin). As a consequence of the increase in entropy with increasing temperature, elements as well as compounds have substantial positive entropies at room temperature. Patterns exist in these molar entropies that can be correlated with molecular structure.

As part of the entropy principle, the entropy change accompanying an energy change in a thermal reservoir depends inversely on the kelvin temperature. An important consequence of this temperature dependence is the temperature dependence of the outcome of chemical reactions. A familiar example of this effect is the reversal in direction of spontaneity for phase changes as seen in the melting of ice above 0°C and the freezing of water below 0°C.

The Second Law (Entropy Principle)

We begin by expressing the second law as an algebraic statement of the entropy principle. For most applications of thermodynamics the entropy-principle form of the second law is directly useful because it provides a numerical index for the spontaneous direction of change and for the extent to which change is possible. On first encounter, this approach suffers from being abstract. Consequently, we shall take steps immediately to show how the entropy principle applies to familiar processes.

With the prototypical σ–θ–wt system in mind, as shown in Fig. 2.1, we use S as the symbol for the entropy function and express the entropy principle as

$$
\boxed{
\begin{array}{c}
\textit{Second Law of Thermodynamics} \\[4pt]
\Delta S_{\text{tot}} = \Delta S_{\sigma} + \Delta S_{\theta} \geq 0 \\
S_{\sigma} \text{ and } S_{\theta} \text{ are independently} \\
\text{state functions and are} \\
\text{extensive functions.} \\
\Delta S_{\theta} = \Delta U_{\theta}/T_{\theta} \text{ and } \Delta S_{\text{wt}} = 0
\end{array}
}
\qquad (4.1)
$$

ΔS_{tot} is the change in the total entropy, that is, the change in entropy of the overall system or "universe." ΔS_{σ} is the change in entropy in the reactive system; ΔS_{θ} is the change in entropy in the thermal reservoir. In parallel with the formulation of the first law, this statement of the second law: (1) focuses on the sum of the changes of entropy contributed by each part of the overall system; (2) designates the entropy function as a state function; (3) designates S_{σ} and S_{θ} as extensive functions; and (4) relates entropy change in a thermal reservoir to experimentally accessible quantities.

The first expression in the entropy principle gives ΔS_{tot}. For *spontaneous* processes the change in total entropy is greater than zero. Such processes are also called *natural* or *irreversible* processes. When $\Delta S_{\text{tot}} = 0$, the process under consideration is at *equilibrium*. When a spontaneous change takes place with ΔS_{tot} only infinitesimally different from zero, the process passes through a succession of near-equilibrium states and is said to be *reversible*. In a reversible process changes in the reverse direction are the exact undoing of *all* the changes of the universe in the forward direction. In our development we shall use $\Delta S_{\text{tot}} = 0$ as a criterion for a reversible or equilibrium process. When $\Delta S_{\text{tot}} < 0$, the exact reverse of the process under consideration is spontaneous. It is important to recognize that ΔS_{tot} does not include ΔS_{wt} because $\Delta S_{\text{wt}} = 0$ in all cases. The reason is that the energy of the weight is ordered. This reason will be clearer after our discussion of entropy from a microscopic point of view in Chapter 6.

The second part of the entropy principle asserts that the entropy function is a state function, independently for the σ and θ subsystems. Because entropy is a state function, its change depends only on the initial and final states and not on the details of the transformation. As we shall see, this state function property is very important for applications of the entropy function. Entropy is also an *extensive* function. This property means that S_{σ} is proportional to the amount of material present, and ΔS_{σ} is proportional to the moles of material which are transformed. This property also means that the entropy function is an additive function for two chemical systems that are considered together but do not interact. The entropy function shares the state function and extensive property with the energy and the enthalpy functions.

The third expression, $\Delta S_\theta = \Delta U_\theta/T_\theta$, provides an experimentally well-defined way to obtain ΔS_θ, since we already know how to measure ΔU_θ and T_θ. Note well that the absolute or kelvin temperature is used in this expression. The units for entropy are joules/kelvin. Although the temperature changes a bit as energy is exchanged with a thermal reservoir, in this text we shall stress applications in which ΔT_θ is small compared with T_θ. Thus, the expression $\Delta S_\theta = \Delta U_\theta/T_\theta$ may be applied directly. Calculus methods must be used if the condition $T_\theta \gg \Delta T_\theta$ is not satisfied. For processes occurring under constant pressure conditions, $\Delta U_\theta = -\Delta H_\sigma$, which means we can relate ΔS_θ to tabulated enthalpies through the relationship, $\Delta S_\theta = -\Delta H_\sigma/T_\theta$. The restriction of the $\Delta S_\theta = \Delta U_\theta/T_\theta$ expression to thermal reservoirs must be strongly emphasized. In general, a similar expression does not apply to the entropy change in reactive systems. Thus, commonly, $\Delta S_\sigma \neq \Delta U_\sigma/T_\sigma$ and $\Delta S_\sigma \neq \Delta H_\sigma/T_\sigma$.

The entropy principle stands in sharp contrast to the energy principle. Whereas the energy principle is a conservation law, the entropy principle is a growth law. The very symbols that are used suggest this difference. The shape of the letter "S" seems to move forward; "U" contains. The total entropy or, as it is often said, the "entropy of the universe" increases in all spontaneous processes. As a consequence, the entropy principle is an action principle. It tells the direction of change. Indeed, the Greek roots for entropy are "change in."

Although the total entropy must increase, it is possible to have local decreases in entropy. For example, the entropy change for the reactive system (chemical reaction) may decrease, provided this entropy decrease is offset by a larger entropy increase in the thermal reservoir. Thus, while ΔS_σ is negative, ΔS_θ is positive and larger in this case. Some people have suggested that living systems violate the second law because such systems depend on many processes for which $\Delta S_\sigma < 0$. Localized decreases in entropy in living systems can be traced, however, back to compensation by larger entropy increases as the concentrated, ordered energy in sunlight is ultimately degraded into thermal energy.

Let us apply the entropy principle to equilibrium between two thermal reservoirs and show that the two temperatures must be equal. Can you make a sketch of such an overall system? For an overall system of two thermal reservoirs in which some energy is exchanged between them, we have from the first law

$$\Delta U_{\theta 1} + \Delta U_{\theta 2} = 0 \tag{4.2}$$

and from the second law for a process occurring at equilibrium ($\Delta S_{tot} = 0$)

$$\Delta S_{tot} = \Delta S_{\theta 1} + \Delta S_{\theta 2} = \frac{\Delta U_{\theta 1}}{T_{\theta 1}} + \frac{\Delta U_{\theta 2}}{T_{\theta 2}} = 0 \tag{4.3}$$

Using the first law expression to eliminate $\Delta U_{\theta 2}$ from the second law expression, we have

$$\frac{\Delta U_{\theta 1}}{T_{\theta 1}} - \frac{\Delta U_{\theta 1}}{T_{\theta 2}} = \Delta U_{\theta 1}\left(\frac{1}{T_{\theta 1}} - \frac{1}{T_{\theta 2}}\right) = 0 \tag{4.4}$$

The resulting expression is a *combined first- and second-law expression*. We shall often develop such combinations. Since we are considering an energy transfer, $\Delta U_{\theta 1} \neq 0$. Hence, $T_{\theta 1}$ must equal $T_{\theta 2}$ in order for that expression to equal zero. This familiar condition of equal temperatures for thermal equilibrium between two thermal reservoirs is consistent with the entropy principle. Another way of viewing equilibrium between two thermal reservoirs at the same temperature is to say that the entropy decrease in one due to a small energy transaction exactly balances the entropy increase in the other.

From what has been said so far, it may appear that we do not have access to definite values of ΔS_{σ}. Yet, for chemical applications we need such values. We can obtain them from studies of *reversible* processes, for which

$$\Delta S_{tot} = \Delta S_{\sigma} + \Delta S_{\theta} = 0 \tag{4.5}$$

and

$$\Delta S_{\sigma} = -\Delta S_{\theta} = \frac{-\Delta U_{\theta}}{T_{\theta}} = \frac{-\Delta U_{\theta}}{T} \tag{4.6}$$

We have replaced T_{θ} with T because for a reversible energy transaction with a thermal reservoir the temperature gradient must be negligible. Of course, once found, such a ΔS_{σ} can be applied to irreversible (spontaneous) processes connecting the same initial and final states because the entropy function is a state function. Once again, we have an example of the indirect strategy of thermodynamics, which depends on the path-independent property of state functions as well as on the energy and entropy principles.

As part of the entropy principle, we have written explicitly that $\Delta S_{wt} = 0$, that is, no entropy change occurs in the weight system *itself* when the weight changes height in the gravitational field. That $\Delta S_{wt} = 0$ is implicit in the absence of a ΔS_{wt} term from the ΔS_{tot} expression, even though the overall system includes a weight part. Most persons new to this formulation need, however, to be alerted to this aspect of the entropy principle.

Although we have attempted to draw out the implications of the entropy principle and set the stage for its application, this principle probably still appears to be an abstract mathematical one, unrelated to familiar events. We shall therefore embark upon a three-phase investigation in order to breathe life into the entropy principle and show its many applications. In the first phase we shall apply the entropy principle to chemical reactions and look for patterns in molar entropies. We shall show, for example, that the entropy principle is consistent with our knowledge of the conditions under which "cold water" freezes and "warm ice" melts. In the second phase, Chapter 5, we shall show that the entropy principle is consistent with the classical statements of the second law which are expressed in terms of energy transactions of thermal reservoirs. These statements apply directly to the everyday energy conversion processes in heat engines and refrigerators. In the third phase, Chapter 6, we shall investigate the relationship of the entropy function to processes occurring at the atomic–molecular level. In doing so, we shall distinguish *thermal entropy*, which measures the extent to which energy is dispersed among the motions of atoms and molecules, and *configurational entropy*, which measures the extent to which atoms and molecules are dispersed in space in mixtures.

Application of the Entropy Principle to Chemical Systems

As the first phase in our investigation of the entropy principle, we apply it to phase changes and to chemical reactions. We also consider how the values for standard molar entropies for perfect crystalline substances are naturally given zero values at absolute zero (zero kelvin) by the third law of thermodynamics. As a consequence of this choice of reference state and of the increase in entropy of a substance with increase in temperature, all entropies at room temperature, except for some ions, are substantially positive. Useful patterns related to atomic and molecular structure can be found in these molar entropies.

Entropy of Reaction. Since entropy is a state function, the calculation of entropies of reaction proceeds from tabulated molar entropies in a fashion exactly like that used in calculating enthalpies of reaction from tabulated enthalpies of formation. First, a balanced chemical equation is written, in which states of each reactant and product are carefully specified. Then, the relationship

$$\boxed{\Delta_r S_\sigma \; = \; \sum v_P S(\text{prod}) - \sum v_R S(\text{react})} \qquad (4.7)$$

is applied. The units of the entropy of reaction are J/K mol rxn, or simply J/K mol. For example, eq. (4.7) gives for the reaction of carbon monoxide and oxygen to form carbon dioxide

$$CO(g) + 1/2O_2(g) \; \rightleftharpoons \; CO_2(g)$$

$S^\circ_{\sigma,298}$ (J/K mol):   197.7   1/2(205.1)   213.7 $\Delta_r S^\circ = -86.6$ J/K mol

Once again, we use the recommended systematic procedure. The molar entropies, weighted by appropriate stoichiometric coefficients, are written under each species in the balanced, state-specified chemical equation. The values of the molar entropies are from the table in Appendix D. The sum of the entropies of the reactants is subtracted from the sum of the entropies of the products. *Note that units of entropies are expressed in joules not kilojoules*, which are the commonly used unit for enthalpies. Note too that the elementary substance, oxygen, has a substantial molar entropy at room temperature. For this reaction, as for other gas-consuming reactions, a sizeable decrease in entropy occurs. This generalization and its converse for gas-producing reactions are ones we shall use frequently.

It is the entropy change in the reactive system (σ) that we calculate from tabulated entropies. Such entropy changes may be negative for spontaneous reactions as in the present case provided ΔS_θ, the entropy change in the thermal reservoir, is positive and large enough to offset the negative value of ΔS_σ. We shall return to this issue and the general problem of assessing spontaneity in chemical reactions and phase changes after discussing molar entropies.

Molar Entropies

We consider molar entropies under standard state conditions at 298 K (25°C) that are placed in typical tables. We begin by discussing the way in which these values are derived from experiments. Two concepts are involved: (1) the third law of thermodynamics, which establishes 0 K as the natural reference temperature for entropies; and (2) the increase in entropy with temperature as substances are warmed from 0 K to 298 K. First, we consider the third law.

Third Law. As we shall see fully in Chapter 6, the entropy function measures disorder — disorder of energy distributed over the motions of atoms and molecules and disorder of position of molecules in space. The more such disordering, the higher the entropy. Thus, it is quite reasonable to assign a zero value of entropy to a *perfect crystalline* substance at absolute zero (0 K). Such a crystal is a *pure* substance and has all its atoms and molecules properly aligned relative to one another. At absolute zero the crystal has no more energy than its electronic energy and the zero-point energy required by the Heisenberg Uncertainty Principle of quantum mechanics. For carbon monoxide Fig. 4.1 shows schematically a possible perfect alignment of molecules in a crystal and an imperfect alignment. In the perfect alignment the molecules in successive rows point in opposite directions, thereby optimizing dipole interactions. In the imperfect alignment, some molecules are turned around relative to the others in their rows. Specifically, our statement of the third law will be

$$\boxed{\begin{array}{c} \textit{Third Law of Thermodynamics} \\[4pt] S^\circ_0 = 0 \text{ for a perfect crystalline substance} \end{array}} \qquad (4.8)$$

$$
\begin{array}{ll}
\begin{array}{l}
\text{C}\!\equiv\!\text{O C}\!\equiv\!\text{O C}\!\equiv\!\text{O C}\!\equiv\!\text{O} \\
\text{O}\!\equiv\!\text{C O}\!\equiv\!\text{C O}\!\equiv\!\text{C O}\!\equiv\!\text{C} \\
\text{C}\!\equiv\!\text{O C}\!\equiv\!\text{O C}\!\equiv\!\text{O C}\!\equiv\!\text{O} \\
\text{O}\!\equiv\!\text{C O}\!\equiv\!\text{C O}\!\equiv\!\text{C O}\!\equiv\!\text{C}
\end{array}
&
\begin{array}{l}
\text{C}\!\equiv\!\text{O C}\!\equiv\!\text{O }\boxed{\text{O}\!\equiv\!\text{C}}\text{ C}\!\equiv\!\text{O} \\
\text{O}\!\equiv\!\text{C O}\!\equiv\!\text{C O}\!\equiv\!\text{C O}\!\equiv\!\text{C} \\
\boxed{\text{O}\!\equiv\!\text{C}}\text{ C}\!\equiv\!\text{O C}\!\equiv\!\text{O C}\!\equiv\!\text{O} \\
\text{O}\!\equiv\!\text{C O}\!\equiv\!\text{C }\boxed{\text{C}\!\equiv\!\text{O}}\text{ O}\!\equiv\!\text{C}
\end{array}
\end{array}
$$

$$\text{aligned, } S^\circ_0 \equiv 0 \qquad\qquad \text{imperfectly aligned, } S^\circ_0 > 0$$

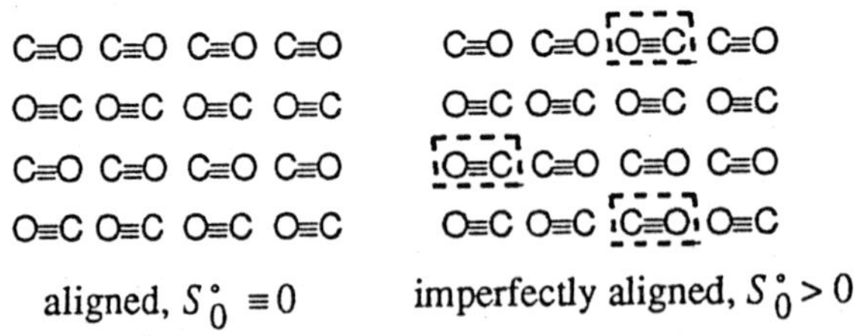

Figure 4.1. Perfect and imperfect alignments of carbon monoxide molecules in a crystal. The misaligned molecules are enclosed with dashed lines.

The standard state entropy of a perfect crystalline substance is zero at absolute zero. The superscript zero, °, means the standard state condition of 1 bar; the subscript 0 means the temperature of 0 K. The third law applies to pure compounds as well as to pure elementary substances. For three different, but perfect crystalline forms of the same substance, such as diamond, graphite, and C_{60}, all have zero entropy at absolute zero. The third law does not apply to solutions because they have configurational entropy and are thus not perfectly crystalline.

The third law rests on much experimental data which demonstrate that ΔS_σ's for chemical reactions involving crystalline reactants and products approach zero as the temperature approaches absolute zero. If $\Delta S_\sigma = 0$ for a reaction, then reactants and products have the same entropies, which can be zero. The third law also rests on much evidence about the structure of crystals obtained from x-ray studies and about the energy states accessible to atoms and molecules in crystals. If one assigns zero values to entropies at absolute zero and uses the methods of statistical thermodynamics to compute entropies at room temperature for reactants and products in chemical reactions, the calculated ΔS_σ's agree with values obtained from direct measurements of ΔS_σ's based on warmup experiments. The third law is confirmed.

Through the third law we have a convenient and natural zero for entropies. Thus, we shall not have to make the arbitrary choice of zero values that we made for enthalpies of formation of elementary substances at 298 K. We must take account experimentally, however, of the entropy that a substance, an elementary substance or a compound, accumulates as it is warmed from absolute zero to room temperature. Thus, all substances (except some ions in aqueous solution) have positive entropies at room temperature.

Temperature Dependence of the Entropy Function. Having introduced the principle that $S°_0 = 0$ for perfect crystalline substances, we turn to a brief discussion of the temperature dependence of the entropy function. To do so we consider, as in the first section of this chapter, the reversible transfer of energy from a thermal reservoir into a reactive system, which is a single, pure substance for the present purpose. Thus,

$$\overset{(+)}{} \quad \overset{(-)}{} \qquad \Delta S_\sigma = \frac{-\Delta U_\theta}{T} \qquad\qquad T_\sigma = T_\theta = \text{const.} \qquad (4.9)$$

As an aid to our thinking, we show the signs of ΔS_σ and ΔU_θ above the terms in the previous equation. To obtain a standard entropy at 298 K for use in a table of data, the increments of entropy, which are acquired at each temperature at temperatures between 0 K and 298 K must be summed. To do so precisely calls for the application of calculus methods. Phase transitions (solid-to-liquid transitions and the like) occur at constant temperature. For these steps in the warmup process $\Delta S_\sigma = \Delta H_\sigma / T$ exactly at a constant temperature. Because of the third law, we obtain "absolute" or "third-law" entropies by this method,

$$\Delta S^\circ_\sigma = S^\circ_{\sigma,298} - S^\circ_0 = S^\circ_{\sigma,298} - 0 = S^\circ_{\sigma,298} \qquad (4.10)$$

Thus, the entropy accumulated in warming the substance from absolute zero to room temperature becomes S°_{298}.

As an example of the contributions to the entropy of a substance as it is warmed from near absolute zero to room temperature, we consider gaseous sulfur dioxide. This process has five distinct contributions: (1) warming crystalline SO_2 from near absolute zero to its melting point at 198 K; (2) melting SO_2 at 198 K; (3) warming liquid SO_2 from 198 K to its normal boiling point at 263 K ($-10°C$); (4) vaporizing SO_2 at 263 K and 1 bar pressure; and (5) warming gaseous SO_2 at 1 bar pressure from 263 K to 298 K.

$$S^\circ_{298}(SO_2) = \Delta S^\circ_c(0 - 198 \text{ K}) + \Delta S^\circ_{c \to l}(198 \text{ K}) + \Delta S^\circ_l(198 - 263 \text{ K})$$

$$+ \Delta S^\circ_{l \to g}(263 \text{ K}) + \Delta S^\circ_g(263 - 298 \text{ K})$$

$$= 85.4 + 37.4 + 25.1 + 95.3 + 5.0 = 248.2 \text{ J/K mol} \qquad (4.11)$$

Note that the vaporization process makes a large contribution, especially in comparison with the melting process.

Patterns in Molar Entropies. Now that we know how absolute entropies depend on the third law and how they may be obtained from warm-up experiments, we examine tabulated molar entropies in Appendix D for patterns that can help us get better acquainted with entropy and anticipate relationships to atomic-molecular models. From a consideration of the molar entropies of single substances we see that entropies increase as a substance goes from the solid state to the liquid state and then on to the gaseous state. For water this sequence is: $S^\circ_{298}(c) \approx 44.6$ J/K mol; $S^\circ_{298}(l) = 69.9$ J/K mol; and $S^\circ_{298}(g) = 188.7$ J/K mol. In general, the increase in entropy in going to the gaseous state is the dominant change. Thus, as we have already seen in the reaction of carbon monoxide and oxygen, the net production or consumption of gases in chemical reactions that involve gases dominates the entropy change for these reactions.

The second generalization about entropies is that entropy increases as the complexity of molecules or ions increases within the same phase. Thus, for example, we find the following sequence of molar entropies for gaseous substances (in J/K mol at 298 K): Kr, 164.1; Cl_2, 223.1; SO_2, 248.2; SiF_4, 282.5. In the solid phase we have the sequence: NaCl, 72.1; Na_2S, 83.7; Na_2CO_3, 134.4; Na_2SO_4, 149.6.

The third generalization is that entropy increases as mass increases. We see this effect directly in the molar entropies for a series of noble gases (in J/K mol at 298K): He, 126.2; Ne, 146.3; Ar, 154.8; Kr, 164.1; Xe, 169.7. In selecting examples to illustrate the effect of molecular complexity on entropy, we selected sequences in which the mass did not change greatly and thereby also contribute substantially to the change in entropy.

The fourth generalization is that entropy increases as an element is replaced with periodic table family members of increasing atomic number. We find this trend for crystalline elementary substances in the sequences (in J/K mol at 298 K): Li, 29.1; Na, 51.2; K, 64.2; Rb, 76.8; Cs, 85.2 and C(graphite), 5.7; Si, 18.8; Ge, 31.1; Sn(white), 51.6; Pb, 64.8. We also find this trend when one species in a compound is replaced with family members of increasing atomic number, as in the series of crystalline substances (in J/K mol at 298 K): LiCl, 59.3; NaCl, 72.1; KCl, 82.6; RbCl, 95.9; CsCl; 101.2. This latter pattern in molar entropies is a combination of the effects of decreasing bond strength and increasing mass. Both effects cause an increase in entropy. As we shall see for solids in Chapter 6, a decrease in bond strength and an increase in mass have comparable effects on decreasing energy level spacings of atomic oscillations and thus of increasing entropy.

Returning to the trend in entropy that accompanies increasing molecular or ionic complexity, we note that it is important to compare substances with comparable bond strengths as well as comparable masses. Thus, ionic compounds should be compared only with ionic compounds, metals with metals, molecular substances with molecular ones, and macromolecular substances with macromolecular ones. In order of decreasing importance of the various influences on entropies, we have

1) The physical state: entropy increases in the sense solid < liquid << gas.
2) Complexity: entropy increases with complexity of molecules or ions.
3) Bond strength: entropy increases with decreasing bond strength;
   mass: entropy increases with increasing mass.

Effects of bond strength and mass are comparable. From the foregoing discussion we conclude that good estimates of molar entropies of untabulated substances can be made by using the entropies of known substances of the same physical state, same composition, similar bond strength, and similar mass. For example, we could estimate the molar entropy of $O_3(g)$ as being that of $NO_2(g)$, which is 240 J/K mol. The actual value for O_3 is 239 J/K mol. These molecules have similar masses, are bent, and have some double-bond character. The reason that NO_2 has a slightly higher entropy is that it has an unpaired electron and therefore two ground electronic energy states.

Table 4.1   Temperature Dependence of $\Delta_r S^\circ$

	$\Delta_r S^\circ{}_{298}$ J/K mol	$\Delta_r S^\circ{}_{598}$ J/K mol	Percentage change
Reactions Involving Gases			
$NO(g) + 1/2 O_2(g) \rightleftharpoons NO_2(g)$	–72.8	–77.4	6.3
$CO(g) + 1/2 O_2(g) \rightleftharpoons CO_2(g)$	–86.6	–91.2	5.3
$C_2H_4(g) + H_2(g) \rightleftharpoons C_2H_6(g)$	–120.5	–132.2	9.7
Reactions Involving Solids and Gases			
$CaCO_3(c) \rightleftharpoons CaO(c) + CO_2(g)$	160.7	156.5	2.7
$C(c) + 1/2 O_2(g) \rightleftharpoons CO(g)$	89.5	93.7	4.5

Adapted from G. C. Pimentel and R. D. Spratley, *Understanding Chemistry*, Holden-Day, 1971, p. 389.

Weak Temperature Dependence of the Entropy of Reaction

In the last chapter we showed that the temperature dependence of the enthalpy of reaction, $\Delta_r H^\circ$, is weak. As a useful approximation, we took $\Delta_r H^\circ$ to be a constant as temperature changed. A similar generalization applies to the entropy of reaction. Table 4.1 contains the entropy changes for the same reactions that were considered in the enthalpy discussion. While the percentage changes in $\Delta_r S^\circ$ over the 300 K temperature interval are somewhat larger than for $\Delta_r H^\circ$, they are all less than 10%. For our purposes we shall regard $\Delta_r S^\circ$ as having a negligible temperature dependence *above 250 K*, provided no reactant or product changes its physical state and no ions in aqueous solution are involved. As was the case with $\Delta_r H^\circ$, the partial cancellation of heat capacities in $\Delta_r C p^\circ$ can also be shown to be the reason for the weak temperature dependence of $\Delta_r S^\circ$. The reason for the restriction of this approximation to temperatures above 250 K is the third law. As the temperature goes toward absolute zero, $\Delta_r S^\circ \rightarrow 0$ since both reactants and products have $S^\circ{}_0 = 0$.

Direct Application of the Entropy Principle to Phase Changes and Chemical Reactions

In this section we apply the entropy principle to the familiar ice to liquid water phase transition and to a simple chemical reaction.

By combining the first and second laws, we can express the total entropy change in terms of the entropy and enthalpy changes *within the reactive system*. In doing so, we will have moved from the global point of view in which the laws are expressed initially to a reactive-system-oriented point of view. This is an application of the familiar change-of-view strategy that was used in developing $\Delta U_{wt} = P_\sigma \Delta V_\sigma$ and the enthalpy function. At constant temperature and pressure, the most common experimental constraints, we have

$$\Delta H_\sigma = -\Delta U_\theta \qquad\qquad \text{first law, const. pressure} \qquad (4.12)$$

$$\Delta S_{tot} = \Delta S_\sigma + \Delta S_\theta = \Delta S_\sigma + \frac{\Delta U_\theta}{T} \geq 0 \quad \text{sec. law, const. temp.} \qquad (4.13)$$

The significance of constant temperature is that $T_\sigma = T_\theta = T$. Combining these expressions, we have

$$\boxed{\begin{array}{c} \Delta S_{tot} = \Delta S - \dfrac{\Delta H}{T} \geq 0 \\ \text{at constant } T \text{ and } P \end{array}} \qquad\qquad (4.14)$$

In eq. (4.14) we have omitted the σ subscripts on ΔS and ΔH on the understanding that this equation is specifically adapted to reactive system quantities. For phase changes and chemical reactions, values of $\Delta_r S°_{298}$ and $\Delta_r H°_{298}$ can be calculated from tabulated thermodynamic functions. Thus, eq. (4.14) can be applied readily to a process occurring in a reactive system.

Since $\Delta_r S°$ and $\Delta_r H°$ are weak functions of temperature, $\Delta_r S°_{298}$ and $\Delta_r H°_{298}$ can be used in eq. (4.14) to estimate ΔS_{tot} at temperatures other than 298 K. Because the weak temperature dependences of $\Delta_r S°$ and $\Delta_r H°$ tend to cancel in eq. (4.14), this approximation for ΔS_{tot} is better than the approximations for the separate $\Delta_r S°$ and $\Delta_r H°$ terms.

Melting of Warm Ice; Freezing of Cold Water. We begin by studying a very familiar process, the melting and freezing of water. At 0°C, ice and water are at equilibrium. ΔS_{tot} is zero for melting and freezing. Above 0°C, ice melts. ΔS_{tot} is greater than zero for this spontaneous process. Below 0°C, water freezes. ΔS_{tot} is greater than zero for this spontaneous reaction.

As always, the first step is to write a chemical equation to establish the stoichiometric coefficients and the direction of the reaction and to specify the states of reactants and products. A pressure of 1 bar is usually chosen in order to make direct use of tabulated data. Note that these data, however, are for 273 K (0°C). Thus,

$$H_2O(c) \rightleftharpoons H_2O(l) \qquad\qquad P = 1 \text{ bar, } T = 273 \text{ K}$$

$Hf°_{273}$ (J/mol):	$-293{,}700$	$-287{,}700$	$\Delta_r H°_{273} = 6000$ J/mol
$S°_{273}$ (J/K mol):	41.3	63.3	$\Delta_r S°_{273} = 22.0$ J/K mol

Assuming $\Delta_r H°_{273}$ and $\Delta_r S°_{273}$ are essentially constant over the temperature range of interest, we have

$$\Delta S_{tot} = 22.0 \text{ J/K mol} - \frac{6000 \text{ J/mol}}{T} \tag{4.15}$$

We have expressed $\Delta_r H^\circ$ in joules to make it compatible with the units of $\Delta_r S^\circ$. In the following tabulation we compare ΔS_{tot} for 10°C, 0°C, and −10°C.

T (°C)	T (K)	$\Delta_r S^\circ{}_\sigma$	$-\Delta_r H_\sigma/T$ ΔS_θ	ΔS_{tot}	Spontaneous direction of reaction
10	283	22.0	−21.1	0.9 J/K mol	ice melts
0	273	22.0	−22.0	0	equilibrium
−10	263	22.0	−22.8	−0.8 J/K mol	water freezes (reverse rxn)

We have used σ's to emphasize the distinction between changes occurring in the reactive system and in the thermal reservoir. Warm ice (above 0°C) melts because in doing so the entropy of the universe increases. At 10°C the positive entropy change in the reactive system, ΔS_σ, due to melting ice outweighs the negative entropy change in the thermal reservoir, ΔS_θ. The negative entropy change in the thermal reservoir accompanies the withdrawal of the enthalpy of melting from the thermal reservoir. The entropy change in the thermal reservoir is expressed by the $-\Delta H_\sigma/T$ term. At 0°C the ΔS_σ and ΔS_θ ($-\Delta H_\sigma/T$) terms balance; ice and liquid water are in equilibrium. At −10° the ice to liquid water process is not spontaneous, but its reverse is. For the freezing process,

$$H_2O(l) \;\rightleftharpoons\; H_2O(c)$$

the signs of all of the entropy terms are changed. Thus,

$$\overset{(-)}{\Delta S_{tot}} = \overset{}{\Delta S_\sigma} + \overset{(+)}{\Delta S_\theta} > 0 \tag{4.16}$$

Cold water (below 0°C) freezes because in doing so the entropy of the universe increases. The entropy decrease in the reactive system, ΔS_σ, due to the freezing process is outweighed by the entropy increase in the thermal reservoir, ΔS_θ. This entropy increase in the thermal reservoir is caused by the release of the enthalpy of freezing. The ΔS_θ term is dominant at temperatures below 0°C.

A temperature dependence of the direction of spontaneous reaction is common to phase transitions. It is a consequence of the inverse temperature dependence of ΔS_θ, expressed as $-\Delta H_\sigma/T$. At lower temperatures ΔS_θ is larger than at higher temperatures for a given energy transaction. The entropy "price" that must be paid for taking energy from a thermal reservoir at lower temperatures is more than the entropy "price" that must be paid for the same energy withdrawal at higher temperatures.

As we have seen for the ice to liquid water transition, the equilibrium temperature is where $\Delta S_{total} = \Delta_r S° - \Delta_r H°/T = 0$, $\Delta_r S° = \Delta_r H°/T$. We can use this condition to find the equilibrium temperature (mp = melting point) under standard state conditions (1 bar pressure) if it is not already known. The result is

$$T_{mp} = \Delta_r H°/\Delta_r S° = (6000 \text{ J/mol})/(22.0 \text{ J/K mol}) = 273 \text{ K} \qquad (4.17)$$

to three significant figures. It is essential, however, to note that $\Delta_r S°$ does *not* equal $\Delta_r H°/T$ at temperatures other than the equilibrium one.

Two Limiting Regimes of Spontaneous Processes. Two important generalizations about the spontaneous direction of reaction may be drawn from eq. (4.14). *Exothermic reactions are favored at lower temperatures.* This outcome is true because $-\Delta H_\sigma/T$, the ΔS_θ term, becomes large and positive and dominates the ΔS_σ term regardless of the sign of ΔS_σ. Thus, water freezes, an exothermic process, below 0°C. *Reactions accompanied by an increase in entropy in the reactive system are favored at higher temperatures.* This outcome is true because $-\Delta H_\sigma/T$ decreases in magnitude as the temperature increases, and ΔS_{total} is then dominated by the ΔS_σ term regardless of the sign of ΔH_σ. Thus, ice melts, an entropy-increasing process in the reactive system, above 0°C. More generally, we can say that liquids freeze and gases condense at lower temperatures because in both cases $-\Delta H_\sigma/T$ is dominantly positive. On the other hand, solids melt and liquids vaporize at higher temperatures because in both cases ΔS_σ is dominantly positive.

A Chemical Reaction. ΔS_{tot}, as calculated by eq. (4.14), can be used to assess spontaneity in chemical reactions. The gas-phase reaction of carbon monoxide and oxygen to form carbon dioxide considered earlier in this chapter serves as a good example. $\Delta S_\sigma = \Delta_r S°_{298} = -86.6$ J/K mol. For $\Delta_r H°_{298}$ we have

$$CO(g) + 1/2 O_2(g) \rightleftharpoons CO_2(g)$$

$Hf°$ (kJ/mol): -110.5 0 -393.5 $\Delta_r H°_{298} = -283.0$ kJ/mol

Then,

$$\Delta S_{tot} = \Delta S_\sigma - \frac{\Delta H_\sigma}{T} = -86.6 \text{ J/K mol} + \frac{283{,}000 \text{ J/mol}}{298 \text{ K}}$$

$$= (-86.6 + 949.7) \text{ J/K mol} = 863.1 \text{ J/K mol} \qquad (4.18)$$

Joules have been used as the units of $\Delta_r H°$ in order to match the units of $\Delta_r S°$. Since ΔS_{tot} is substantially greater than zero, this reaction is highly favored at room temperature under standard state conditions. The enormous entropy increase in the thermal reservoir, represented by the $-\Delta H_\sigma/T$ term, for this exothermic reaction more than offsets the entropy decrease in the reactive system.

At very high temperatures the $-\Delta H_\sigma/T$ term becomes small enough that the negative ΔS_σ term dominates. Under these conditions the reverse reaction with a positive ΔS_σ becomes spontaneous. A very rough estimate of the turn around or equilibrium temperature can be made by setting $\Delta S_{tot} = 0$. Approximating $\Delta S°_T$ and $\Delta_r H°_T$ by their 298 K values, and solving for the T_{equil} value, we have

$$\Delta S_{tot} = 0 \approx \Delta_r S°_{298} - \Delta_r H°_{298}/T_{equil} \qquad (4.19)$$

$$T_{equil} \approx \frac{\Delta_r H°_{298}}{\Delta_r S°_{298}} = \frac{-283{,}000 \text{ J/mol}}{-86.6 \text{ J/K mol}} \approx 3300 \text{ K} \qquad (4.20)$$

This result is a very rough estimate because we have stretched too far the approximation that $\Delta_r H°$ and $\Delta_r S°$ are independent of temperature.

Consequence of a Net Change in Moles of Gas in a Reaction. For reactions that involve a net change in moles of gas, a prediction can be made about the sign and magnitude of $\Delta_r S°$. The basis of the prediction is the dominant contribution of the entropy of gases. According to Campbell's Rule, the magnitude of $\Delta_r S°$ is *roughly* 140 J/K for a net production of one mole of gas. If the reaction is one in which the net change in moles of gas is a decrease, as in the CO/O_2 reaction, $\Delta_r S° < 0$. If the net change in moles of gas is an increase, as in the decomposition of $CaCO_3$,

$$CaCO_3(c) \rightleftharpoons CO_2(g) + CaO(c)$$

then $\Delta_r S° \approx 140$ J/K mol. These predictions about the sign and magnitude of $\Delta_r S°$ can be augmented with predictions about the sign and even the magnitude of $\Delta_r H°$. For example, in a dissociation reaction, such as

$$H_2(g) \rightleftharpoons 2H(g)$$

we can be sure that $\Delta_r H° \gg 0$ as well as $\Delta_r S° > 0$. As a consequence, bond formation is favored at low temperature, and bond dissociation is favored at high temperature.

Summary

The entropy principle provides the means to assess spontaneous change through the expression $\Delta S_{tot} = \Delta S_\sigma + \Delta S_\theta \geq 0$. The equals sign is for processes occurring essentially at equilibrium. Numerical values for one of the entropy terms, ΔS_θ, is experimentally accessible through the expressions $\Delta S_\theta = \Delta U_\theta / T_\theta$ and $\Delta U_\theta = m_\theta c_\theta \Delta T_\theta$. The other term, ΔS_σ, can be found experimentally for equilibrium processes. Once known, however, ΔS_σ values can be used for spontaneous processes, since S is a state function.

For phase changes and chemical reactions, the entropy of reaction, $\Delta_r S^\circ$, can be computed from tabulated molar entropies. The molar entropies depend on assuming zero values at zero kelvin for elements as well as compounds based on the third law of thermodynamics. Consequently, the tabulated molar entropies consist of the entropy acquired as the substance is warmed from absolute zero to room temperature.

Several patterns exist in molar entropies. Molar entropies increase with solid $\rightarrow$ liquid $\rightarrow$ gas phase changes. The gas-phase values are dominantly large. Molar entropies increase with increasing molecular or ionic complexity within a given phase for approximately the same molar mass. Molar entropies increase with increasing molar mass. Molar entropies increase as one element is replaced with its family members of increasing atomic number. From the dominance of gas-phase entropies, an important generalization exists for values of $\Delta_r S$. If a process is net gas producing, then $\Delta_r S^\circ \approx 140$ J/K mol gas formed. If a process is net gas consuming, then $\Delta_r S^\circ < 0$. Another important generalization about the entropy of reaction $\Delta_r S^\circ$ is that it is a weak function of temperature above 250 K. Thus, a useful approximation is $\Delta_r S^\circ_T \approx \Delta S^\circ_{298}$.

When applying the entropy principle to phase changes and chemical reactions, we reexpress ΔS_{tot} in reactive system variables. Thus, $\Delta S_{tot} = \Delta S_\sigma - \Delta H_\sigma / T \geq 0$ at constant T, P. Under standard state conditions, $\Delta S_{tot} = \Delta_r S^\circ - \Delta_r H^\circ / T$. From this expression we see that the spontaneous sense of a process depends on the temperature. Ice melts above $0°C$ because the positive $\Delta_r S^\circ$ term dominates. Ice does not melt below $0°C$ because the negative $\Delta S_\theta = -\Delta_r H^\circ / T$ term dominates. However, the reverse process of water freezing is spontaneous. In general, at high temperatures the $\Delta_r S^\circ$ term dominates, and processes that have an entropy increase in the reactive system are spontaneous. At low temperatures, the $-\Delta_r H^\circ / T$ term dominates, and exothermic processes are spontaneous.

The entropy principle works as a means for assessing spontaneity in phase changes and chemical reactions.

Problems

1. Addition of 10 J of thermal energy to a substance increases its entropy 1 J/K. Consider the substance to be a large thermal reservoir. What is its temperature on the kelvin scale? Is this substance hot or cold?

2. Calculate $\Delta_r S^\circ_{298}$ for the hydrogenation of ethylene in the reaction $C_2H_4(g) + H_2(g) \rightleftharpoons C_2H_6(g)$. Could you have predicted that $\Delta_r S^\circ_{298}$ was

positive, negative, or nearly zero without performing a calculation? Ans: $\Delta_r S°_{298} = -120.6$ J/K mol.

3. For the set of three reactions used to illustrate Hess' law of constant enthalpy summation on p. 20 in Chapter 3 show that there is a corresponding law of constant *entropy* summation. (This must be true since entropy is a state function.)

4. For the excess stomach acid quenching reaction of solid sodium bicarbonate ($NaHCO_3$) with aqueous hydronium ion, compute $\Delta_r S°_{298}$. Could this spontaneous reaction be endothermic? Check your conclusion by computing $\Delta_r H°_{298}$. One ans: $\Delta_r S°_{298} = 241$ J/K mol.

5. (a) For the reaction $Cu(c) + Hg_2^{2+}(aq) \rightleftharpoons Cu^{2+}(aq) + 2Hg(l)$ compute the standard state enthalpy change and the standard state entropy change at 25°C.
    (b) For this reaction what are the signs of the following quantities: ΔS_σ, ΔS_θ, ΔS_{tot}? Why? Three ans: $\Delta_r S°_{298} = -65.2$ J/K mol; $\Delta S_\theta > 0$; $\Delta S_{tot} > 0$.

6. Is there any reactive-system (σ) entropy change for the *spontaneous* process, $Sn(c,white) \rightleftharpoons Sn(c,gray)$, at 0 K (absolute zero)? What would the entropy change be in the thermal surroundings (θ) near 0 K? Ans: $\Delta_r S°_0 = 0$; $\Delta S_{tot} \approx \Delta S_\theta > 0$.

7. From the following list: $N_2(g)$, $Cl_2(g)$, $Si(c)$, $SO_3(g)$, $H_2(g)$, $Sn(c)$ without consulting a table select the substance with (a) the largest entropy, (b) the smallest entropy, (c) the strongest bond (largest $DH°$), and (d) the weakest bond (smallest $DH°$).

8. For the reaction, $I_2(g) \rightleftharpoons 2I(g)$, $\Delta_r H°_{298} = 151.3$ kJ/mol and $\Delta_r S°_{298} = 100.9$ J/K mol. At approximately what temperature would ΔS_{tot} for this reaction be zero under standard state conditions? What is the significance of the temperature at which $\Delta S_{tot} = 0$? In terms of the contributions to ΔS_{tot}, why is diatomic iodine the stable form at room temperature? One ans: $T \approx 1500$ K.

9. Give an example of a chemical reaction involving one or more gases that you predict will have a negative entropy change in the reactive system ($\Delta S_\sigma < 0$). From the tabulated data compute $\Delta_r S°_{298}$ to confirm your prediction.

10. *Without consulting a table of thermodynamic data* put the following substances in order of decreasing molar entropies: KCl(c, 0 K), MgO(c), C(graphite), $H_2O(l)$, $PCl_3(g)$, Ar(g), $F_2(g)$, $N_2(g)$, Si(c). All are at room

temperature except the KCl, which is at 0 K. Check your predictions against the tabulated data.

11. By considering similar substances estimate the molar entropies of $CF_2(g)$ and $AgCl(c)$. The similar substances should have the same composition, the same type of bonding, similar masses, and the same shape, if appropriate. Compare your estimates with the tabulated values for $CF_2(g)$ and $AgCl(c)$.

12. Nitric oxide (NO) formed in high-compression automobile engines can be decomposed to nitrogen and oxygen with a suitable catalyst in the exhaust system (a catalytic converter).
    (a) Show that this reaction is thermodynamically feasible by calculating ΔS_{tot} for the reaction. Assume the reaction occurs at room temperature. Ans: ΔS_{tot} = 290.4 J/K mol for decomposition of one mole of nitric oxide.
    (b) From tabulated thermodynamic data estimate the temperature at which 1 bar of gaseous nitrogen and 1 bar of gaseous oxygen are in equilibrium with 1 bar of gaseous nitric oxide, i.e., ΔS_{tot} = 0. Ans: $T \approx 7300$ K.

13. Given that $\Delta_r H° = 40.67$ kJ/mol for vaporization of H_2O at 100°C, what is ΔS_{tot} for vaporization of 1 mol of water at 1 bar pressure at 125°C? Is this process spontaneous? (Hint: compute $\Delta_r S°_{373}$ from $\Delta_r H°_{373}$.) Ans: ΔS_{tot} = 7 J/K mol, spontaneous.

14. *Without reference to tabulated data* give +, 0, or – for $\Delta_r S°$, $\Delta_r H°$, and ΔS_{tot} for each process: (a) $H_2O(g) \rightleftharpoons H_2O(l)$ at 100°C, (b) $2H(g) \rightleftharpoons H_2(g)$ at 25°C. In each case give your reasoning and cite algebraic expressions where possible. Make use of your specific knowledge about the direction of spontaneous change in these systems as well as generalizations about entropy changes and bond dissociation enthalpies.

15. Starting with an expression for ΔS_{tot} show why exothermic reactions are favored at low temperatures.

16. Explain how living systems, in which ΔS_σ is negative for many reactions, do not violate the second law of thermodynamics.

17. Look up molar entropies for various ions in aqueous solution and look for trends with charge and size. Explain the trends.
    Ans: $S°_{298}$ decreases with increasing charge and decreasing size.

5. EVERYDAY ENERGY CONVERTORS: REFRIGERATORS AND HEAT ENGINES

Two classical statements of the second law of thermodynamics concern the familiar events of energy transfer between two thermal reservoirs and between a fallen object and its resting place. These classical statements, which are expressed in everyday language, do not appear to relate to the algebraic form of the entropy principle introduced and applied in the last chapter. By arguments too arduous to give here, the entropy principle can be coaxed out of the classical statements. It is much easier to show that the algebraic form of the entropy principle is consistent with the classical statements. Doing so is one goal of this chapter.

An investigation of the two classical statements of the second law leads naturally to an analysis of refrigerators and heat engines. In particular, we find the thermodynamic constraints on energy conversions in these devices and how these constraints are expressed in terms of the kelvin temperatures of the thermal reservoirs that are involved. The resulting expressions are among the most important relationships for industrial societies, which depend on innumerable energy convertors of both small- and large-scale types.

Through the application of the entropy principle to the two classical statements and through the development of the consequences for possible refrigerators and heat engines, we make the entropy principle less abstract. Such domestication of the entropy principle is another goal of this chapter.

Two classical statements are of importance. Both are cast in the negative terms of what does *not* happen and are thus known as "principles of impotence."

Clausius Statement and Its Consequences

First, we consider the statement of Clausius.

> *It is impossible to construct a device that, operating in a cycle,*
> *will produce no other effect than the transfer of heat (thermal*
> *energy) from a cooler to a hotter body.*

This statement describes cost-free or "automatic" refrigeration. From everyday experience we know that such a process does not occur. We have to plug a refrigerator into an electric power line. Nor are people's hands warmed by grasping icicles. Figure 5.1 shows the essentials of the process described by the Clausius statement. T_h is the temperature of the hot reservoir; T_c is the temperature of the cold one. The significance of the reference to a "device" in the

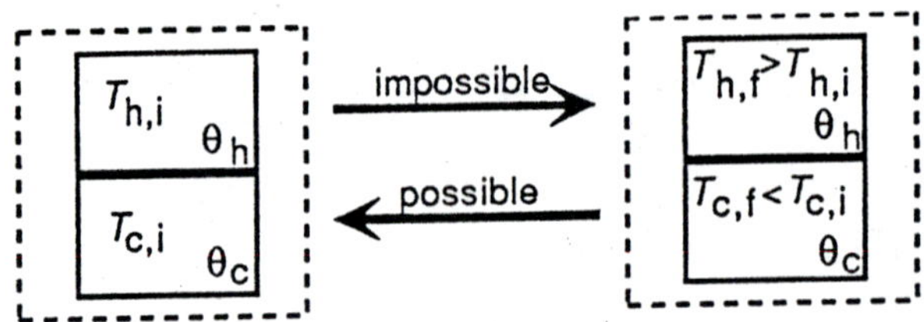

Figure 5.1. The essentials of a proposed transfer of energy from a low-temperature thermal reservoir at T_c to a high-temperature one at T_h, an impossible process.

Clausius statement is that, even if energy transfer between the two thermal reservoirs is coupled by some device or reactive system, the *net* process of up-temperature energy transfer remains impossible. "Operating in a cycle" means that the *net* energy change in any reactive system is zero. "Produce no other effect" means that the net energy change in any weight system or its equivalent is zero. Classical thermodynamics is implicitly reactive-system oriented in its formulation. That is why "device" and "operating in a cycle" refer to the reactive system.

We now apply the first and second laws to the Clausius nonevent with the intention of showing that the Clausius statement is consistent with these laws. For the Clausius statement the first law becomes

$$\Delta U_{\theta h} + \Delta U_{\theta c} = 0 \tag{5.1}$$

or

$$\Delta U_{\theta c} = -\Delta U_{\theta h} \tag{5.2}$$

From the second law we have

$$\Delta S_{\text{tot}} = \Delta S_{\theta h} + \Delta S_{\theta c} = \frac{\overset{(+)}{\Delta U_{\theta h}}}{T_h} + \frac{\overset{(-)}{\Delta U_{\theta c}}}{T_c} \tag{5.3}$$

after replacing the entropy terms with the energy-related equivalents. Above each term its algebraic sign is shown as an aid to our thinking. When the expression derived from the first law is used to eliminate $\Delta U_{\theta c}$ from the second law expression, we have as a combined first- and second-law equation

$$\Delta S_{\text{tot}} = \frac{\Delta U_{\theta h}}{T_h} - \frac{\Delta U_{\theta h}}{T_c} = \Delta U_{\theta h}\left(\overset{(+)}{\frac{1}{T_h}} - \overset{(-)}{\frac{1}{T_c}}\right) < 0 \tag{5.4}$$

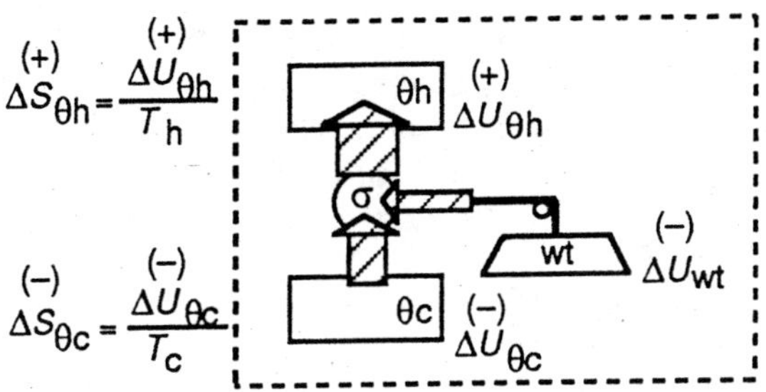

Figure 5.2. **The essentials of the refrigeration (or heat pumping) process. The widths of the arrows represent the relative magnitudes of the energies being transferred.**

Because $\Delta U_{\theta h}$ is positive and $T_h > T_c$ in the nonevent described by Clausius, $\Delta S_{tot} < 0$. In accordance with the entropy principle, this process is not possible. For the reverse process, a down-temperature transfer of thermal energy, the sign of the $\Delta U_{\theta h}$ term is negative and now $\Delta S_{tot} > 0$. This familiar process is spontaneous. Thus, the entropy principle is consistent with the Clausius statement and its converse.

Refrigeration. Of course, refrigeration, in which the purpose is to cool a low-temperature thermal reservoir, is possible if the two thermal reservoirs are coupled by a suitable device and some weight-system energy or its equivalent is converted into thermal energy. Figure 5.2 shows the essentials of the refrigeration process in which energy is transferred from a low-temperature reservoir to a high-temperature one. The widths of the arrows indicate the relative magnitudes of the energy transfers. For the refrigeration process the energy principle is

$$\overset{(+)}{\Delta U_{\theta h}} + \overset{(-)}{\Delta U_{\theta c}} + \overset{(-)}{\Delta U_{wt}} = 0 \tag{5.5}$$

or

$$\Delta U_{\theta h} = -\Delta U_{\theta c} - \Delta U_{wt} \tag{5.6}$$

The coupling device or reactive system, which may be a motor and a pump, keeps cycling around so no *net* changes occur in σ. Thus, $\Delta U_\sigma = 0$. From the entropy principle we have

$$\Delta S_{tot} = \overset{(+)}{\Delta S_{\theta h}} + \overset{(-)}{\Delta S_{\theta c}} = \frac{\overset{(+)}{\Delta U_{\theta h}}}{T_h} + \frac{\overset{(-)}{\Delta U_{\theta c}}}{T_c} \geq 0 \tag{5.7}$$

Just as the energy of the reactive system undergoes no net change, so is $\Delta S_\sigma = 0$. When the first-law result is substituted into the second-law expression, we have the combined first- and second-law expression

$$\frac{-\Delta U_{\theta c}}{T_h} - \frac{\Delta U_{wt}}{T_h} + \frac{\Delta U_{\theta c}}{T_c} \geq 0 \tag{5.8}$$

Solving for the ratio $\Delta U_{wt}/\Delta U_{\theta c}$, we have

$$\frac{-\Delta U_{wt}}{T_h} \geq \Delta U_{\theta c}\left(\frac{1}{T_h} - \frac{1}{T_c}\right) = -\Delta U_{\theta c}\left(\frac{T_h - T_c}{T_h T_c}\right) \tag{5.9}$$

$$\frac{-\Delta U_{wt}}{-\Delta U_{\theta c}} \geq T_h\left(\frac{T_h - T_c}{T_h T_c}\right) \tag{5.10}$$

$$\boxed{\frac{\overset{(-)}{\Delta U_{wt}}}{\underset{(-)}{\Delta U_{\theta c}}} \geq \frac{T_h - T_c}{T_c}} \tag{5.11}$$

We have divided by $-\Delta U_{\theta c}$ in order to avoid dividing by a negative number. (Multiplication or division by a negative number changes the sense of an inequality.) Since both ΔU_{wt} and $\Delta U_{\theta c}$ are negative energy changes, their ratio is a positive number. This ratio is always positive and depends in the limit only on the kelvin temperature. The equality sign applies to the limiting, reversible process; the inequality sign applies to the actual, spontaneous process.

Let us apply eq. (5.11) to the familiar refrigeration process in a kitchen. The high-temperature reservoir is at room temperature. Thus, $T_h = 20°C + 273$ K = 293 K. The low-temperature reservoir is the freezer compartment at $-5°C + 273$ K = 268 K. We have

$$\frac{\Delta U_{wt}}{\Delta U_{\theta c}} \geq \frac{293 \text{ K} - 268 \text{ K}}{268 \text{ K}} = \frac{25}{268} = 0.093 \tag{5.12}$$

For each 100 joules of energy that are removed from the freezer we must supply more than 9 joules of weight-lifted (or electrical) energy. The sum of these energies, 109+ joules, is discharged into the surrounding room. Had the difference in temperature been greater between the two reservoirs as in the summertime, the investment of weight-system energy would have been greater. Note that we must use kelvin temperature in eq. (5.11) and in related expressions.

Temperature Dependence of the Entropy Change Accompanying Energy Transactions. In view of the entropy principle, why is simple up-temperature energy transfer impossible and practical refrigeration possible? Both outcomes are a consequence of the inverse temperature dependence in the $\Delta S_\theta = \Delta U_\theta / T_\theta$ expression. At a high temperature a given energy transaction with a thermal reservoir is accompanied by a smaller entropy change than would accompany the same energy transaction at a lower temperature. For example, when 100 joules are supplied to a thermal reservoir at 400 K, we have

$$\Delta S_{\theta h} = \frac{100 \text{ J}}{400 \text{ K}} = 0.250 \text{ J/K} \tag{5.13}$$

When the same amount of energy is removed from a thermal reservoir at 300 K, we have

$$\Delta S_{\theta c} = \frac{-100 \text{ J}}{300 \text{ K}} = -0.333 \text{ J/K} \tag{5.14}$$

Thus, $\Delta S_{tot} = \Delta S_{\theta h} + \Delta S_{\theta c} = 0.250 - 0.333$ J/K $= -0.083$ J/K < 0, and this energy transfer is impossible. For the reverse process, a down-temperature energy transfer, $\Delta S_{tot} = 0.083$ J/K, and the process is spontaneous. If in the up-temperature process we supplement the energy transferred to the high-temperature reservoir with 34 J from a weight system or its equivalent, *which suffers no entropy change*, then the entropy increase in the high-temperature thermal reservoir is large enough to offset the entropy decrease in the low-temperature one. Overall, $\Delta S_{tot} > 0$. We have a practical refrigeration process.

$$\Delta S_{\theta h} = \frac{100 + 34 \text{ J}}{400 \text{ K}} = \frac{134 \text{ J}}{400 \text{ K}} = 0.335 \text{ J/K} \tag{5.15}$$

$$\Delta S_{tot} = \Delta S_{\theta h} + \Delta S_{\theta c} = 0.335 - 0.333 \text{ J/K} = 0.002 \text{ J/K} \tag{5.16}$$

Heat Pumping. A *heat pump* is like a refrigerator, but its purpose is to warm a high-temperature thermal reservoir rather than to cool a low-temperature one. Since the energy transactions are the same in heat pumps and refrigerators, Fig. 5.2 applies to heat pumps as well as to refrigerators. In a home heating application of a heat pump, thermal energy is "pumped" from the out-of-doors with the aid of electrical energy input, which is equivalent to ΔU_{wt}. The sum of these two energies, $\Delta U_{\theta c} + \Delta U_{wt}$, is the thermal energy input into the house, $\Delta U_{\theta h}$. If we return to the equations preceding eq. (5.8), we can derive an expression for $\Delta U_{\theta h}/\Delta U_{wt}$. It is

$$\frac{\overset{(+)}{\Delta U_{\theta h}}}{\underset{(-)}{-\Delta U_{wt}}} \leq \frac{T_h}{T_h - T_c} \tag{5.17}$$

This expression is adapted to heat pumps, whereas eq. (5.11) is adapted to refrigerators. If the temperature difference between the out-of-doors, which may be a buried rock pile or the water of a lake, and the interior of the house is not great, then the amount of thermal energy supplied to the house is substantially larger than the electrical energy input. For an outside temperature of 0°C ($T_c = 273$ K) and an inside temperature of 20°C ($T_h = 293$ K),

$$\frac{\Delta U_{\theta h}}{-\Delta U_{wt}} \leq \frac{293 \text{ K}}{293 \text{ K} - 273 \text{ K}} = \frac{293}{20} = 15 \tag{5.18}$$

In the reversible limit the heat pump would deliver 15 times as much energy into the house as the electrical energy input. A practical heat pump would be much less efficient due to thermal losses in the mechanism and incomplete energy exchanges with the hot and cold thermal reservoirs.

Kelvin–Planck Statement and Its Consequences

The other important classical statement of the second law of thermodynamics is the Kelvin–Planck formulation:

> *It is impossible to construct an engine that, operating in a cycle, will produce no other effect than the extraction of heat (thermal energy) from a reservoir and the performance of the equivalent amount of work (weight lifting).*

Such an imaginary *heat engine* is known as "a perpetual motion machine of the second kind." None has ever been successfully constructed. The process described by the Kelvin–Planck statement is equivalent to a book rising in the gravitational field at the expense of the thermal energy of a table top. Figure 5.3 depicts the essentials of this impossible process.

As we did above for the nonevent described by the Clausius statement, we now show that the entropy principle confirms the impossibility of the process described by the Kelvin–Planck statement. Any "engine" or reactive system is understood to cycle around so that $\Delta U_\sigma = 0$ and $\Delta S_\sigma = 0$. Also, for the present we have only the weight system and a single thermal reservoir. From the energy principle we have

$$\overset{(-)}{\Delta U_\theta} + \overset{(+)}{\Delta U_{wt}} = 0 \qquad (5.19)$$

or

$$\Delta U_\theta = -\Delta U_{wt} \qquad (5.20)$$

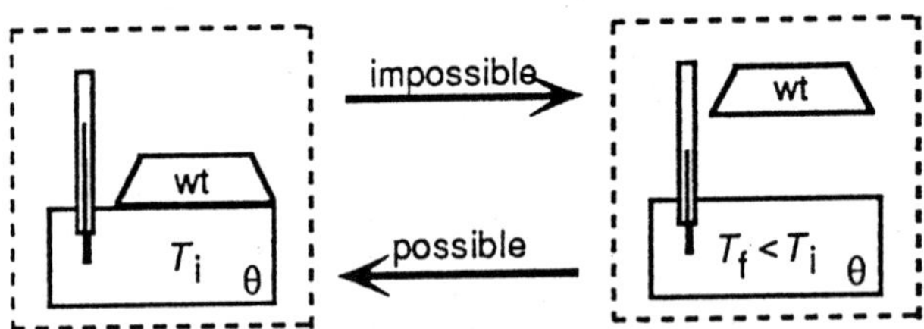

Figure 5.3   Raising a weight at the expense of the energy of a thermal reservoir.   The temperature drops slightly in the thermal reservoir: $T_f < T_i$.

From the entropy principle, where $\Delta S_{wt} = 0$ as always, we have

$$\Delta S_{tot} = \Delta S_\theta = \frac{\overset{(-)}{\Delta U_\theta}}{T_\theta} \qquad (5.21)$$

When the expressions from the two laws are combined, we have

$$\Delta S_{tot} = \frac{\overset{(+)}{-\Delta U_{wt}}}{T_\theta} < 0 \qquad (5.22)$$

Since the energy of the weight system is supposed to increase, ΔS_{tot} would be less than zero. This process is impossible. The reverse process, however, is an everyday occurrence. For it, $\Delta U_{wt} < 0$, and $\Delta S_{tot} > 0$.

Heat Engines. Of course, it is possible to lift a weight at the expense of the energy in a thermal reservoir provided part of the energy removed is discarded into a lower temperature thermal reservoir. Such is the operation of *heat engines* of the steam and internal combustion type. The essential features of a heat engine are shown in Fig. 5.4. The widths of the arrows reflect the relative magnitudes of the energy transfers.

Comparison of Fig. 5.4 with Fig. 5.2, which is for a refrigerator, shows that the processes of a heat engine and a refrigerator differ principally in the signs of the energy transactions. For heat engines the supply of thermal energy in the high-temperature thermal reservoir is usually from a chemical or nuclear reaction. (In Fig. 5.4 we show $\Delta U_{\theta h}$ equal to ΔH_σ for the chemical reaction. Since energy is passed through θh, an alternative description would have been $\Delta U_{\theta h} = 0$ and ΔH_σ taking the place of $\Delta U_{\theta h}$ in the subsequent analysis.) From the energy and entropy principles we can derive an expression for the efficiency of a heat engine. For each cycle of the reactive system, $\Delta U_\sigma = 0$ and $\Delta S_\sigma = 0$.

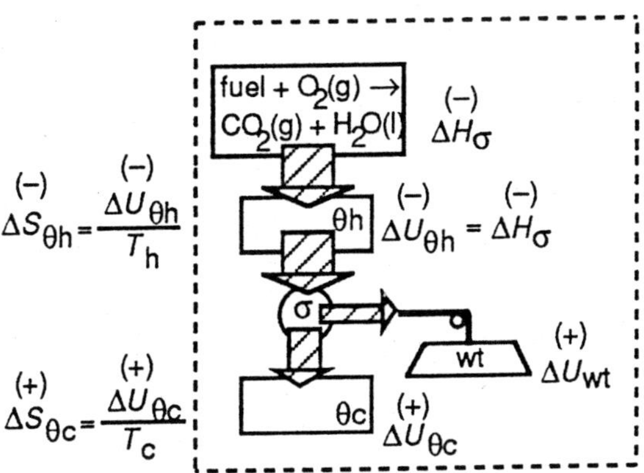

Figure 5.4.   The essential features of a heat engine. $T_h > T_c$.

Thus,

$$\overset{(-)}{\Delta U_{\theta h}} + \overset{(+)}{\Delta U_{\theta c}} + \overset{(+)}{\Delta U_{wt}} = 0 \qquad (5.23)$$

or

$$\Delta U_{\theta c} = -\Delta U_{\theta h} - \Delta U_{wt} \qquad (5.24)$$

And

$$\Delta S_{tot} = \overset{(-)}{\Delta S_{\theta h}} + \overset{(+)}{\Delta S_{\theta c}} = \frac{\Delta U_{\theta h}}{T_h} + \frac{\Delta U_{\theta c}}{T_c} \geq 0 \qquad (5.25)$$

Assembling these two expressions into a combined first and second law expression and solving for the ratio $\Delta U_{wt}/(-\Delta U_{\theta h})$, which is defined as the efficiency of the heat engine, *Eff*, we have

$$\frac{\Delta U_{\theta h}}{T_h} - \frac{\Delta U_{\theta h}}{T_c} - \frac{\Delta U_{wt}}{T_c} \geq 0 \qquad (5.26)$$

$$\Delta U_{\theta h}\left(\frac{T_c - T_h}{T_h T_c}\right) \geq \frac{\Delta U_{wt}}{T_c} \qquad (5.27)$$

$$-\Delta U_{\theta h}\left(\frac{T_h - T_c}{T_h}\right) \geq \Delta U_{wt} \qquad (5.28)$$

$$Eff \equiv \frac{\overset{(+)}{\Delta U_{wt}}}{\underset{(-)}{-\Delta U_{\theta h}}} \leq \frac{T_h - T_c}{T_h} \qquad (5.29)$$

We have divided by $-\Delta U_{\theta h}$ in order to use a positive number that does not change the sense of the inequality. Note that the limiting efficiency, which is the fraction of available thermal energy that is converted into mechanical energy, depends only on the kelvin temperatures of the two thermal reservoirs and is always less than unity and equal to or greater than zero. The limiting efficiency of conversion of thermal energy into weight-lifted energy increases as the temperature *difference* between the two reservoirs increases. The equality sign applies to the limit of ideal, reversible engines. For practical heat engines the inequality sign applies, and the extent of weight lifting is reduced for a given $\Delta U_{\theta h}$. These actual efficiencies are lower than for reversible heat engines because of finite temperature and pressure differences in the convertor (reactive system) and thermal energy losses from friction and imperfect insulation.

Let us apply this expression for the limiting efficiency of a heat engine to an old-time steam engine. In such engines the boiler (high-temperature thermal reservoir) is heated by a combustion reaction. Steam is produced in the boiler, delivered to a cylinder that is coupled to a flywheel, and condensed at the temperature of the surroundings. Thus,

$$T_h \approx 100°C + 273 \text{ K} = 373 \text{ K} \tag{5.30}$$

and

$$T_c \approx 20°C + 273 \text{ K} = 293 \text{ K} \tag{5.31}$$

$$Eff \equiv \frac{\Delta U_{wt}}{-\Delta U_{\theta h}} \leq \frac{373 \text{ K} - 293 \text{ K}}{373 \text{ K}} = \frac{80 \text{ K}}{373 \text{ K}} = 0.21 \tag{5.32}$$

In the reversible limit such a steam engine would convert only about 20% of the thermal energy, traceable to the combustion reaction, into weight-lifting energy. In practice the conversion is much less efficient. Since T_c is fixed by the temperature of the surroundings, the only practical way to increase the efficiency of a heat engine is to raise T_h. Modern steam turbines, in which the high temperature is about 800 K, have much higher limiting efficiencies.

Possible Energy Conversions. The energy conversion in a heat engine is possible for the same reason that refrigeration is possible, namely, the inverse temperature dependence in $\Delta S_\theta = \Delta U_\theta / T_\theta$. Thus, when energy leaves a high-temperature thermal reservoir, a smaller entropy change occurs than would occur if all this energy were deposited in a thermal reservoir at a lower temperature. When only an appropriate fraction of the energy is transferred to the low-temperature reservoir, the entropy increase is sufficient to give an overall entropy increase. The remaining fraction of the energy can be used to lift a weight or do the equivalent. Suppose 100 J are removed from a high-temperature reservoir at 400 K, then

$$\Delta S_{\theta h} = \frac{-100 \text{ J}}{400 \text{ K}} = -0.25 \text{ J/K} \tag{5.33}$$

If only 75 J are delivered to a low-temperature reservoir at 300 K, then

$$\Delta S_{\theta c} = \frac{75 \text{ J}}{300 \text{ K}} = 0.25 \text{ J/K} \tag{5.34}$$

Overall, $\Delta S_{tot} = \Delta S_{\theta h} + \Delta S_{\theta c} = 0$, and a maximum of 25 J may be converted into weight-lifted energy, for which $\Delta S_{wt} = 0$.

As will become increasingly apparent, we distinguish two general types of energy, disordered and ordered energy. On the one hand, we have thermal energy, which is disordered. The change in thermal energy is accompanied by an entropy change, as reflected in $\Delta S_\theta = \Delta U_\theta / T_\theta$. As we have just seen, changes in energy content of high-temperature thermal reservoirs are accompanied by smaller entropy changes than are the same energy changes in low-temperature reservoirs. Thus, higher temperature thermal energy is more useful than lower temperature thermal energy. In sharp contrast to thermal energy, we have various forms of ordered energy. These ordered forms include mechanical energy, of which weight-lifted energy is an example, electrical energy, light energy, and chemical energy. No net entropy change accompanies the change in amount of ordered energy. Thus,

$$\Delta S_{wt} = \Delta S_{el} = \Delta S_{light} = 0 \qquad (5.35)$$

Chemical energy is not related simply to the enthalpy of reaction but rather to the Gibbs free energy of reaction, which we will present later. This outcome is a consequence of $\Delta S_\sigma \neq 0$ for chemical reactions. Ordered forms of energy may be completely interconverted without any *net* entropy change. However, as we have seen, thermal energy cannot be converted completely into an ordered form of energy.

Direct conversion of ordered chemical energy into ordered mechanical energy would be much more efficient than going through the entropy-profligate step of converting ordered chemical energy into disordered thermal energy, followed by the use of this thermal energy in a heat engine. Although biological systems make extensive use of direct chemical-to-mechanical energy conversion in muscles, no practical devices of this sort have been developed. Discovering such a device remains a distinct possibility for a major invention.

Summary

Two classical statements of the second law of thermodynamics in the form of principles of impotence have been shown to be consistent with the entropy principle. Were energy to be transferred directly from a low-temperature thermal reservoir to a high-temperature one, ΔS_{tot} would be less than zero—an impossibility for a spontaneous process. Were an object to rise in the earth's gravitational field at the expense of the energy of a thermal reservoir, ΔS_{tot} would also be less than zero.

In practical refrigeration, thermal energy is transferred from a low-temperature thermal reservoir to a high-temperature one, but augmented with energy obtained from a weight system or its equivalent. This energy transaction is possible for two reasons. No entropy change accompanies the loss of energy from the weight system itself. The augmented energy flowing into the high-temperature thermal reservoir produces a sufficient entropy increase to offset the entropy decrease in the low-temperature thermal reservoir. Thus, $\Delta S_{\theta h} = \Delta U_{\theta h}/T_h = (-\Delta U_{\theta c} - \Delta U_{wt})/T_h$ is equal to or greater than $-\Delta S_{\theta c} = -\Delta U_{\theta c}/T_h$. The thermodynamic limits on the energy transfers in the refrigerator (cooling device) or the comparable heat pump (heating device) are expressed in terms of kelvin temperatures.

A thermodynamic analysis of heat engines as energy convertors leads to conclusions similar to those for refrigerators. A fraction of the energy that flows from a high-temperature thermal reservoir can be diverted into weight-lifted energy. The remaining energy is transferred to a low-temperature thermal reservoir in order to produce an entropy increase that compensates for the entropy decrease in the high-temperature thermal reservoir. Thus, $\Delta S_{\theta c} = \Delta U_{\theta c}/T_c = -(\Delta U_{\theta h} + \Delta U_{wt})/T_c$ is equal to or greater than $-\Delta S_{\theta h} = -\Delta U_{\theta h}/T_h$. The efficiency of conversion of thermal energy to fully useful weight-lifted energy is $Eff = \Delta U_{wt}/(-\Delta U_{\theta h}) \leq (T_h - T_c)/T_h$. This expression is of great importance for an industrial society.

Because an entropy change accompanies a change in energy in a thermal reservoir, where $\Delta S_\theta = \Delta U_\theta/T_\theta$, thermal energy is very different from the energy of a weight system, where $\Delta S_{wt} = 0$. For a given ΔU_θ, the entropy change is smaller at higher temperature than at lower temperature. As a consequence, energy from high-temperature thermal reservoirs is more useful in energy convertors than is energy from low-temperature thermal reservoirs. In contrast, there are no limitations on the use of weight-system energy in energy conversions.

Problems

1. Calculate ΔS_{tot} for a process in which 100 J of energy are transferred directly from a thermal reservoir at 100°C to a thermal reservoir at 0°C. How does the temperature dependence of the entropy change of a thermal reservoir make this process possible? Ans: $\Delta S_{tot} = 0.098$ J/K.

2. See problem 1. How much of the 100 J from the 100°C reservoir can be diverted into lifting a weight (forming ordered energy) without violating the second law? Include a sketch of the essentials of the heat engine. One ans: $\Delta U_{wt} = 26.8$ J.

3. Suppose methyl alcohol (CH_3OH, bp 65°C) were used as the working substance in a simple "steam" engine. Compare the maximum efficiency of converting thermal energy into mechanical energy in this engine with the maximum efficiency of a simple steam engine (H_2O, bp 100°C). One ans: $Eff \leq 0.13$ for the methyl alcohol engine ($T_c = 20°C + 273$ K).

4. Currently a heat pump is being advertised to "heat your home in winter and cool your home in summer." This device is said to deliver "more energy to heat your home than it consumes in electrical energy." This system employs electrical energy (ordered energy of the weight-lifting type) to help transfer thermal energy from a cold body (outside in winter) to a warm body (inside in winter). Let us assume the indoor and outdoor temperatures to be

20°C (68°F) and –10°C (14°F) respectively. Calculate the maximum amount of thermal energy that can be made available to heat the home for each 100 J of electrical energy transformed in operating the heat pump. Include a sketch of the essentials of this heat pump. Ans: $\Delta U_{\theta h} = 977$ J.

5. Ocean thermal energy conversion (OTEC) is a possible technology for converting thermal energy into electrical energy. OTEC makes use of the temperature difference between surface waters in the tropics (~30°C) and deep-water "rivers" (~10°C). What is the maximum efficiency of energy conversion in such a system? Do you see why an OTEC system would have to be built on a large scale? (The source of this temperature difference is the light from the sun. Thus, OTEC is a solar-energy system.) Ans: $Eff \leq 0.066$.

6. What is the limiting efficiency of a steam turbine for which the steam is at 500°C? Such turbines are used in producing electricity in modern plants. Ans: $Eff \leq 0.61$.

7. Derive eq. (5.17) for the operation of a heat pump. Draw a well-labeled sketch of the overall system. Begin your derivation with algebraic statements of the energy and entropy principles.

8. What is the maximum efficiency of converting gravitational energy, such as that stored in water behind a dam, into electrical energy? What is the maximum efficiency of converting chemical energy into electrical energy, as, for example, when a battery is discharged?

6. ENTROPY FROM A MICROSCOPIC POINT OF VIEW

As the final phase of our investigation of the entropy principle itself, we consider entropy from a microscopic (atomic–molecular) point of view. We shall show with atomic–molecular models how the entropy function measures: (1) the disordering of energy among the motions of atoms and molecules, which we call *thermal entropy*, and (2) the disordering of atoms and molecules themselves due to spreading in space in mixtures, which we call *configurational entropy*. Interpreting thermal energy as disordered energy will prove useful in considering the classical statements of the second law. We shall show why molar entropies have the patterns that we find. We shall see why the entropy of a solute increases with dilution in a solution. We shall also investigate the microscopic basis for the relationship $\Delta S_\theta = \Delta U_\theta / T_\theta$ and the reason why a chemical reaction may change its direction of spontaneity as temperature changes.

In our investigation the second law will be seen to be statistical in predictive power rather than absolute as is the first law. Thus, processes equivalent to a book raised at the expense of the energy of a table top (thermal reservoir) that are impossible at the macroscopic (laboratory scale) level have a noticeable probability of occurrence at the microscopic level. Indeed, the Brownian motion observed under an optical microscope is just such a process in which local, temporary violations of the second law occur.

Boltzmann Equation

The fundamental equation that links the macroscopic-level entropy function to microscopic-level atomic–molecular models is the Boltzmann equation.

$$\boxed{S = k \ln \Omega} \tag{6.1}$$

This equation is expressed in terms of the natural logarithm function, which is abbreviated "ln." The base of natural logarithms is $e = 2.718....$ The relationship between the common logarithm, or base 10 "log" function, and the ln function is $2.303 \log_{10} N = \ln_e N$. Usually base e is understood for ln, which is pronounced "lin," and base 10 is understood for log, which is pronounced "log." The base e logarithm of a number is larger because it takes a bigger exponent to express a number in a smaller base,

$$M = (2.718...)^{\ln M} = (2.718...)^{2.303 \log M} = 10^{\log M} \tag{6.2}$$

In eq. (6.1) k is the Boltzmann constant (1.38×10^{-23} J/K molecule). k is simply the gas constant per molecule, i.e., $k = R/N_0$, where N_0 is the Avogadro number. Ω is the number of *microstates*, i.e., number of arrangements of energy and matter in the system, that are distinguishable at the microscopic (atomic–molecular) level but indistinguishable at the macroscopic level. To be indistinguishable at the macroscopic level two systems must have the same energy, volume, and composition. Two systems with the same composition have the same numbers of molecules (or ions) of each type in the same volume. *A fundamental assumption is that all microstates consistent with a macroscopic description of a system are equally probable.*

In eq. (6.1) we already see the general relationship between entropy and disorder that we seek. A system with a large number of ways to arrange itself microscopically, that is, a large Ω, has a large entropy.

That the logarithmic relationship in the Boltzmann equation is the correct relationship between entropy and Ω, the number of microstates, can be seen by considering the properties of these two functions. The overall entropy of two separate systems, A and B, is the sum of the entropies of the two systems. Thus, $S_{tot} = S_A + S_B$ because entropy is an extensive or additive function. In contrast, the numbers of microstates for the two systems combine by multiplication. If there are 10 distinguishable ways to distribute the energy over atoms and molecules in system A, then $\Omega_A = 10$. If there are 20 distinguishable ways to distribute the energy in B, then $\Omega_B = 20$. The combined number of ways to distribute the energy, Ω_{tot}, is the product of the separate $\Omega's$ because any one of the 10 ways of distributing energy in A can occur with any of the 20 ways of distributing energy in B. Thus,

$$\Omega_{tot} = \Omega_A \cdot \Omega_B = 10 \cdot 20 = 200 \qquad (6.3)$$

If $S = k \ln \Omega_A$, then the combining properties of $S's$ and $\Omega's$ are consistent. We have

$$S_{tot} = S_A + S_B = k \ln \Omega_A + k \ln \Omega_B$$

$$= k \ln (\Omega_A \cdot \Omega_B) = k \ln \Omega_{tot} \qquad (6.4)$$

The logarithmic relationship is the proper one. k is the necessary numerical constant.

To count or calculate Ω we must have an explicit mechanical, geometrical, or mathematical *model* for a microscopic system. For *thermal entropy* our model will be a collection of mass-spring oscillators, which is a mechanical model. For *configurational entropy* our model will be the *cell model*, in which the space available to a molecular mixture is divided into cells of equal size and the different molecules are distributed into these cells. This is a geometrical model. For much of our investigation our model systems will contain such a small number of atoms or molecules that we can evaluate Ω by counting. We call such small systems *countable systems*.

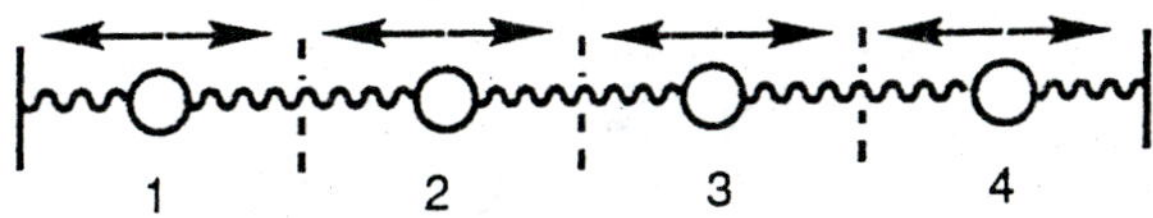

Figure 6.1. A model for a microsystem composed of four harmonic oscillators.

To say merely that "entropy measures disorder" is inadequate. This characterization takes on meaning only when we specify *what* is disordered. For *thermal entropy*, energy is disordered or dispersed. For *configurational entropy*, atoms and molecules are disordered or dispersed. Thus, entropy may measure the disorder of energy and the disorder of atoms and molecules. For each case an explicit model of matter at the atomic–molecular level is needed.

Thermal Entropy

Model for Thermal Entropy. Our model for thermal entropy is a solid composed of a set of identical mass-spring oscillators, which are *harmonic oscillators*. Figure 6.1 shows a solid composed of four such oscillators, all of which have the same vibration frequency because they consist of the same atoms (masses) and the same bonds (spring constants). The numbers identify the oscillators, which are localized in space. Our model consists of one-dimensional harmonic oscillators. This model is a simplification of the well-known Einstein model of a crystal. In the full model each oscillator is held by three mutually perpendicular pairs of springs, and combinatorial mathematics is used in order to deal with an Avogadro number of such oscillators. Because these are atomic harmonic oscillators, the possible energy levels are *quantized* in accordance with quantum mechanics. These energy levels are equally spaced and thus are simply ladderlike. Figure 6.2 shows the first five rungs of this endless energy level scheme, which applies to each oscillator. The spacing between the possible energy levels is $h\nu$, where h is Planck's constant (6.63×10^{-34} J sec) and ν is the vibration frequency. The symbol ν is the Greek letter "nu" and should not be confused with the English letter "v" in speaking or writing. The frequency increases with the spring constant (bond strength) and decreases with mass. In detail this relationship is

$$\nu = \frac{1}{2\pi}\sqrt{\frac{f}{m}} \tag{6.5}$$

where f is the constant that reflects the stiffness of the spring and m is the mass.

We consider the implications of Fig. 6.2 for the harmonic oscillator model of a solid. The possible energy levels of an harmonic oscillator are indexed with a *quantum number* which may be 0, 1, 2, 3 .... The vibration

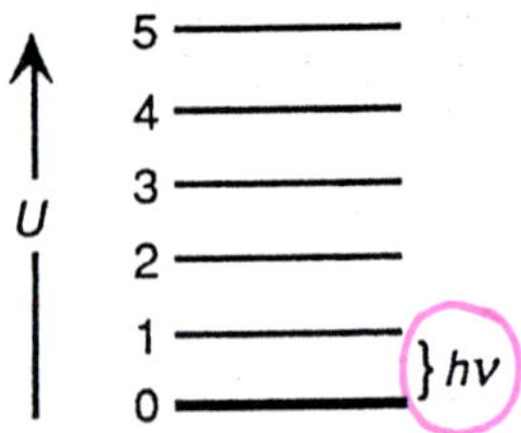

Figure 6.2. Energy level diagram for a quantum mechanical harmonic oscillator.

frequency v is also the frequency of the photons of light, which are involved when an oscillator changes energy between adjacent levels by absorbing or emitting light. Typically, these photons fall in the infrared region of the spectrum. The energy of a given atomic oscillator can be specified by giving the quantum number and the frequency, for example, as $2hv$. For a collection of four identical atomic oscillators of known v we can specify the total energy by giving the sum of the quantum numbers. Thus, for example,

$$U = 0hv + 1hv + 2hv + 3hv = 6hv \tag{6.6}$$

where oscillator one has a quantum number of 0, oscillator two a quantum number of 1, oscillator three a quantum number of 2, and oscillator four a quantum number of 3. We shall use n as the symbol for the *total number of units of energy*, which is simply the sum of the quantum numbers for the individual oscillators. Thus,

$$\boxed{U = nhv} \tag{6.7}$$

We shall use the capital letter, N, as our symbol for the *number of oscillators*.

We are now in a position to evaluate Ω for our model of a one-dimensional crystal. We shall do so for the case of four oscillators ($N = 4$) for several values of the number of units of energy n. If $n = 0$, then $U = 0hv$. All four oscillators are in their lowest energy or *ground states*. There is a single microstate for this energy; $\Omega = 1$. If the system has one unit of energy ($n = 1$), any one of the four oscillators may have this unit of energy. Thus, there are four ways to arrange the energy; $\Omega = 4$. For two units of energy ($n = 2$), we find two different *distributions* of the energy, as diagrammed in Fig. 6.3. In one distribution, one oscillator has two units of energy, and the others have none. There are four ways to choose the favored oscillator. If we use W_1 to express the number of microstates contributed by this distribution, we have $W_1 = 4$. These four microstates are shown in the top row of Fig. 6.3. A second way in

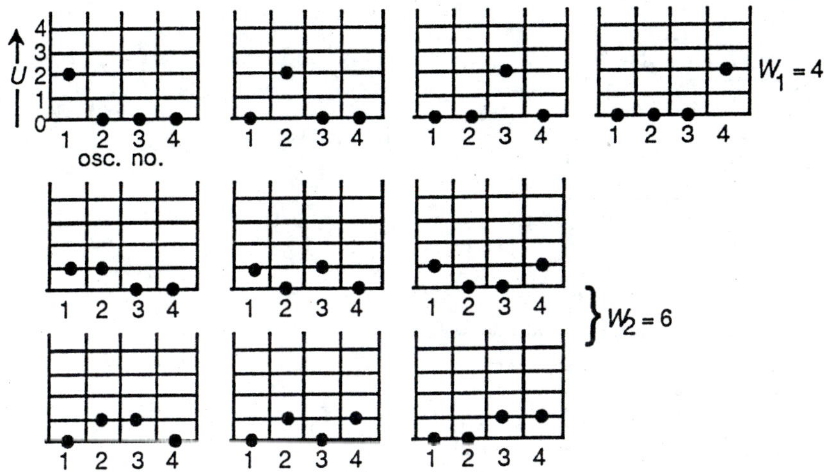

Figure 6.3.   Energy level diagrams for a four-oscillator ($N = 4$) solid showing microscopically distinguishable microstates for two units ($n = 2$) of energy.   The system has two types of microstates, i.e., two distributions. $\Omega = W_1 + W_2 = 4 + 6 = 10.$

which two units of energy can be distributed among four equivalent oscillators is to give one unit to each of two oscillators. The number of ways of doing so is $6 = (4 \times 3)/2$. Any one of four oscillators can be chosen for the first unit of energy, and then any one of the remaining three can be chosen for the second. We must divide the 4×3 product by 2, however, because the order in which the two oscillators are chosen makes no difference. If we use W_2 for the count of this second kind of distribution, we have $W_2 = 6$. These six microstates are shown in the second and third rows of Fig. 6.3.

These 10 different microstates are microscopically distinguishable because the four oscillators have spatially distinct positions. Since the number of oscillators ($N = 4$) and the energy ($n = 2$, $U = 2h\nu$) are the same for all of the microstates in Fig. 6.3, they correspond to one macroscopically indistinguishable state.

To write out the individual microstates in as much detail as in Fig. 6.3 is not practical as n gets larger. An abbreviated diagram, as is shown in Fig. 6.4, will do. All cases in Fig. 6.4 are for four oscillators ($N = 4$), and the previously considered case of two units of energy ($n = 2$) is repeated. The different kinds of distributions are shown, and the count for each distribution is shown under each ladder diagram. Only four different kinds of distributions are found for the three cases.

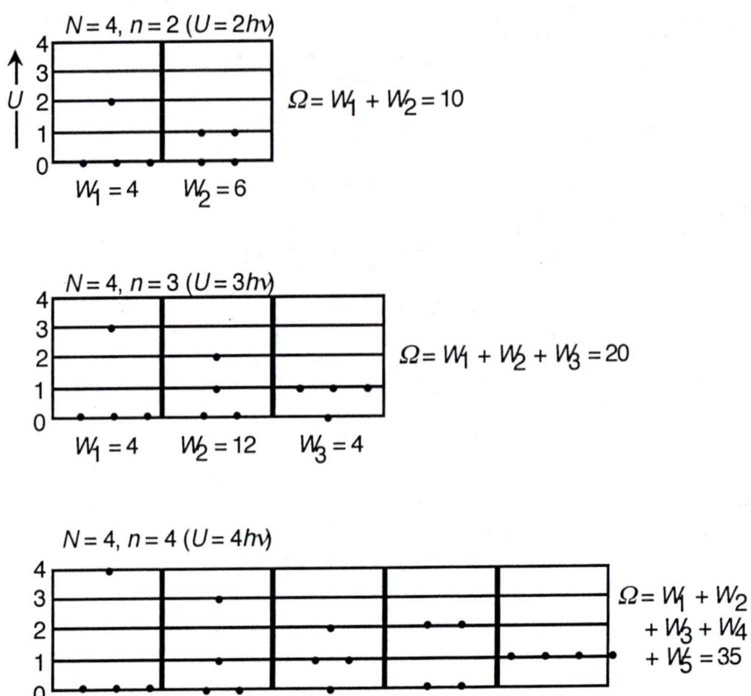

Figure 6.4.   **Numbers of microstates for four-oscillator solids arranged by distribution (W_i).**

To go to a larger number of units of energy or a larger number of oscillators gets time consuming even with this abbreviated diagram. A combinatorial formula is desirable. For the present model this formula is

$$\Omega = \frac{(N + n - 1)!}{(N - 1)!\,n!} \tag{6.8}$$

where ! stands for the factorial of the number. The factorial is the extended product of the number down to one. For example, $5! = 5 \cdot 4 \cdot 3 \cdot 2 \cdot 1 = 120$, The factorial of zero is one, i.e., $0! = 1$. Check the validity of this formula for Ω by applying it to the set of cases diagrammed in Fig. 6.4.

Table 6.1 gives Ω for up to 12 oscillators ($N = 12$) and up to 12 units of energy ($n = 12$). This table shows that Ω, the number of ways of arranging the energy among the oscillators, increases rapidly as the number of oscillators or number of units of energy increase. In most of the applications that follow, we shall concentrate on cases in which the number of oscillators is four.

Table 6.1. Ω Values* as a Function of the Number of Oscillators (N) and Number of Units of Energy (n)

N \ n	0	1	2	3	4	5	6	7	8	9	10	11	12
1	1	1	1	1	1	1	1	1	1	1	1	1	1
2	1	2	3	4	5	6	7	8	9	10	11	12	13
3	1	3	6	10	15	21	28	36	45	55	66	78	91
4	1	4	10	20	35	56	84	120	165	220	286	364	455
5	1	5	15	35	70	126	210	330	495	715	1001	1365	1820
6	1	6	21	56	126	252	462	792	1287	2002	3003	4368	6188
7	1	7	28	84	210	462	924	1716	3003	5005	8008	12376	18364
8	1	8	36	120	330	792	1716	3432	6435	11440	19448	31824	50388
9	1	9	45	165	495	1287	3003	6435	12870	24310	43758	75582	125970
10	1	10	55	220	715	2002	5005	11440	24310	48620	92378	167960	293930
11	1	11	66	286	1001	3003	8008	19448	43758	92378	184758	352716	646646
12	1	12	78	364	1365	3368	12376	31824	75582	167960	352716	705432	1352078

*Computed from $\Omega = (N + n - 1)!/(N - 1)!n!$

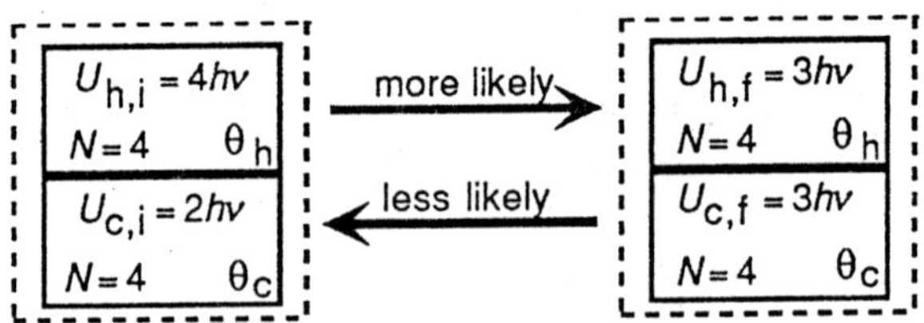

Figure 6.5. System for the microscopic analysis of the transfer of energy from a higher temperature thermal reservoir (*h*) to a lower temperature thermal reservoir (*c*). Each reservoir consists of four harmonic oscillators.

Thermal Entropy and Energy Transfer Between Thermal Reservoirs. We shall now apply this countable system analysis to the thermal energy transactions associated with the classical statements of the second law, which were given in Chapter 5.

Consider the transfer of thermal energy from a higher temperature thermal reservoir to a lower temperature one. This spontaneous process is the converse of the process that is ruled out by the Clausius statement of the second law. We model each of the two thermal reservoirs with four equivalent harmonic oscillators. The hotter reservoir (subscript h) initially has four units of energy, and the cooler one (subscript c) has two units of energy. Then, the energy content of the two reservoirs is equalized by transferring one unit from the hotter one to the cooler one. Figure 6.5 depicts the essentials of this energy-transfer process.

We can express this process as

$$\begin{pmatrix} \text{4 oscillators} \\ U_{h,i} = 4h\nu \\ \Omega_{h,i} = 35 \end{pmatrix} + \begin{pmatrix} \text{4 oscillators} \\ U_{c,i} = 2h\nu \\ \Omega_{c,i} = 10 \end{pmatrix} \rightarrow 2\begin{pmatrix} \text{4 oscillators} \\ U_{h,f} = U_{c,f} = 3h\nu \\ \Omega_{h,f} = \Omega_{c,f} = 20 \end{pmatrix}$$

(θ_h) hotter reservoir (θ_c) cooler reservoir   both reservoirs

Of course, we have seen to it that $\Delta U_{\text{tot}} = \Delta U_{\theta h} + \Delta U_{\theta c} = 0$ as required by the energy principle. Since heat (thermal energy) capacities are positive and the two thermal reservoirs are the same in structure and size, more energy content means a higher temperature for a reservoir.

To see the extent to which energy is dispersed or disordered in the initial and final states, we consider the Ω's. We have

$$\Omega_{\text{tot},i} = \Omega_{h,i} \cdot \Omega_{c,i} = 35 \cdot 10 = 350 \tag{6.9}$$

$$\Omega_{\text{tot},f} = \Omega_{h,f} \cdot \Omega_{c,f} = 20 \cdot 20 = 400 \tag{6.10}$$

As we have argued before, Ω's for separate subsystems combine by multiplication. In this example the final (f) energy-balanced state is favored over the initial (i) energy-unbalanced state in that it is realized in 50 more ways. Expressed another way, for 350 of 750 possible microstates for the two states under consideration, the system is in the initial state, whereas for 400 of 750 microstates the system is in the final state. (Once the hotter and cooler thermal reservoirs are brought into contact, states other than the energy-balanced state will also be accessible. These possibilities include $U_h = 6hv$, $U_c = 0hv$, for which $\Omega = 84$; $U_h = 5hv$, $U_c = 1hv$, for which $\Omega = 224$; "U_h" = $2hv$, "U_c" = $4hv$; "U_h" = $1hv$, "U_c" = $5hv$; "U_h" = $0hv$, "U_c" = $6hv$.) Chance favors the state that is realized most often and thus is associated with the greatest disordering of energy. Using the Boltzmann relation, we can express this outcome in terms of entropy. ΔS_{tot} for this thermal energy-transfer process is

$$\Delta S_{tot} = S_{tot,f} - S_{tot,i} = k \ln \Omega_{tot,f} - k \ln \Omega_{tot,i} = k \ln (\Omega_{tot,f}/\Omega_{tot,i})$$

$$= (1.38 \times 10^{-23} \text{ J/K})(2.303) \log (400/350) = 1.8 \times 10^{-24} \text{ J/K} \qquad (6.11)$$

a tiny entropy change, but nevertheless an increase.

With the aid of the entries in Table 6.1 we can see how scaleups in the number of oscillators and in number of units of energy increase the odds of energy flowing from a higher temperature to a lower temperature one. Consider the following case

$$\begin{pmatrix} 12 \text{ oscillators} \\ U_{h,i} = 12hv \\ \Omega_{h,i} = 1.35 \times 10^6 \end{pmatrix} + \begin{pmatrix} 12 \text{ oscillators} \\ U_{c,i} = 6hv \\ \Omega_{c,i} = 1.24 \times 10^4 \end{pmatrix}$$

$$\rightarrow 2 \begin{pmatrix} 12 \text{ oscillators} \\ U_{h,f} = U_{c,f} = 9hv \\ \Omega_{h,f} = \Omega_{c,f} = 1.68 \times 10^5 \end{pmatrix}$$

$$\Omega_{tot,i} = (1.35 \times 10^6)(1.24 \times 10^4) = 1.67 \times 10^{10} \qquad (6.12)$$

$$\Omega_{tot,f} = (1.68 \times 10^5)(1.68 \times 10^5) = 2.82 \times 10^{10} \qquad (6.13)$$

Thus, $\Omega_{tot,f}/\Omega_{tot,i} = 2.82/1.67 = 1.69$ compared with 1.14 for the four-oscillator case and smaller numbers of units of energy.

The Statistical Nature of the Second Law. In these small systems we have found that the state, hotter-reservoir cooler and cooler-reservoir warmer, is favored as is true in our direct experience with the comparable process in macroscopic systems. In a macroscopic system a comparable change would be, however, a certainty. In Fig 6.5 we used the designations "more likely" and "less likely" over the arrows rather than "possible" and "impossible" as we did in our earlier discussion at the macroscopic level in Chapter 5. Thus, our countable system analysis brings out the inherently *statistical nature of the second law*. A larger, positive value of ΔS means a statistically more favorable process. Suppose, for example, $\Delta S = 1$ J/K at the macroscopic level. Then, since

$$\ln (\Omega_f/\Omega_i) = \Delta S/k = (N_o \Delta S/R) \tag{6.14}$$

$$\log (\Omega_f/\Omega_i) = (6 \times 10^{23} \text{ mol}^{-1})(1 \text{ J/K})/(2.303)(8.31 \text{ J/K mol}) \approx 3 \times 10^{22}$$

or

$$\Omega_f/\Omega_i = 10^{3 \times 10^{22}} \tag{6.15}$$

which is an astronomically large number. It has a large exponential *in the exponent*. Thus, when we have a macroscopically measurable value of ΔS, the final state is favored over the initial state beyond any shadow of doubt.

At its core the second law says that the outcome of physical and chemical events is governed by chance. Microscopically, a system explores all the possible microstates that are consistent with its overall, macroscopic description and the atomic–molecular energy levels available to it. The system is then found most of the time in the state which has the distribution with the dominant number of microstates. For a system of macroscopic size this dominance of a single distribution at the microscopic level is so great that we are unaware of the contributions of the occasional deviant microstates. In our thermal energy-transfer example, the overall system was partitioned into two thermal reservoirs. This partitioning made it possible to distinguish the initial and final states which had different energies for the two thermal reservoirs even though the overall energy and composition of the two reservoirs taken together was constant.

Thermal Entropy and Weight Lifting at the Expense of a Thermal Reservoir. Having applied a countable system analysis to the process that is the converse of Clausius' classical statement of the second law, we turn to an application related to the Kelvin–Planck classical statement. We examine the type of change said to be impossible by a variant of this latter statement. Namely, *processes whose NET effects are equivalent to cooling a thermal reservoir and raising a weight are impossible.* Figure 6.6 shows the essentials of such processes.

The proposed change can be expressed as

$$\begin{pmatrix} 0 \text{ oscillators} \\ U_{wt,i} = 0 \\ \Omega_{wt,i} = 1 \end{pmatrix} + \begin{pmatrix} 4 \text{ oscillators} \\ U_{\theta,i} = 4h\nu \\ \Omega_{\theta,i} = 35 \end{pmatrix} \rightarrow \begin{pmatrix} 0 \text{ oscillators} \\ U_{wt,f} = 3h\nu \\ \Omega_{wt,f} = 1 \end{pmatrix} + \begin{pmatrix} 4 \text{ oscillators} \\ U_{\theta,f} = 1h\nu \\ \Omega_{\theta,f} = 4 \end{pmatrix}$$

$$\quad\;\; \text{weight} \qquad \text{thermal reservoir} \qquad\quad \text{weight} \qquad \text{thermal reservoir}$$

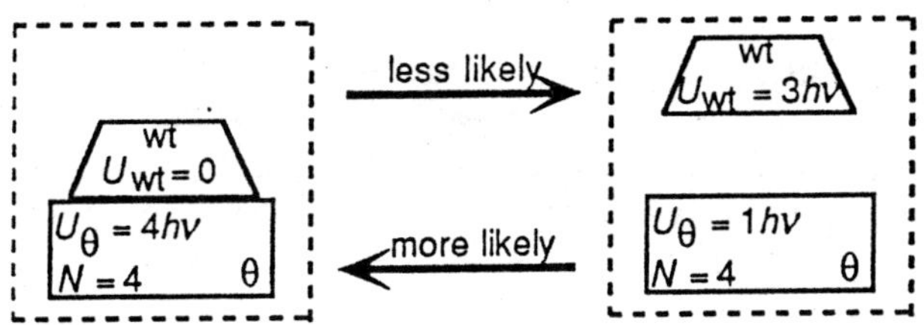

Figure 6.6. System for the microscopic analysis of the transfer of energy from a thermal reservoir to a weight system.

Ω for a weight system is always unity because the gravitational energy of the weight is arranged only one way at a given height, namely as mgh. Said another way, the gravitational energy of a weight system is ordered. The structure and identity of the weight are unimportant; only the mass counts. Since $S_{wt} = k \ln \Omega_{wt} = 0$, it should now be clear why we have given $\Delta S_{wt} = 0$ as part of the second law. The overall numbers of microstates for the initial and final states are

$$\Omega_{tot,i} = \Omega_{wt,i} \cdot \Omega_{\theta,i} = 1 \cdot 35 = 35 \tag{6.16}$$

$$\Omega_{tot,f} = \Omega_{wt,f} \cdot \Omega_{\theta,f} = 1 \cdot 4 = 4 \tag{6.17}$$

Thus, the particular weight-lifted, thermal-reservoir-cooler state that we have considered is found only 4/39ths of the time in this system. ΔS_{tot} for this process is negative, since

$$\Delta S_{tot} = S_f - S_i = k \ln 4 - k \ln 35 = k \ln (4/35) < 0 \tag{6.18}$$

As we found in our previous countable system analysis at the four-oscillator level, we have the same tendency but not the certainty that we know at the macroscopic level. For the proposed process to occur three units of energy, which are dispersed or disordered over four oscillators, must by chance assemble into a single portion of ordered energy resident in the lifted weight.

Brownian Motion. The odds against a weight rising at the expense of a thermal reservoir increase as the number of oscillators increases. For example, if the thermal reservoir consisted of 100 oscillators with 1000 units of energy distributed among them and 50 units of this energy were used to raise a weight, $(\Omega_i - \Omega_f)/\Omega_i \approx 1/70$. Although these are strong odds against the weight-higher, thermal-reservoir-cooler state, they are far from a certainty. In fact, this example is roughly in the domain of Brownian motion, where, for example, a particle viewed under the optical microscope may increase temporarily its mechanical energy through favorable collisions by the surrounding molecules of liquid. As a result, the immediately surrounding liquid (thermal reservoir) cools. For a moment the entropy principle has been "violated" *in the local region*. In subsequent collisions the energetic particle gives back its mechanical energy to the surrounding liquid, where the energy again gets dispersed among molecular motions. A similar process of brief, localized "violations" of the second law is seen in the erratic dance of dust particles in an intense beam of light. Of course, these events are not really violations of the second law but simply confirm the statistical nature of this law.

Equation (6.8) was used to compute Ω for this example. When factorials get large, it is necessary to resort to an approximation to evaluate them. Stirling's approximation serves: $\ln N! \approx N \ln N - N$. Thus, $\ln \Omega = \ln (N + n - 1)! - \ln (N - 1)! - \ln n! \approx (N + n - 1) \ln (N + n - 1) - (N + n - 1) - (N - 1) \ln (N - 1) + (N - 1) - n \ln n + n = (N + n - 1) \ln (N + n - 1) - (N - 1) \ln (N - 1) - n \ln n$.

You should be able to adapt the countable system analysis to a model of a heat engine. The two thermal reservoirs would be represented with four oscillators, and a weight system would have to be added. A portion of the energy leaving the high-temperature reservoir would be transferred to the weight system and the remainder transferred to the low-temperature thermal reservoir. Select numbers of units of energy that are easy to use.

Spontaneous Change in a Primitive Chemical Reaction. Next, we apply a countable system analysis to an investigation of how a primitive chemical reaction system can alter its direction of spontaneous change as does the ice-to-water phase transition at temperatures above and below 0°C. To do so we consider two crystalline forms of an element such as the gray and white forms of tin. Such different forms are called *allotropes*. In the past during cold winters in churches in Europe, organ pipes occasionally suffered "tin disease," in which the melodious metallic white form of tin changed into the dull nonmetallic gray form of tin. We model an A form (like gray tin) with oscillators that have both a somewhat lower ground-state energy and a wider spacing between energy levels because the bonds are strong. We model a B form (like white tin) with oscillators that have a somewhat higher ground state energy and a narrower spacing between energy levels because the bonds are weak. Figure 6.7 shows the first few levels of the energy diagrams for oscillators of the two types.

To simplify our discussion we have chosen the spacing of the A-oscillator states to be twice the spacing of the B-oscillator states. For the same reason we have chosen the *ground state* of the B oscillators to be at the second energy level of the A oscillators. As before, we use four oscillators to model the A and the B forms. Of course, each of the four oscillators of A has the energy scheme on the left. Each of the four oscillators of B has the energy scheme on the right. The primitive chemical reaction is

$$A(c) \; \rightleftharpoons \; B(c)$$

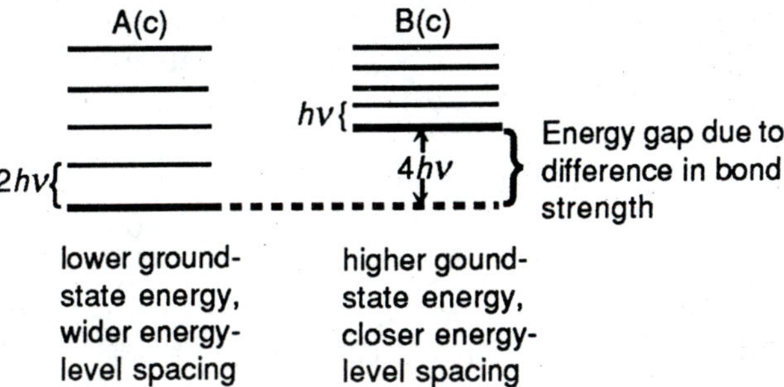

Figure 6.7. **Energy-level diagrams for the two types of oscillators, A and B, which represent two forms of a solid element.**

Now, we ask which form is favored when the system has a small amount of energy and which form is favored when the system has a large amount of energy. For the *low-energy case* we start by giving the A form $18hv$ of energy. Because the energy level spacing for the A oscillators is $2hv$, these four oscillators have $n_A = 18hv/2hv = 9$ units of thermal energy. $\Omega_A = 220$, as shown in Table 6.1. When the A oscillators are converted to B oscillators, $4hv$ must be acquired by *each* oscillator to go from the ground state of an A oscillator to the ground state of a B oscillator. This $4(4hv) = 16hv$ of energy, which is needed to convert the stronger bonds of the four A oscillators into the weaker bonds of the four B oscillators, is essentially ΔH ($\Delta H \approx \Delta U$) for this reaction. For the B oscillators only $18hv - 4(4hv) = 2hv$ of energy is left for distribution. For the form B, $n_B = 2hv/hv = 2$ units of thermal energy. $\Omega_B = 10$ from Table 6.1. Since $\Omega_A > \Omega_B$, the A form is favored in this low-energy case.

For the *high-energy case* we start by giving the A form $50hv$ of energy. Then, $n_A = 50hv/2hv = 25$ units of thermal energy for which $\Omega_A = 3280$, as calculated with the combinatorial formula, eq. (6.8). When this same amount of energy is given to the four B oscillators, once again $4(4hv) = 16hv$ is needed to reach the ground states. Thus, $n_B = [50hv - 4(4hv)]/hv = 34$ units of thermal energy and $\Omega_B = 7760$, which is also calculated with eq. (6.8). Since $\Omega_B > \Omega_A$, the B form is favored for this high-energy case.

We summarize the two cases as follows

Low-energy case

4 A oscillators		4 B oscillators
$U_A = 18hv$		$U_B = 18hv$
	less likely →	
$n_A = 9$	← more likely	$n_B = 2$
$\Omega_A = 220$		$\Omega_B = 10$

High-energy case

4 A oscillators	4 B oscillators
$U_A = 50h\nu$	$U_B = 50h\nu$

$$n_A = 25 \quad \xrightarrow{\text{more likely}} \quad n_B = 34$$
$$\xleftarrow{\text{less likely}}$$

$$\Omega_A = 3280 \qquad\qquad \Omega_B = 7760$$

To assess the direction of change in these two cases of equal numbers of oscillators, knowing the number of units of energy to distribute is sufficient. Thus, in the low-energy case the A form is favored because $n_A > n_B$, whereas in the high-energy case the B form is favored because $n_B > n_A$. The Ω values are useful in assessing the relative probabilities of existence of the two forms of the crystal and in calculating the entropy change.

Qualitatively, why is B favored in the high-energy case and A favored in the low-energy case? If the system has enough energy, then, even after some energy is ordered in converting each A oscillator into a more weakly bound B oscillator, many units of energy are left over to distribute over the closely spaced oscillator states of the B form. On the other hand, if the system has a small amount of energy, then not enough remains for significant distribution over the B-oscillator states after the A-to-B conversion. There are more ways to distribute the limited amount of energy over the more widely spaced A-oscillator states.

In the foregoing analysis of the interconversion of two solids from a microscopic point of view, we have kept the overall energy constant. This choice has been made to simplify the argument even though the customary constraint on chemical reactions is constant temperature. In a constant temperature process, the energy for the bond changes is essentially the enthalpy of reaction, ΔH, and is drawn from a surrounding thermal reservoir. This energy withdrawal is accompanied by an entropy decrease in the thermal reservoir. This negative ΔS_θ is compensated by an entropy increase as the less dispersed energy of the A oscillators is converted wholly into more dispersed energy of the B oscillators. In our constant-energy treatment the entropy decrease due to the demand for ordered energy, as the stronger A bonds are converted to weaker B bonds, occurs within the reactive system itself. For the spontaneous process in the constant-energy system, this entropy decrease is compensated within the reactive system by populating more closely spaced levels of the B oscillators. Thus, a parallel exists between the constant-temperature and constant-energy treatments. For most purposes we can think of the low-energy case as comparable to a low temperature one and the high-energy case as comparable to a high-temperature one. Appendix B gives a countable system analysis of the constant-temperature process and confirms this generalization.

Because of the conclusion of the previous paragraph, our analysis of the model for the primitive A-to-B conversion helps illuminate the melting of a solid or the evaporation of a liquid. The increase in enthalpy upon melting or evaporation is equivalent to the increase in electronic energy in going from A to

B. The liquid state has more closely spaced energy levels than the solid state, and the gaseous state has more closely spaced levels than the liquid state.

We can also understand a simple bond dissociation process such as

$$Cl_2(g) \; \rightleftharpoons \; 2Cl(g)$$

with the aid of the A-to-B model. The bond dissociation enthalpy is comparable to the bond energy difference between A and B oscillators. The product atoms have more closely spaced energy levels than the reactant molecules because translational motion of two atoms has replaced the translational motion and more constrained rotational/vibrational motions of a diatomic molecule. (See below for more discussion of this difference.)

An Analogy to Thermal Entropy. In Chapter 1, the Introduction, we mentioned an analogy between forms of money and forms of energy. This difference in forms or quality of money was related to entropy. In light of the discussion of thermal entropy from a microscopic point of view, we recall this analogy and extend it.

The two forms of money were a large sum of money in a single bank account (*capital* to economists) and the same amount of money distributed in small denominations and coins to many people. The money in the bank account is a concentrated, ordered form that has zero entropy. This bank account is analogous to energy stored in a weight system or an equivalent potential energy reservoir. Such capital funds can be transformed directly into a large capital item such as a new fire truck for a community, just as mechanical energy can be transformed completely into electrical energy. The money in the bank account is ordered; the energy in the weight system is ordered.

The money distributed to the populace is like energy in a thermal reservoir which is energy dispersed among a collection of harmonic oscillators. Each person who can accept, say, quarters, one-dollar bills, and five-dollar bills, is analogous to a molecule which is a composite of oscillators or the like that can accept different units of energy. Entropy is associated with the money dispersed to the populace, as is entropy associated with the energy distributed over the motions of the molecules in the thermal reservoir. The more people, the more different small denominations of money, and the more money, then the higher is the entropy. The more oscillators, the more types of oscillators with different energy-level spacings, and the more energy, then the higher is the entropy. The money dispersed to the populace is disordered; the energy dispersed in a thermal reservoir is disordered. So far, the money analogy is equivalent to the energy exchange between a weight system and a thermal reservoir, as in the problem of a book falling on a table top.

How does the money analogy extend to the more general chemical problem in which the ground state energy differs as well as does the spacing between the energy levels? The A-to-B conversion discussed above is just such a case. We may extend the money analogy by introducing the idea of mandatory bank accounts for each person of one type, say B. Suppose a large sum of money, say \$10,000, is to be distributed to 100 A-type people in \$10 bills and to the same number of B-type people in \$5 bills. Likewise, suppose now that although the full \$10,000 is distributed to the A-type people, \$20 is held back in mandatory, individual bank accounts for each of the 100 B-type people. Then, only \$8,000 remains for distribution to B-type people. These individual bank accounts are analogous to the energy needed to convert the more strongly bonded A atoms into the less strongly bonded B atoms. The consequence is that a reduced amount of money is available for random distribution to the B-type people. Nonetheless, in this case, the number of distributable \$5 bills, 1600, is greater than the number of distributable \$10 bills, 1000. Thus, the distribution to the B-type people is favored by higher entropy. This case is analogous to the high-temperature case of the A-to-B conversion.

Microscopic Basis for the Relation $\Delta S_\theta = \Delta U_\theta/T_\theta$. As another phase of our investigation of thermal entropy from a microscopic point of view, we explore the all-important relationship, $\Delta S_\theta = \Delta U_\theta/T_\theta$.

Why is the entropy change accompanying a given energy change larger in a low-temperature thermal reservoir than in a high-temperature one? For our microscopic analysis we again use a four-oscillator solid with an energy-level spacing of hv as a model. Table 6.2 contains a tabulation of the results.

The first column has the number of units of energy, the second column has the fixed increment of energy, and the third has the corresponding number of microstates, Ω. See Table 6.1 for these values of Ω. To obtain the ΔS_θ corresponding to each energy increment, we need the *ratios of successive* Ω *values* as are given in the fourth column. This relationship is true because

Table 6.2. Consequences of Adding Equal Increments of Energy (hv) to a Four-Oscillator Solid.

				"ΔS_θ"	
n $(= U/hv)$	ΔU_θ	Ω	Ω_f/Ω_i	$\log(\Omega_f/\Omega_i)$	
0		1			
	hv		4	0.60	
1		4			Increasing
	hv		2.5	0.40	
2		10			temperature
	hv		2.0	0.30	
3		20			
	hv		1.75	0.24	
4		35			↓

$$\Delta S = k \ln \Omega_f - k \ln \Omega_i = k \ln (\Omega_f/\Omega_i) = k(2.303) \log (\Omega_f/\Omega_i) \qquad (6.19)$$

The values of log (Ω_f/Ω_i) in the fifth column are proportional to ΔS_θ and thus are also labeled "ΔS_θ." Of course, adding energy to a thermal reservoir raises its temperature. As temperature increases in the oscillator system, the number of microstates, Ω, increases, and the entropy increases. However, the *increments* of ΔS_θ, as reflected in the ratios of successive Ω values, *decrease* for a fixed increment of energy. Adding a unit of energy to a lower temperature thermal reservoir opens up relatively more new ways to distribute all of the energy than does adding a unit of energy to a high-temperature reservoir. It is just this behavior that the expression $\Delta S_\theta = \Delta U_\theta/T_\theta$ has. Thus, an energy transaction with a thermal reservoir at a lower temperature is accompanied by a larger *change* in the spread of energy than is the same energy transaction at a higher temperature. We encountered an example of this result in the analysis of the transfer of energy between two thermal reservoirs as depicted in Fig. 6.5.

Table 6.2 shows that, as expected, the entropy associated with the dispersed energy in a thermal reservoir increases with the amount of energy. The temperature increases also, as can be seen from $T = \Delta U_\theta/\Delta S_\theta$ and the decrease in ΔS_θ (expressed as "ΔS_θ") as each fixed increment of energy is added. Thus, although the entropy, S_θ, *increases* with increasing temperature, the *change* in entropy, ΔS_θ, for a fixed energy change *decreases.*

Another way to understand the decrease in ΔS_θ with increasing temperature for a given energy transaction is to consider the accumulation of energy in each oscillator as the temperature rises. As more energy is added to a system consisting of a fixed number of oscillators, the temperature rises and the average energy per oscillator increases. Thus, at higher temperatures more oscillators have increased amounts of energy, and thus the average oscillator is able to transfer a larger amount of energy in an energy transaction. The energy being *transferred* is less dispersed. As a consequence, the entropy change in such a transaction is reduced compared to the same energy transfer from a low-temperature thermal reservoir where the average oscillator has less energy.

The incremental behavior of the entropy function that we have uncovered in our countable system analysis is a familiar phenomenon. Picture two classrooms in an elementary school that differ in the degree of disorder. One is so orderly that you can "hear a pin drop"; the other is so disorderly that you cannot "hear the teacher speak." If one of the active children from the disorderly (hot) classroom is moved out, the loss is hardly noticeable in this classroom. However, think of the difference that the active child will make when put in the orderly (cold) classroom.

In many of our applications of the entropy principle, we have emphasized the consequences of the inverse temperature dependence of the $\Delta S_\theta = \Delta U_\theta/T_\theta$ expression. In a heat engine a partial conversion of disordered thermal energy drawn from a high-temperature reservoir into ordered weight-lifted energy is possible if some of the energy is given to a low-temperature thermal reservoir. In the ice-to-water phase transition the spontaneous direction depends on temperature through the temperature dependence of ΔS_θ in the thermal reservoir. As a consequence of our microscopic-level investigation of the relationship between entropy change and temperature in a thermal reservoir, you should now have a deeper understanding of the relationship of such processes to the entropy function.

Atomic–Molecular Basis for Patterns in Molar Entropies. Remaining on our agenda for investigation of thermal entropy from a microscopic point of view is a discussion of the basis for the patterns that we noted in molar entropies. These patterns included the increase in molar entropy as: (1) a substance goes from solid to liquid to gas, (2) molecular or ionic compounds increase in complexity, (3) bond strength decreases, and (4) mass increases. These patterns are understandable in terms of the dependence of the energy level spacings in atoms and molecules on the degree of spatial confinement of the particles, on mass, and on bond strength. When we introduced the mass-spring oscillator model, we said that the spacing of the allowed energy levels, $h\nu$, depended on the mass and the spring constant (approximately, bond strength) according to the relationship

$$\nu = \frac{1}{2\pi}\sqrt{\frac{f}{m}} \qquad (6.20)$$

Thus, the frequency of an atomic oscillator increases as bond strength increases and decreases as mass increases. For motions of electrons or atoms or molecules, in general, energy-level spacings depend inversely on the size of the volume in which a particle is confined. For the exceedingly light electrons confined in the small space of atoms, energy-level spacings are usually very large ($\sim$400 kJ/mol or more). These electronic energy-level spacings are so large as to play little role in entropies at room temperature. Vibrational motions of atoms, which are more than 2000 times heavier than electrons, take place over a distance of a fraction of a bond length. Thus, because of the much greater mass and despite the smaller space of movement in vibrational motions, the energy-level spacings are much smaller (5 kJ/mol or less). For molecular rotations that involve collections of atoms moving over the volume of a molecule, the energy-level spacings are yet smaller ($\sim 10^{-2}$ kJ/mol). For translational motions of molecules in the gas phase the energy-level spacings are exceedingly small ($\sim 10^{-19}$ kJ/mol) because the volume is so large compared to molecular dimensions. Of course, the closer is the energy-level spacing, the larger is the entropy due to the dispersal of thermal energy. For a fixed number of "oscillators" a given amount of energy can be arranged in more different ways the smaller the energy spacing of the energy levels of each oscillator type. A quantitative discussion of the effect of a change in energy-level spacing on the thermal energy and entropy content of a four-oscillator system at a given temperature is given in Appendix C.

Table 6.3. Contributions to the Entropies (J/K mol) at 298 K for the Participants in the Reaction: $CO(g) + 1/2O_2(g) \rightleftharpoons CO_2(g)$

	$CO(g)$	$O_2(g)$	$CO_2(g)$
Translational	150	152	156
Rotational	47	44	54
Vibrational	~0	~0	3
Electronic*	0	9	0
$S°_{298}$ = Total	197	205	213

*The electronic contribution of $R \ln 3$ for O_2 is due to the three spin states associated with the two unpaired-electron spins in the ground state of this molecule. The rotational contributions for O_2 and CO_2 are decreased by $R \ln 2 = 6$ J/K mol because of the center of symmetry in each of these molecules. The two lower frequency bending modes of CO_2 (667 cm^{-1}) give the small vibrational contribution. $S°_{298} = S°_0 + S°_{th,298} = S°_{th,298}$ since $S°_0 \equiv 0$ by the third law.

As a quantitative example of the contribution of various motions to thermal entropies of molecules and to a chemical reaction, we consider the participants in the reaction

$$CO(g) + 1/2O_2(g) \rightleftharpoons CO_2(g)$$

This reaction is the same one that we examined in our discussion of energy contributions given in association with Table 3.3. Table 6.3 shows contributions to thermal entropies at 298 K from translational, rotational, and vibrational motions in these three molecules. An electronic contribution must also be considered for O_2, which has two unpaired electrons in its lowest electronic state. The dominant contributions for each molecule are from translational motions, which have the most closely spaced energy levels. Rotational motions, which have the next most closely spaced energy levels, also make substantial contributions. As in these examples, vibrational contributions are usually small at room temperature. Since we have chosen the standard state entropy at 0 K, $S°_0$, to be zero on the basis of the third law, the total entropy at 298 K is the sum of the *thermal* (th) contributions, $S°_{th}$. The $S°_{298}(CO_2)$ value is somewhat larger than the values for the two diatomic molecules due to its greater mass and greater complexity. The substantial negative entropy change for the reaction reflects the net consumption of 0.5 mol of gaseous reactants.

$$\Delta_r S°_{298} = (1)(214 \text{ J/K mol}) - (1)(197 \text{ J/K mol}) - (0.5)(205 \text{ J/K mol})$$
$$= -86 \text{ J/K mol} \tag{6.21}$$

We now apply the qualitative information about energy-level spacings to the patterns we found in molar entropies. When a solid melts, lattice vibrations are converted into rotations and confined translational motion. As a consequence, energy-level spacings decrease, and the entropy increases. When a liquid vaporizes, a very large change occurs in the volume in which each molecule can move. Translational energy-level spacing decreases markedly, and entropy increases appreciably. As molecular complexity increases, such as in the series $Kr(g)$, $Cl_2(g)$, $SO_2(g)$, and $SiF_4(g)$, more energy-level manifolds become accessible because rotational and vibrational motions are added. With more energy levels available into which to disperse energy, the entropy is larger. Weakening of chemical bonds reduces the spacing of vibrational energy levels. Entropy increases. Soft solids have weak bonds and thus relatively high entropies. Increasing the mass of atoms in a substance decreases the spacing of vibrational, rotational, and translational energy levels, and thus the entropy increases.

Configurational Entropy

Role of Configurational Entropy. Up to this point in our examination of entropy from a microscopic point of view we have been concerned exclusively with thermal entropy, the degree of microscopic disordering of energy. Now we shall consider configurational entropy contributions, the degree of microscopic disordering of position of particles in space.

Configurational entropy effects are evident in everyday events. All gases mix spontaneously and do not become unmixed. The same is true for similar liquids such as hexane and cyclohexane. In both mixing processes the enthalpy change is almost zero ($\Delta H_{mix} \approx 0$), and the *thermal entropy* remains essentially unchanged. We shall call such processes *ideal mixing*. In most reactive systems both thermal and configurational entropy effects contribute to the overall entropy. For chemical reactions such contributions are usually hopelessly entangled. At equilibrium both reactants and products are present even though the concentration of one or the other may be quite small. That the species in low concentration do not disappear altogether is a consequence of configurational entropy increasing with degree of dilution. The large, positive entropy of a dilute species offsets other negative entropy terms associated with a reaction.

Although we begin our investigation of configurational entropy at the microscopic level with a countable system analysis, we shall extend the expressions to apply to the macroscopic level. The dependence of entropy on concentration will be needed for the treatment of chemical equilibrium and related phenomena.

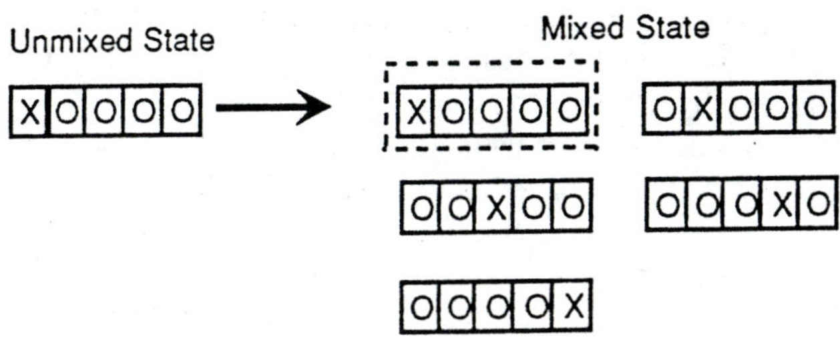

Figure 6.8. Application of the cell model to mixing one X molecule with four O molecules. The "mixed" microstate with the dashed lines around it is the same as the unmixed state.

Model for Configurational Entropy. To develop configurational entropy from a microscopic point of view we must have a model. We use a *cell model* in which the appropriate space is divided into cells of equal size. Into the cells different types of molecules are distributed one by one. This model is a *geometrical* one as distinct from the mechanical model that was used for thermal entropy. We begin at the countable system level. Figure 6.8 shows the application of the cell model to mixing one molecule of X with four molecules of O. The mixed state is favored over the unmixed state 4 to 1.

As a step toward a general expression for the number of microstates for the mixed state consider the mixing of two X's and four O's. Figure 6.9 shows the possible microstates (arrangements). In the unmixed state the two X's are localized in the two cells on the left and the four O's are localized in the four cells on the right. $\Omega_{cf} = 1$ for this state (cf stands for "configurational"). After mixing, the X's and O's may be found in any of the cells in the overall space. There are 15 such microstates (arrangements), of which one corresponds to the original unmixed state. This latter one is singled out with the dashed frame around it. Thus, $\Omega_{cf} = 14$ for the mixed state, and the probability of the mixed state to the unmixed state is 14/1.

General Formula for Entropy of Mixing. In anticipation of developing a general formula for the microstates of a mixture, we have written out the microstates in Fig. 6.9 in a systematic way that includes duplicates. In each grouping of possible microstates one of the X's is the fixed one and is intensified for reference. In the first grouping the key X is in the upper left hand corner, and the other X is systematically moved to the other five cells. In the second grouping, the key X is in the second cell, and the other X moves about. The first case in this second grouping is a duplicate of one from the first grouping and is therefore crossed out. In the third grouping the key X is placed in the third cell. Two duplicates arise. When we come to the last grouping, all arrangements are duplicates. As far as the O's are concerned, they simply fill up the vacant cells left by placing the X's in all possible arrangements. The combinatorial formula for the arrangements of X's is $\Omega = 6 \cdot 5/2 = 30/2 = 15$. There are six cells in which to place the first X and then five cells remaining in

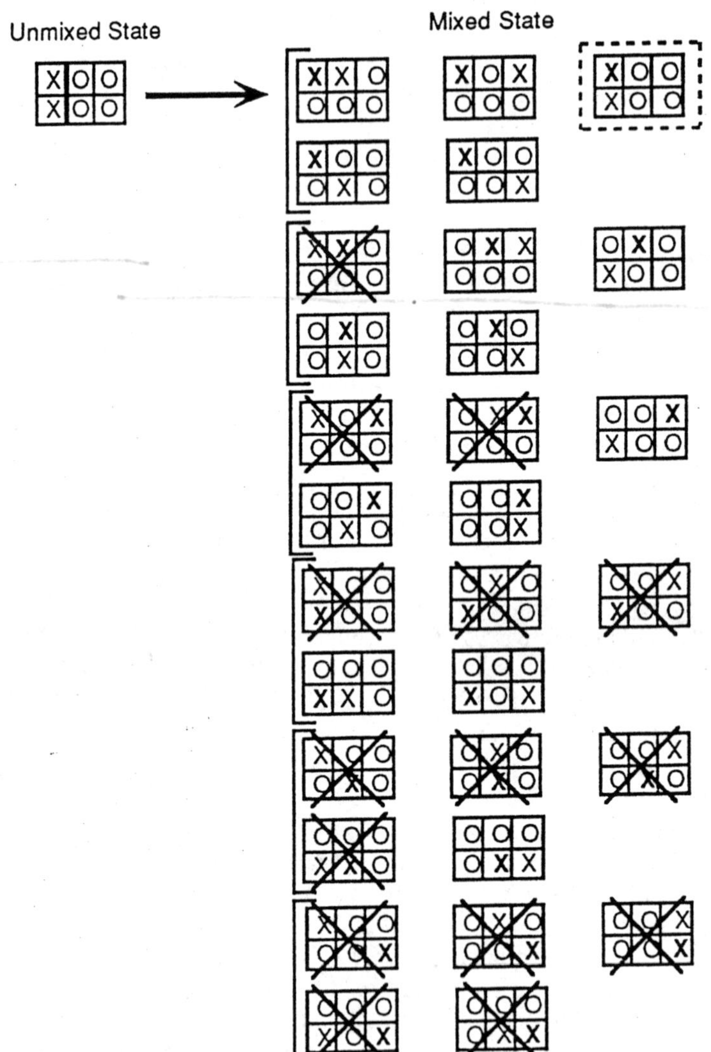

Figure 6.9. Cell model for the mixing of two X molecules and four O molecules.

which to place the second. Thus, we have 30 ways in which to arrange the X's if the X's are distinguishable. Even though the locations in cells are distinguishable, the X's are indistinguishable. Thus, we must correct for this indistinguishability by dividing by 2, the number of ways of arranging two X's among themselves. Had we chosen to focus attention on the O's instead of the X's we would have had $\Omega = (6 \cdot 5 \cdot 4 \cdot 3)/(4 \cdot 3 \cdot 2 \cdot 1) = 15$, which is of course the same numerical result. The combinatorial formula may be generalized to

$$\Omega = \frac{N(N-1)(N-2)...(N_2+1)}{N_1!} \tag{6.22}$$

where N_1 is the number of molecules of substance 1 (X's in our example), N_2 is the number of molecules of substance 2 (O's in our example), and $N = N_1 + N_2$ is the total number of molecules. For subsequent development it is useful to express Ω in a more symmetrical form in terms of N_1 and N_2. Thus,

$$\Omega = \frac{(N_1+N_2)(N_1+N_2-1)...(N_2+1)}{N_1!} \cdot \frac{N_2!}{N_2!} = \frac{(N_1+N_2)!}{N_1!N_2!}$$

$$= \frac{N!}{N_1!N_2!} \tag{6.23}$$

Although we were led to this equation by considering a countable system, the equation is general and can be applied to large values of N_1 and N_2, i.e., to moles of material where, for example, N_1 and N_2 are of the order of Avogadro's number.

Another way to derive eq. (6.23) is as follows. The number of ways to fill $N = N_1 + N_2$ cells with distinguishable objects is $N!$ Correction for indistinguishability among the N_1 molecules of substance 1 and the N_2 of substance 2 is achieved by dividing by $N_1!$ and by $N_2!$.

Now we are in a position to develop a general expression for the change in configurational entropy that accompanies ideal mixing. For a pure substance only one *configurational* arrangement exists. Thus, we take the Ω_{cf}'s of the pure substances as unity. Of course, the pure substances have large contributions to Ω due to thermal entropy, Ω_{th}, but these parts of Ω do not change during the ideal mixing process and may be disregarded when focusing on the mixing process.

$$S_{cf,1} = k \ln \Omega_1 = k \ln 1 = 0 \quad \text{and} \quad S_{cf,2} = 0 \tag{6.24}$$

For the mixture (m)

$$S_{cf,m} = k \ln \Omega_m = k \ln \frac{(N_1+N_2)!}{N_1!N_2!} \tag{6.25}$$

where N_1 is the number of molecules of substance 1 and N_2 is the number of molecules of substance 2. The single arrangement that corresponds to the unmixed state normally makes such a tiny contribution to Ω_m that it is not subtracted from Ω_m. We simplify this factorial expression by using Stirling's approximation for large factorials, which is $\ln N! \approx N \ln N - N$.

$$\frac{S_{cf,m}}{k} = (N_1 + N_2) \ln (N_1 + N_2)$$

$$- (N_1 + N_2) - N_1 \ln N_1 + N_1 - N_2 \ln N_2 + N_2$$

$$= -N_1 \ln \left(\frac{N_1}{N_1 + N_2}\right) - N_2 \ln \left(\frac{N_2}{N_1 + N_2}\right) \qquad (6.26)$$

The total number of particles is $N = N_1 + N_2$. With the Avogadro number N_0 the moles of substance 1 are $n_1 = N_1/N_0$ and the moles of substance 2 are $n_2 = N_2/N_0$. For a mixing formula for ideal solutions, concentrations are conveniently expressed as mole fractions, which are the fractions of the total number of moles or molecules of each substance. Expressions for mole fractions expressed in number of molecules are

$$X_1 = \frac{N_1}{N_1 + N_2} = \frac{N_1}{N} \qquad (6.27)$$

and

$$X_2 = \frac{N_2}{N_1 + N_2} = \frac{N_2}{N} \qquad (6.28)$$

Using these definitions, we have

$$\frac{S_{cf,m}}{N_0 k} = \frac{S_{cf,m}}{R} = -\frac{N_1}{N_0} \ln X_1 - \frac{N_2}{N_0} \ln X_2 = -n_1 \ln X_1 - n_2 \ln X_2 \qquad (6.29)$$

Finally, for the mixing of n_1 moles of pure substance 1 and n_2 moles of pure substance 2 to form a solution with mole fractions X_1 and X_2 we have

$$\Delta S_{cf} = S_{cf,m} - S_{cf,1} - S_{cf,2} = -R(n_1 \ln X_1 + n_2 \ln X_2) - 0 - 0 \qquad (6.30)$$

$$\boxed{\Delta S_{cf} = -R(n_1 \ln X_1 + n_2 \ln X_2)} \qquad (6.31)$$

Although the cell model that we have developed in order to calculate the entropy change upon mixing may appear to apply only to solutions of solids, this model is satisfactory for ideal gas and liquid solutions as well. The cells are merely the average volumes that the gas or liquid molecules occupy in space. Equation (6.31) may be generalized to any number of components making up an ideal solution by adding equivalent terms for additional components. The general equation is

$$\Delta S_{cf} = -R \sum n_i \ln X_i \qquad (6.32)$$

ΔS_{cf} is always positive for forming ideal solutions since mole fractions are less than 1 and thus logarithms of mole fractions are negative.

For 1 mol of a 50–50 mixture of two ideal solution-forming liquids such as hexane and cyclohexane we have

$$\begin{aligned} \Delta S_{cf} &= -(8.314 \text{ J/K mol})(2.303)[(0.5 \text{ mol}) \log 0.5 + (0.5 \text{ mol}) \log 0.5] \\ &= 5.76 \text{ J/K} \end{aligned} \qquad (6.33)$$

Let us also see how ΔS_{cf} increases as increasingly dilute solutions containing *1 mol of solute* are formed. Of course, this means that increasingly large amounts of solvent (the more concentrated component) must be used. For a 10:1 solution per mole of solute we have

$$\begin{aligned} \Delta S_{cf} &= -(8.314 \text{ J/K mol})(2.303)[(1) \log 0.0909 + (10) \log 0.909] \\ &= -(19.143)(-1.041 - 0.414) = 27.9 \text{ J/K mol} \end{aligned} \qquad (6.34)$$

This result and those for 1:1 and 1000:1 mixtures are assembled in the following tabulation

n_1	n_2	X_1	X_2	ΔS_{cf}, J/K mol, 1 mol of solute
1	1	0.5	0.5	11.5
10	1	0.909	0.091	27.9
1000	1	0.999	0.0010	65.7

Thus, entropy increases in the formation of increasingly dilute solutions, provided the amount of solute is fixed. These increases may compensate for large thermal entropy decreases in the overall thermodynamic system that may accompany mixing. We may also conclude that almost everything is soluble in almost everything else to some degree.

For subsequent use in this text it is desirable to break up eq. (6.31) into configurational entropy terms associated with each component. Thus, we see that the configurational entropy associated with *a mole* of substance 1 in the mixture is $-R \ln X_1$ and that associated with substance 2 per mole is $-R \ln X_2$. In general then, the configurational entropy *per mole* for substance i is

$$S_{cf,i} = -R \ln X_i \qquad (6.35)$$

As before, we see that the configurational entropy contribution increases as the concentration of 1 mol of a substance is decreased by adding solvent.

We have used the conventional terminology of "entropy of mixing" in developing eqs. (6.31) and (6.32). A reconsideration of the derivation of eq. (6.23) for Ω_{cf} shows that mixing, as such, is not crucial. The expression for Ω_{cf} is a consequence of finding all the possible microstates for one type of molecule, say the X's. The molecules of the other type, the O's, simply fill the empty cells. It is the spreading out of the molecules in space that is crucial, not the intermixing of them. The "entropy of mixing" might better be called the "entropy of dilution."

Configurational entropy is a measure of the extent to which matter is spread out and therefore diluted in some medium. In short, *configurational entropy is a measure of the spread of matter at the microscopic level.*

A Final Consideration of the Relationship Between Entropy Change and Energy Change

When one first encounters the entropy function, it is natural to wonder why it is expressed in terms of an energy change through $\Delta S_\theta = \Delta U_\theta / T_\theta$. Energy and entropy are very different concepts. After all, entropy is said to be a measure of disorder of energy or matter and indeed is related to the number of arrangements, Ω, of energy or matter at the microscopic level. If entropy is a measure of the quality or disorder of energy, however, then it should be related to the amount of energy change and the circumstances of this energy change. The expression $\Delta S_\theta = \Delta U_\theta / T_\theta$ tells us that the proper measure of the circumstances is the $1/T$ factor. As we have emphasized in our development of the entropy principle, a given energy transaction at low temperature is accompanied by large entropy change, whereas the same transaction at high temperature is accompanied by small entropy change.

One may also wonder about the distinction we have made between configurational and thermal entropies. It is artificial, but useful. The expression, $\Delta S_\theta = \Delta U_\theta / T_\theta$, which is part of the statement of the second law, refers only to thermal energy changes. Although we shall not bother to do so here, it can be shown that configurational entropy is a special case of thermal entropy. For example, the entropy increase accompanying the mixing of two ideal gases at constant pressure is the same as the sum of the entropy changes when each gas independently expands to its final pressure.

Often, in presentations of thermodynamics at the introductory level, what we are calling configurational entropy is all that is described. From such discussions the student is assumed to have a grasp of entropy that applies to all cases, including those for which thermal entropy is the only consideration. Such a generalization from configurational entropy to thermal entropy is not possible conceptually or analytically. On the other hand, as we have indicated, configurational entropy can be derived from thermal entropy. Clearly, thermal entropy is the more important concept. It is what we have focused our attention on in this text.

The Third Law Revisited

The third law states that the entropy of a perfect crystalline substance can be taken as zero at absolute zero; $S°_0 = 0$. Since a perfect crystalline substance is pure, its configurational entropy is zero. Since a perfect crystalline substance has no residual thermal energy at absolute zero, its thermal entropy (S_{th}) is zero. In an imperfectly aligned crystal, some excess interaction energy remains, due, for example, to misaligned molecular dipoles, and thus $S_{th} \neq 0$ in such cases.

Evolution Toward Equilibrium

Overall systems that are not at equilibrium evolve toward equilibrium by maximizing the number of microstates consistent with the constraints on the overall system. For example, an overall system may not be at equilibrium because it includes some liquid below its freezing point or because it includes two reactive chemicals that have just been mixed. Constraints on the *overall* system are constant energy and volume. Locally, the constraint on the reactive system itself is often constant pressure and constant temperature. Through the interplay of thermal and configurational entropy effects, usually hopelessly intertwined in chemical systems, the overall system explores various microstates until the number of microstates (Ω) is maximized. For a macroscopic system the distribution (W) that makes the maximum contribution to Ω is overwhelmingly larger than alternative distributions that differ significantly. Thus, it is unnecessary to consider all the distributions as we did with the countable systems. To prove this last assertion about the dominance of the largest W, analysis with combinatorial mathematics is necessary.

Summary

At the microscopic level, entropy can be associated with thermal entropy, the disordering or dispersal of energy as in a thermal reservoir. Entropy can also be associated with configurational entropy, the disordering or dispersal of matter. The Boltzmann equation, $S = k \ln \Omega$, connects entropy to the number of microstates, Ω, that is, the number of arrangements of energy or molecules at the microscopic level. To evaluate Ω an explicit model is needed. For thermal entropy our model consists of quantum mechanical harmonic oscillators. For configurational entropy our model is a cell model, space divided into equal volumes. At the outset the number of oscillators or molecules is kept small enough so that Ω can be evaluated by counting. Such small systems are called countable systems.

For small systems the probability of change in the favored sense is not overwhelmingly larger than in the unfavored sense. Thus, for small systems, momentary processes for which $\Delta S_{tot} < 0$ are possible. Brownian motion seen under a microscope is just such a local violation of the second law. The second law is fundamentally statistical in nature. For macroscopic systems, however, the difference in Ω values for the initial and final states is so large that more probable outcomes are certainties.

The thermal entropy analysis is applied to energy transfers between two thermal reservoirs and between a weight system and a thermal reservoir. The one-wayness in these processes is illuminated. The thermal entropy analysis is also applied to a primitive chemical reaction or phase transition. The outcome is an improved understanding of how such processes are favored in one direction at low temperature and in the other direction at high temperature. Exploring how thermal entropy relates to the spacing of energy states in molecular systems helps explain the pattern of molar entropies in relationship to the physical state, to molecular complexity, to bond strength, and to mass.

The investigation of thermal entropy also clarifies why the entropy change accompanying a given energy transfer is larger at low temperature than at high temperature, as described by $\Delta S_\theta = \Delta U_\theta / T_\theta$.

Configurational entropy applies to the dilution processes that occur when ideal solutions are formed. Such solutions form with $\Delta H_\sigma = 0$ and thus include no direct thermal entropy change. The entropy change is due entirely to molecules spreading out in space. The general expression for the entropy change accompanying mixing is $\Delta S_{cf} = -R\Sigma n_i \ln X_i$, where the X_i are mole fraction measures of concentration. The configurational entropy contribution of a single species, i, is $S_{cf,i} = -R \ln X_i$ per mole of this species. As a consequence, the configurational entropy contributed by a single solute increases with dilution by added solvent.

At absolute zero a perfect crystal of a pure substance has no thermal entropy and no configurational entropy. Thus, $S°_0 = 0$.

In nonideal systems, the common ones, thermal entropy and configurational entropy effects are intertwined. Furthermore, configurational entropy is a special case of thermal entropy. Nonetheless, distinguishing between thermal entropy and configurational entropy effects is a useful aid to our thinking.

Problems

1. For a solid consisting of three oscillators find Ω *by counting* for the cases $n = 0, 1, 2, 3,$ and 4 units ($h\nu$) of energy. Include ladder diagram sketches for each case. Two ans: $n = 2, \Omega = 6$; $n = 4, \Omega = 15$.

2. *Without referring to a table or the general formula,* tell which system has the largest value of Ω: (a) a six-oscillator solid with one unit ($h\nu$) of energy; (b) a four-oscillator solid with two units ($h\nu$) of energy. Ans: $\Omega_{(a)} < \Omega_{(b)}$.

3. By *counting*, i.e., not using a general formula, show that a mixture of two molecules of A and three molecules of B has a higher configurational entropy than a mixture of one molecule of A and five molecules of B.

4. (a) Which has the larger entropy:
        (i) A five-oscillator solid with two units of energy?
        (ii) A mixture of three (motionless) argon atoms and three (motionless) xenon atoms?
    (b) What kinds of entropy do these two examples illustrate? Why?
    Ans: $\Omega_{(i)} = 15$, $\Omega_{(ii)} = 20$.

5. Two kinds of molecules, A and B, mix to form an ideal solution. There are five molecules of A and ten of B. Assume the thermal entropy part is constant throughout.
    (a) Give Ω_i for the unmixed state and Ω_f for the mixed state. Use the general expression for Ω for the cell model.
    (b) Set up algebraically but do not evaluate an expression for ΔS_{cf} for this process.
    One ans: $\Omega_i = 1$, $\Omega_f = 3003$.

6. Explain why two four-oscillator solids have a larger Ω when the available thermal energy is shared equally between them than when one of the solids has more of the energy than the other.

7. Consider a thermal reservoir consisting of six identical harmonic oscillators with energy levels spaced by $h\nu$. In the initial state the thermal reservoir has $6h\nu$ of energy, and a weight system is coupled to it. In the final state the weight has risen in the gravitational field to the extent of $4h\nu$ at the expense of the thermal reservoir. What is Ω_i for the initial state of the overall system, and what is Ω_f for the final state of the overall system? What are the odds of finding the system in the initial state instead of the final state? Use Table 6.1 for values of Ω. One ans: $\Omega_i = 462$, $\Omega_f = 21$.

8. Redo the countable system argument associated with Fig. 6.5 but assume that the high-temperature reservoir contains $10h\nu$ of energy and the low-temperature reservoir contains $2h\nu$. Each reservoir consists of four harmonic oscillators. Calculate Ω_f/Ω_i and ΔS_{tot} for the transfer of $4h\nu$ from the high-temperature reservoir to the low-temperature reservoir. Appropriate values of Ω can be found in Table 6.1. One ans: $\Omega_{tot,f}/\Omega_{tot,i} = 7056/2860$.

9. Redo the analysis of the energy transfer between two thermal reservoirs as shown in Fig. 6.5, but have the "low temperature" reservoir consist of eight oscillators and contain $4h\nu$ of energy initially. The "high temperature" reservoir still has four oscillators and $4h\nu$ initially. Allow $1h\nu$ to transfer so that the h reservoir has $3h\nu$ and the c reservoir has $5h\nu$ Is this a favored

process? Which reservoir was initially at the higher temperature? One ans: $\Omega_{tot,f}/\Omega_{tot,i} = 15840/11550$. Use $T = \Delta U_\theta/\Delta S_\theta$ to find temperatures.

10.

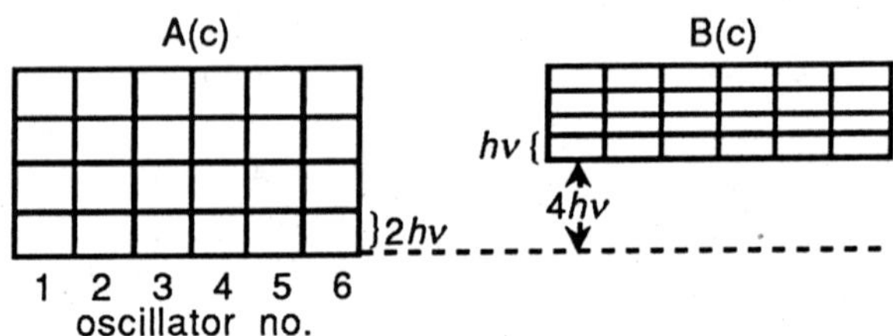

Consider the interconversion between two solid forms (A and B) of an element modeled with six harmonic oscillators. The energy level diagrams for six oscillators of the two forms are shown. If the system contains $36hv$ of energy, which form is favored? Why? Ans: $\Omega_A > \Omega_B$.

11. Consider the conversion of solid A to solid B. A has weaker bonds than B. A is therefore the favored form when the system contains much energy. Explain.

12. Brownian motion, as observed under a biologist's microscope, is an everyday violation of the second law of thermodynamics. Explain why this statement is true in a sense.

13. As a model of Brownian motion, calculate the probability (Ω_f/Ω_i) that $10hv$ units of energy from the $100hv$ units of energy in a 100-oscillator thermal reservoir are converted to mechanical energy. To do this calculation use the general formula, eq. (6.8), and Stirling's approximation for factorials, $\ln N!$ $\approx N \ln N - N$. Ans: $\Omega_f/\Omega_i = 1/1340$.

14. Calculate the entropy change caused by mixing 20 mL of hexane (C_6H_{14}) and 10 mL of pentane (C_5H_{12}). Assume densities of 0.66 g/mL and 0.63 g/mL, respectively, for these liquids. Ans: $\Delta S_{cf} = 1.31$ J/K.

15. Assuming that an ideal solution forms, compute the entropy change in making a 1 M solution from liquid methanol (CH_3OH) and water. Pure water is 55.5 M. Ans: $\Delta S_{cf} = 41.8$ J/K mol methanol.

16. Between each pair of entropies insert a >, =, or < sign and give a brief reason for your answer. N is the number of oscillators or number of molecules. All are molar entropies except S_θ.
$S°_{298}[CaCO_3(c)]$ $S°_{298}[CaO(c)]$;
$S°_{298}[Ca(c)]$ $S°_{298}[Sr(c)]$;

$S°_0[Sn(gray)]$ $S°_0[Sn(white)]$;
$S_\theta(N = 4, 8hv$, spacing $2hv)$ $S_\theta(N = 4, 4hv$, spacing $hv)$;
$S[0.1\ M\ SO_2(aq)]$ $S[0.2\ M\ SO_2(aq)]$.

17. (See Appendix C.) Two thermal reservoirs, 1 and 2, *at the same temperature* consist of an equal number of harmonic oscillators but with different energy-level spacings. Let reservoir 1 have the closer energy-level spacings. Compare S_θ, U_θ, and C_θ (heat capacity) of the two reservoirs. Compare ΔS_θ for the two reservoirs when $\Delta U_{\theta 1} = -\Delta U_{\theta 2}$.

18. In the case described in problem 17 what can be done to thermal reservoir 2 to make its S_θ and U_θ equal to the values in thermal reservoir 1 *without changing the oscillators in reservoir 2*. Do the values of S_θ and U_θ become equal in the two reservoirs for the same change?

Chapter 7. The Gibbs Free Energy

As we have emphasized from the point of introduction of the second law, this "change in" law is expressed globally in terms of the total entropy. To evaluate ΔS_{tot} for chemical processes, we have used differences in two reactive system variables, ΔH_σ and ΔS_σ. Can we not have a single, reactive-system-oriented state function, after the fashion of the enthalpy function, that can serve as the index of spontaneous change? There is great need for such a function under the customary constraints of constant temperature and pressure. Long ago, Gibbs introduced such a function, which is now called the Gibbs energy function and is symbolized with G. Often, G is simply called the Gibbs function.

In this chapter we derive the change in the Gibbs function, ΔG_σ, from ΔS_{tot} and show how to interpret the sign of ΔG. We show the computation of $\Delta_r G^\circ$ from the tabulated Gibbs energies of formation. $\Delta_r G^\circ$ is the Gibbs free energy for a chemical reaction under standard state conditions. The strong dependence of $\Delta_r G^\circ$ on temperature is recognized and approximated with a function that depends on the near-constant values of $\Delta_r H^\circ_{298}$ and $\Delta_r S^\circ_{298}$. The contributions of these two terms to the sign and magnitude of $\Delta_r G^\circ$ are also explored for a number of familiar processes.

The reason for calling $\Delta_r G$ the free energy is also developed in this chapter. Thus, $\Delta_r G$ is shown to be the maximum ordered energy that a chemical reaction can make available to another system, such as an electrical energy system or a second chemical reaction, under the constraints of constant temperature and constant pressure. As part of this discussion, $-T\Delta S_{tot}$ is seen to be the ordered energy that is unnecessarily converted into thermal energy.

The Gibbs Free Energy

When ΔS_{tot} is expressed in terms of ΔH_σ and ΔS_σ *at constant temperature and pressure*, we have the combined first law and second law expression, eq. (4.14),

$$\Delta S_{tot} = \Delta S_\sigma - \frac{\Delta H_\sigma}{T} \geq 0 \tag{7.1}$$

Since T is the same in the reactive system and in the thermal reservoir at constant temperature, it is unsubscripted. After multiplying through this expression by $-T$, we have

$$-T\Delta S_{tot} = \Delta H_\sigma - T\Delta S_\sigma \leq 0 \tag{7.2}$$

$-T\Delta S_{\text{tot}}$ has energy units, and the sense of the inequality sign has been reversed. We equate this function of the reactive system quantities, ΔH_σ, T, and ΔS_σ, to the change in the single reactive system variable, G_σ. Thus,

$$\Delta G_\sigma = \Delta H_\sigma - T\Delta S_\sigma \le 0 \qquad (7.3)$$

and

$$-T\Delta S_{\text{tot}} = \Delta G_\sigma \qquad (7.4)$$

ΔG_σ is the change in the Gibbs function, G. When it is $\Delta_r G$ for a chemical reaction, $\Delta_r G$ is also called the Gibbs free energy for reasons developed below.

Let us consider the implications of eq. (7.3) and the formal definition of the Gibbs function. Whereas S_{tot} *increases* for a spontaneous process, G_σ *decreases* for a spontaneous process occurring at constant temperature and pressure. For an equilibrium process under these conditions $\Delta G_\sigma = 0$, and for a process that is spontaneous in the reverse direction $\Delta G_\sigma > 0$. The formal definition of the Gibbs function is

$$G \equiv H - TS \qquad (7.5)$$

which gives $\Delta G = \Delta H - T\Delta S$, the previous result, at constant temperature

At first glance it appears that constant temperature is the only constraint on eq. (7.3). The pressure must also be constant, however, in order to use ΔH_σ. Only at constant pressure as well as at constant temperature can the sign of ΔG_σ be interpreted as stated. A further, more subtle constraint on ΔG_σ in eq. (7.3) is that no potential energy reservoir other than ΔU_{wt} be part of the overall system. Equation (7.3) applies to the familiar circumstances of the interaction of chemical reactions and surroundings as depicted on Fig. 2.1. Equation (7.3) does not apply, however, if an electrical system with its ΔU_{el} term contributes to the overall system. We consider the important case of such *electrochemical* systems in Chapter 9. The Gibbs function, like the enthalpy function, is only of use for reactive systems. Thus, the σ subscript is usually superfluous for ΔG and ΔH. In the expression $\Delta G = \Delta H - T\Delta S$, it is clear from context that the ΔS term is also for the reactive system. In summary, we have for the Gibbs function

$$\boxed{\begin{array}{c} \Delta G = \Delta H - T\Delta S \le 0 \\ \text{at constant } T \text{ and } P; \text{ no } \Delta U_{\text{pot}} \text{ other than } P\Delta V \\ \Delta G < 0 \quad \text{spontaneous reaction as written} \\ \Delta G = 0 \quad \text{equilibrium} \\ \Delta G > 0 \quad \text{spontaneous reaction in reverse} \end{array}} \qquad (7.6)$$

The constraint "no ΔU_{pot} other than $P\Delta V$" on the relationships in the box represents the absence of *potential* energy reservoirs other than the weight system (ΔU_{wt}).

The Gibbs function is a *state function* because it is defined in terms of state functions. As a consequence, the change in the Gibbs function is independent of the path taken in going from reactants to products. Thus, ΔG for a single-step reaction is the same as for a multistep reaction involving the same initial reactant state and the same final product state. The Gibbs function is also an *extensive* function.

We may calculate $\Delta_r G°$ for a reaction from the tabulated $Gf°$'s of reactants and products in the same manner that we calculate $\Delta_r H°$ and $\Delta_r S°$. Thus,

$$\Delta_r G° = \Sigma v_P Gf°(\text{prod}) - \Sigma v_R Gf°(\text{react}) \qquad (7.7)$$

The units of $\Delta_r G°$ are energy/mol rxn or simply energy/mol, and the individual $Gf°$'s for reactants and products have units of kJ/mol. The *Gibbs free energy of reaction*, $\Delta_r G°$, is an intensive quantity. In analogy to the concept of enthalpies of formation we define *Gibbs energies of formation*. For this purpose the reference substances for the Gibbs function are the stable forms of the elements in their standard states (1 bar). For the reference substances the Gibbs energies of formation are set equal to zero, i.e., $Gf° \equiv 0$ at all temperatures. Compare the discussion for enthalpies of formation in Chapter 3.

As an example of a systematic calculation of $\Delta_r G°$, consider the oxidation of carbon monoxide to carbon dioxide. The fully specified chemical equation and the standard state Gibbs free energies of formation, taken from Appendix D, are

$$CO(g) + 1/2O_2(g) \rightleftharpoons CO_2(g)$$

$Gf°_{298}$(kJ/mol): -137.2 0 -394.4

Applying eq. (7.7), we have

$$\begin{aligned}
\Delta_r G° &= (1)(-394.4 \text{ kJ/mol}) - (1)(-137.2 \text{ kJ/mol}) - (1/2)(0 \text{ kJ/mol}) \\
&= -257.2 \text{ kJ/mol}
\end{aligned} \qquad (7.8)$$

The negative value of $\Delta_r G°$ means that the reaction is spontaneous as written under standard state conditions at room temperature. $\Delta_r G°$ is very large as well as negative. In Chapter 8, we shall develop the relation between the magnitude of $\Delta_r G°$ and the extent of possible reaction as expressed by the equilibrium constant.

Through eq. (7.4) we can relate $\Delta_r G°$ for the combustion of carbon monoxide to ΔS_{tot} and thus to our previous entropy analysis of this reaction in Chapter 4. From $\Delta S_{tot} = 863.1$ J/K mol in Chapter 4, we have

$$\Delta_r G° = -(298 \text{ K})(863.1 \text{ J/K mol}) = -257.2 \text{ kJ/mol} \qquad (7.9)$$

in agreement with the direct calculation of $\Delta_r G°$ from tabulated values. As a review of the calculation of ΔS_{tot} in Chapter 4 shows, the calculation of $\Delta_r G°$

from ΔS_{tot} amounts to calculating $\Delta_r G°$ from $\Delta_r H°$ and $\Delta_r S°$ as in eq. (7.3) which becomes

$$\boxed{\Delta_r G° = \Delta_r H° - T\Delta_r S°} \tag{7.10}$$

Equation (7.10) shows that $\Delta_r G°$ is a strong function of temperature, even if $\Delta_r H°$ and $\Delta_r S°$ are often weak functions of temperature, as we have emphasized before. To estimate $\Delta_r G°_T$ at temperatures other than 298 K, we use eq. (7.10) in the modified form,

$$\Delta_r G°_T \approx \Delta_r H°_{298} - T\Delta_r S°_{298} \tag{7.11}$$

Equation (7.11) can also be used to estimate the temperature at which a reaction comes to equilibrium *under standard state conditions*, i.e., the temperature at which $\Delta_r G°_T = 0$.

Worked Example

What is $\Delta_r G°_{298}$ and its significance for the dissociation of gaseous fluorine at room temperature? At what approximate temperature are F_2 molecules and F atoms at equilibrium when both species are at 1 bar?

	$F_2(g)$	$\rightleftharpoons$	$2F(g)$	
$Gf°_{298}$ (kJ/mol):	0		2(61.9)	$\Delta_r G°_{298} = 123.8$ kJ/mol
$Hf°_{298}$ (kJ/mol):	0		2(80.0)	$\Delta_r H°_{298} = 160.0$ kJ/mol
$S°_{298}$ (J/K mol):	202.8		2(158.8)	$\Delta_r S°_{298} = 114.8$ J/K mol

The large positive value for $\Delta_r G°_{298}$ means that this reaction is not spontaneous at room temperature under standard state conditions. Although the entropy increase in the reactive system, $\Delta_r S°_{298}$, favors the reaction significantly, the energy to dissociate the bond in F_2 molecules must be drawn from the thermal reservoir at a prohibitive entropy price. For the equilibrium temperature, we estimate

$$T \approx \frac{\Delta_r H°_{298}}{\Delta_r S°_{298}} = \frac{160,000 \text{ J/mol}}{114.8 \text{ J/K mol}} \approx 1390 \text{ K}$$

Even though the F—F bond is quite weak, the reactive system must be raised to about 1100°C to produce F atoms *at 1 bar*. Of course, at substantially lower temperature, observable but smaller pressures of F atoms are in equilibrium with 1 bar of F_2 gas. Equilibrium constants are needed to compute these pressures.

We can also use the $\Delta_r G° = 0$ equilibrium condition at constant T, P to compute exactly a $\Delta_r S°$ from a known $\Delta_r H°$ or vice versa. Thus, if the *standard* enthalpy of vaporization of water at 100°C is 40.8 kJ/mol, we have exactly

$$0 = \Delta_r H°_{373} - (373 \text{ K})\Delta_r S°_{373} \tag{7.12}$$

and

$$\Delta_r S°_{373} = \frac{40,800 \text{ J}}{373 \text{ K}} = 109 \text{ J/K} \tag{7.13}$$

This computation of $\Delta_r S°_T$ from $\Delta_r H°_T$, starting from the $\Delta_r G°_T = 0$ condition, is equivalent to the discussion in Chapter 4 based on eq. (4.14) and the condition that $\Delta S_{tot} = 0$.

Why the Change in the Gibbs Function Is Called "Free Energy"

The change in the Gibbs function is the maximum amount of useful, ordered energy that can be obtained from a chemical reaction under conditions of constant temperature and pressure. Thus, $\Delta_r G$ is the amount of energy that is "free" in the useful sense. If a reactive system is coupled to an additional system, such as an electrical one, that can store ordered energy, $\Delta_r G$ is the maximum amount of energy that the chemical reaction can supply to the added system. Consequently, $\Delta_r G$ is often regarded as the "chemical energy" available from a reaction. $\Delta_r G$ is also the amount of chemical energy from one spontaneous chemical reaction that can be applied to reversing another nonspontaneous chemical reaction. Such coupling of chemical reactions is of great importance in biological chemistry. We will discuss it in Chapter 10.

We consider the algebraic basis for characterizing $\Delta_r G$ as free energy. For clarity we shall use σ subscripts throughout this discussion. The second-law expression for ΔS_{tot} consists of two terms, $\Delta S_\theta + \Delta S_\sigma$. For a chemical reaction, ΔS_σ is fixed by the initial state of the reactants and by the final state of the products. In contrast, ΔS_θ depends inversely on temperature and on the interaction of the reactive system with its surroundings. Under the customary conditions depicted in Fig. 2.1, $\Delta U_\theta = -\Delta H_\sigma$ and $\Delta S_\theta = -\Delta H_\sigma/T$. Thus, the entropy change in the thermal reservoir is proportional to ΔH_σ and is often quite large. If the reactive system is coupled to an additional *potential* energy reservoir, such as an electrical system, then the energy principle becomes

$$\Delta U_\theta = -\Delta H_\sigma - \Delta U_{pot} \tag{7.14}$$

where ΔU_{pot} is the energy change in the added reservoir. Now, we have

$$\Delta S_\theta = -\Delta H_\sigma/T - \Delta U_{pot}/T \tag{7.15}$$

If energy is stored in the new reservoir, ΔU_{pot} is positive and ΔS_θ is thereby reduced in magnitude. For ΔS_{tot}, we have

$$\Delta S_{tot} = -\Delta H_\sigma/T - \Delta U_{pot}/T + \Delta S_\sigma \qquad (7.16)$$

For a best-case, reversible (equilibrium) process, $\Delta S_{tot} = 0$ and

$$-\Delta H_\sigma/T - \Delta U_{pot}/T + \Delta S_\sigma = 0 \qquad (7.17)$$

or, after multiplying through by T and rearranging,

$$-\Delta U_{pot} = \Delta H_\sigma - T\Delta S_\sigma \qquad (7.18)$$

Comparing this expression with eq. (7.3), we recognize that $-\Delta G_\sigma = \Delta U_{pot}$. Thus, $-\Delta G_\sigma$ is the maximum amount of energy made available by a chemical reaction at constant temperature and constant pressure that can be stored in a useful form in an electrical system or its equivalent. For irreversible, spontaneous processes, $\Delta S_{tot} > 0$ and $\Delta U_{pot} < -\Delta G_\sigma$. After multiplying through eq. (7.16) by T, we have with the aid of eq. (7.3)

$$T\Delta S_{tot} = -\Delta G_\sigma - \Delta U_{pot} > 0 \qquad (7.19)$$

A portion of the available, useful energy, $-\Delta G_\sigma$, enters the thermal reservoir through frictional, dissipative processes. The remainder is stored as ΔU_{pot}. In the worst case, as in Fig. 2.1, when no additional potential energy reservoir is coupled, all of $-\Delta G_\sigma$ is dissipated as thermal energy. This relationship to excess thermal energy production is explored further in Chapter 10.

As chemical energy, we note that $-\Delta_r G$ can be larger or smaller than $\Delta_r H$ in magnitude. If $\Delta_r S$ is negative as in the reaction of carbon monoxide with oxygen considered above, then $\Delta_r G$ is less than $\Delta_r H$ in magnitude. If $\Delta_r S$ is greater than zero, as in the dissociation of molecular F_2, then $\Delta_r G$ is larger in magnitude than $\Delta_r H$. In this latter case, the entropy increase in the reactive system helps compensate a negative ΔS_θ and thus a withdrawal of energy from the thermal reservoir. Consequently, an endothermic reaction can be spontaneous and a source of free energy, often at an elevated temperature. More generally, we note that $\Delta_r H$ alone is not a proper measure of useful energy available from a chemical reaction.

From this discussion of the free energy character of $\Delta_r G_\sigma$, we see that "free" is being used in the sense of availability as *ordered energy*. Here "free" is not being used in the sense of out of control or without cost. Because of these ambiguities, some scientists shun the use of "free energy." We shall continue to use "free energy" with its refined meaning.

Analyzing $\Delta_r G$ in Terms of $\Delta_r H$ and $\Delta_r S$

Because of the relationship between $\Delta_r G$, $\Delta_r H$, and $\Delta_r S$ in eq. (7.3), it is often said that a decrease in the Gibbs free energy function is a consequence of energy (enthalpy) minimization and entropy maximization. Thus, enthalpy and entropy effects are seen to be in competition. *In our development we have emphasized that spontaneity is always traceable to an increase in the total entropy of the universe.* Thus, we recognize that the $-\Delta_r H/T$ term is merely the entropy change of the thermal reservoir, ΔS_θ, thinly disguised. Two entropy terms compete.

As shown in the following table, there are four possible sign combinations of $\Delta_r H$ and $\Delta_r S$. One of these gives reactions that are only spontaneous in the forward sense at all temperatures. One gives reactions that are spontaneous in the reverse sense at all temperatures. Two give reactions for which the spontaneous direction depends on temperature.

$\Delta_r H \ (= -T\Delta S_\theta)$	$\Delta_r S$	$\Delta_r G$
−	+	− at all T, e.g., $N_2O \rightleftharpoons N_2(g) + 1/2O_2(g)$
+	−	+ at all T, e.g., $N_2(g) + 1/2O_2(g) \rightleftharpoons N_2O(g)$
−	−	− at low T; + at high T, e.g., $2F(g) \rightleftharpoons F_2(g)$
+	+	− at high T; + at low T, e.g., $F_2(g) \rightleftharpoons 2F(g)$

The reactions that switch favorable direction with temperature change are the ones for which the signs of $\Delta_r H$ and $\Delta_r S$ are the same. Those reactions with opposite signs for these quantities are spontaneous in only one direction. We see that there are substances such as N_2O that are unstable with respect to elements at all temperatures. Thus, one could not hope to prepare N_2O by direct reaction of N_2 and O_2. An indirect method would have to be found.

Some Examples. First, we consider the interplay of $\Delta_r H°$ and $\Delta_r S°$ contributions for familiar types of weak acids. One type of weak acid is the representative carboxylic acid, acetic, in which ions are formed when it reacts with water. The other is the ammonium ion, for which the number of ions does not change and for which the type of ion changes only slightly when it reacts with water. For the first type, we shall find that a negative $\Delta_r S°$ is the dominant factor in making the acid weak. In the other, we shall find that a positive $\Delta_r H°$ (i.e., negative ΔS_θ) is the dominant factor.

For the ionization of acetic acid we have

$$HOAc(aq) + H_2O(l) \rightleftharpoons H_3O^+(aq) + OAc^-(aq)$$

$\Delta_r H°_{298} = -0.25$ kJ/mol, $\Delta_r S°_{298} = -92.1$ J/K mol, and $\Delta_r G°_{298} = 27.2$ kJ/mol. $\Delta_r H°$ is almost zero for this reaction and for dissociation reactions of similar carboxylic acids. Thus, the substantial negative value of $\Delta_r S°$ causes acetic acid to be a weak acid as reflected in the sizeable positive value of $\Delta_r G°$. The negative value of $\Delta_r S°$ arises from the "freezing" of water molecules around the ions due to ion–dipole attractions. The dipolar water molecules orient themselves in an energetically favorable way around the positive and negative ions. The decreased mobility of these water molecules lowers their entropy because vibrational degrees of freedom take the place of translational and rotational ones. As a rule, carboxylic acids are weak due to this entropy effect in the reactive system. The spontaneous reaction is in the reverse direction under standard state conditions.

In contrast to the acetic acid example, the ammonium ion is a weak acid because of a sizeable positive value of $\Delta_r H°$. For the reaction

$$NH_4^+(aq) + H_2O(l) \rightleftharpoons NH_3(aq) + H_3O^+(aq)$$

$\Delta_r H°_{298} = 53.2$ kJ/mol, $\Delta_r S°_{298} = -2.1$ J/K mol, and $\Delta_r G°_{298} = 52.8$ kJ/mol. One would expect $\Delta_r S°$ to be close to zero for a reaction of this type because the number of ions is conserved in the reaction, and the NH_4^+ ion is similar to the H_3O^+ ion. The positive value of $\Delta_r H°$ means that an entropy decrease would have to occur in the thermal reservoir. ΔS_θ would be negative were this reaction to take place. The spontaneous reaction is in the reverse direction under standard state conditions.

By examining $\Delta_r H°$ and $\Delta_r S°$ contributions, we can gain an understanding of the so-called *chelate effect*. This effect holds that complex ions involving polydentate, chelating ligands are more stable than ones involving comparable monodentate ligands. Consider the three reactions in Table 7.1. The manner of writing the complexation reactions in Table 7.1 is consistent with standard thermodynamic usage but obscures the role of water molecules. The water molecules that are complexed to the metal ion are covered by the aqueous (aq) designation. The following equation for the first reaction shows the release of water molecules

$$Cd(H_2O)_4^{2+}(aq) + 4NH_3(aq) \rightleftharpoons Cd(NH_3)_4^{2+} + 4H_2O(l)$$

In going from simple ammonia ligands to bidentate ethylenediamine (en) ligands, the bond strength in the complexation process changes little as reflected in the $\Delta_r H°$ values in Table 7.1. On the other hand, $\Delta_r S°$ is substantially larger and positive for the chelate complex formation due to fewer high-entropy translational degrees of freedom being removed when en molecules are the ligands. The two ends of the en molecules are already tied together through the molecular backbone in a configuration suitable for bonding in a ring. The positive value for $\Delta_r S°$ arises from water molecules, which lack translational and rotational degrees of freedom when coordinated to the $Cd^{2+}(aq)$ reactant,

Table 7.1. Thermodynamic Functions for Complex Ion Formation

	$\Delta_r G^\circ$ (kJ/mol)	$\Delta_r H^\circ$ (kJ/mol)	$\Delta_r S^\circ$ (J/K mol)
$Cd^{2+}(aq) + 4NH_3(aq) \rightleftharpoons Cd(NH_3)_4^{2+}(aq)$* 25°C, ionic strength 2.05 M	−42.7	−53.2	−35.6
$Cd^{2+}(aq) + 2en(aq) \rightleftharpoons Cd(en)_2^{2+}(aq)$* 25°C, ionic strength 2.05 M; en = $H_2NCH_2CH_2NH_2$	−60.7	−56.5	13.8
$Ca^{2+}(aq) + EDTA^{4-}(aq) \rightleftharpoons Ca(EDTA)^{2-}(aq)$**	−62.8	−10.5	176

$$EDTA^{4-} = \begin{array}{c} {}^-OOC-CH_2 \\ {}^-OOC-CH_2 \end{array} \!\!\!\! N-CH_2-CH_2-N \!\!\!\! \begin{array}{c} CH_2-COO^- \\ CH_2-COO^- \end{array}$$

*C. G. Spike and R. W. Parry, *J. Am. Chem. Soc.*, 75, 2726 (1953).
**F. F. Carini and A. E. Martell, *J. Am. Chem. Soc.*, 76, 2153 (1954).

acquiring translational and rotational motion in the products. Although the calcium ion has such weak bonds to ligands that it normally does not form well-defined complex ions as reflected in the small value of $\Delta_r H^\circ$, the small calcium ion forms a stable complex with the super, polydentate ligand, ethylenediaminetetraacetate (EDTA) due to the large positive $\Delta_r S^\circ$ associated with this reaction. During formation of the complex, very little immobilization of the EDTA ion ligand is needed while many water molecules are "unfrozen" from around the calcium ion and the charged ends of the EDTA ion. This last case is an outstanding example of the favorable entropy increase in the reactive system associated with the chelate effect.

Finally, we apply this $\Delta_r H^\circ$, $\Delta_r S^\circ$ analysis to some solubility relationships. When "like dissolves like" as in the case of two liquid hydrocarbons mixing, we have a situation in which $\Delta_r H^\circ \approx 0$. Being alike means the interaction energies are essentially the same for both components in pure forms and in solutions. Hence, the positive $T\Delta_r S$ term that accompanies ideal mixing causes $\Delta_r G$ to be negative for all compositions. Thus, "like dissolves like" because of the favorable *configurational* entropy increase in the reactive system due to mixing.

Suppose we try to mix "unlikes" such as a hydrocarbon and water. These molecules are unlike in that stronger hydrogen bonds act between the small polar water molecules, whereas only the weaker van der Waals interactions cause attractions between the larger hydrocarbon molecules. Indeed, were it not for the importance of the hydrogen bonds, water would be a gas at room temperature. In a contemplated mixing process between water and a hydrocarbon, a sizeable positive $\Delta_r H$ would outweigh the positive $T\Delta_r S$ due to mixing, making $\Delta_r G$ overall positive for all solutions except very dilute ones. Thus, unlikes do not dissolve one another to any appreciable extent because of the unfavorable enthalpy increase. Of course, this enthalpy increase would be accompanied by an entropy decrease, ΔS_θ, that would have to occur in the thermal reservoir as energy was withdrawn to supply the positive $\Delta_r H$.

There are many intermediate cases between "likes" and "unlikes" in which $\Delta_r H$ is positive but not overwhelmingly so. Mixing propyl alcohol, $CH_3CH_2CH_2OH$, and water would be such a case. There are also some "symbiotic" cases in which more favorable interactions exist in the mixture. The hydrogen bonding between acetone, $(CH_3)_2C=O$, and chloroform, $CHCl_3$, which occurs in the mixture but not in the pure substances, is an example. In such cases $\Delta_r S$ is less than the ideal mixing value. Why?

The dissolution of solids in liquids, particularly where ions are involved, is a complex matter and thus not readily discussed in general terms. In every case the step of melting of the solid into solution is an entropy-increasing process, as is the subsequent mixing process. This melting step is also an endothermic process, which means that ΔS_θ is negative. Furthermore, $-T\Delta S_\theta = \Delta H_{melt} > T\Delta S_{melt}$ at ordinary temperatures, otherwise the solids would have melted alone without the interaction with the liquid. Specific interaction may occur between the solvent and the species dissolving in the liquid. Highly polar and oxygenated molecules such as sugar enjoy such interactions with water as a solvent. So do the ions in substances such as sodium chloride. An entropy price is paid for these favorable solvent–solute interactions, however, in that the "freezing" of the water molecules around the polar molecules or the ions causes an entropy decrease. The interplay of the three entropy effects, melting (+), mixing (+), and solvating (–), and of the two enthalpy effects, melting (+) and solvating (–), is complex but typically leads to moderate solubilities in water of solids containing small polar molecules or ions, especially large oxygenated ones of low charge. Solids with ions of high charge or strong covalent bonds as reflected in very high melting points are generally insoluble in water.

To obtain a sense of the interplay of the various thermodynamic factors in the solubility of ionic compounds, we consider three examples. They are calcium chloride, calcium sulfate, and ammonium nitrate, for which $\Delta_r G^\circ_{298}$, $\Delta_r H^\circ_{298}$, and $\Delta_r S^\circ_{298}$ are given in Table 7.2. Of the three, calcium chloride is the most soluble salt, since $\Delta_r G^\circ_{298}$ for this compound is large and negative. Calcium sulfate has a very low solubility, since its $\Delta_r G^\circ_{298}$ is substantially positive. Before considering each case, we remind ourselves that an increase in the charge on an ion increases the energy effect of ion–ion and ion–dipole interactions. For ion–ion interactions in a solid, this effect depends on the products of the charges and so is four times as great for two doubly charged ions as for two singly charged ones. The energy effect in a solid is also greater for smaller ions, which can be closer to their partners.

Table 7.2.   Thermodynamic Functions for the Solubility of Three Ionic Substances in Water

	$\Delta_r G°_{298}$ (kJ/mol)	$\Delta_r H°_{298,}$ (kJ/mol)	$\Delta_r S°_{298}$ (J/K mol)
$CaCl_2(c) \rightleftharpoons Ca^{2+}(aq) + 2Cl^-(aq)$	–67.3	–81.4	–44.2
$CaSO_4(c) \rightleftharpoons Ca^{2+}(aq) + SO_4^{2-}(aq)$	23.7	–18.0	–139.7
$NH_4NO_3(c) \rightleftharpoons NH_4^+(aq) + NO_3^-(aq)$	–4.2	27.0	108.7

For calcium chloride the large exothermicity is due to the strong solvation interaction with water, especially of the doubly charged calcium ion, which offsets the positive enthalpy of melting. Also, the negative entropy of solvation of the mix of 2+ calcium ions and the larger 1– chloride ions is not too great. Thus, the dominant term in making $CaCl_2$ soluble is the negative $\Delta_r H°_{298}$. For calcium sulfate the overall process is much less exothermic, due to a large enthalpy of melting attributable to strong attraction between 2+ and 2– ions in the crystal. Also, the addition of the 2– sulfate ions makes the entropy of solvation more negative. Overall, the large negative entropy change in the reactive system is the reason that calcium sulfate is insoluble.

For ammonium nitrate the solubility process is endothermic, presumably because the solvation energies of the rather large, singly charged ions are outweighed by the positive enthalpy of melting. Since $\Delta_r S°_{298}$ is positive, the entropy decrease due to solvation must be outweighed by the entropies of melting and mixing. A small entropy of solvation is what one would expect for large, singly charged ions. Ammonium nitrate dissolves in a strongly endothermic process because of the large positive entropy change, $\Delta_r S°_{298}$.

Generalizations about $\Delta_r S$ and $\Delta_r H$

Before going on to further exploration of the Gibbs function in relation to equilibrium constants in the next chapter, we pause to summarize instances in which we can make qualitative predictions of entropy changes *in the reactive system.* Entropy changes in the reactive system will be substantially positive for:

(1)   Net gas production, $I_2(g) \rightleftharpoons 2I(g)$ and $I_2(c) \rightleftharpoons I_2(g)$
(2)   Net ion consumption in a reaction wholly in solution,
       $H_3O^+(aq) + OAc^-(aq) \rightleftharpoons H_2O(l) + HOAc(aq)$
(3)   Chelate effect, $Ni^{2+}(aq) + EDTA^{4-}(aq) \rightleftharpoons Ni(EDTA)^{2-}(aq)$
(4)   Mixing of gases

(5)   A mixing process or dilution process for liquids in which interactions between solute and solvent molecules do not change appreciably, hexane(l) + pentane(l) $\rightleftharpoons$ hexane,pentane(sol), H_3O^+(aq, 1 M) + Cl^-(aq, 1 M) $\rightleftharpoons$ H_3O^+(aq, 0.1 M) + Cl^-(aq, 0.1 M)

(6)   Dissolving of a *molecular* solid, naphthalene(c) + benzene(l) $\rightleftharpoons$ naphthalene,benzene(sol)

(7)   Depolymerization, $—(CH_2—CH_2)_n—$ (s) $\rightleftharpoons$ $nCH_2=CH_2$(l)

$$\text{polyethylene} \qquad\qquad \text{ethylene}$$

Of course, the reverses of these processes will have substantially negative entropy changes.

Entropy changes in the reactive system will be nearly zero for:

(1)   No net gas production in a reaction wholly in the gas phase, e.g., $H_2(g) + F_2(g) \rightleftharpoons 2HF(g)$

(2)   No change in the number of similar ions in a reaction in solution, e.g., NH_3(aq) + H_3O^+(aq) $\rightleftharpoons$ NH_4^+(aq) + H_2O(l)

(3)   Reactions occurring near absolute zero

Less can be said about estimating $\Delta_r H$ than estimating $\Delta_r S$, unless some bond dissociation enthalpies have been learned. For gas reactions we can predict signs or near zero values of $\Delta_r H°$ from generalized knowledge of bond dissociation enthalpies as described in Chapter 3. For all bond dissociation processes, such as $F_2(g) \rightleftharpoons 2F(g)$, $\Delta_r H° > 0$. Melting and vaporization processes are "physical" dissociation processes for which $\Delta_r H° > 0$ with the value for vaporization being substantially larger. For the formation of ideal solutions or for further dilution of species at low concentration, $\Delta_r H \approx 0$.

Consideration of eq. (4.14) or eq. (7.3) shows that reactions with $\Delta_r S° > 0$ are favored at high temperature and reactions with $\Delta_r H° < 0$ are favored at low temperature.

Summary

The Gibbs energy function, G, has been introduced. $\Delta_r G$, which applies to a reactive system, is a restatement of ΔS_{tot} when T and P are constant and no potential energy reservoirs other than a weight system are involved. Under these three constraints, $\Delta_r G = -T\Delta S_{tot} \leq 0$. Thus, an energy function for a reactive system has replaced an entropy change for the universe, and the significance of the sense of the inequality has been reversed. For a spontaneous process, $\Delta_r G_{T,P} < 0$, whereas $\Delta S_{tot} > 0$.

$\Delta_r G°_{298}$ can be calculated from tabulated standard Gibbs free energies of formation in a manner familiar for $\Delta_r H°_{298}$ and $\Delta_r S°_{298}$. Since $\Delta_r G° = \Delta_r H° - T\Delta_r S°$ at constant temperature, $\Delta_r G°$ can also be calculated at various temperatures from values of $\Delta_r H°_{298}$ and $\Delta_r S°_{298}$. Computed in this way, $\Delta_r G°_{298}$ at 298 K is exact, and $\Delta_r G°_T$ at other temperatures is approximate insofar as $\Delta_r H°$ and $\Delta_r S°$ are weakly temperature dependent. By imposing the equilibrium condition of $\Delta_r G°_T = 0$ on the relationship among $\Delta_r G°$, $\Delta_r H°$, and

$\Delta_r S°$, the temperature at which a reaction is at equilibrium *under standard state conditions* can be estimated. $\Delta_r G$ is a strong function of temperature.

Generalizations about the sign of $\Delta_r S°$ for various processes, such as net gas production, and estimates of $\Delta_r H°$ provide qualitative understanding of the direction of spontaneous change for a number of processes. Examples considered in this way are the weakness of carboxylic acids, the strength of NH_3 as a base, the chelate effect, and solubility processes.

$\Delta_r G$ is called the "free energy" because it tells the maximum amount of ordered energy available from a chemical reaction at constant temperature and constant pressure. This free energy can be stored in a potential energy reservoir, such as an electrical one, or in another chemical reaction system that has been driven in reverse. For a spontaneous process, $T\Delta S_{tot}$ gives the amount of available ordered energy that has been dissipated unnecessarily as thermal energy. In such processes, $-\Delta_r G \geq T\Delta S_{tot} \geq 0$. Some of the available ordered energy may be stored in another system, while the rest is dissipated as thermal energy.

Problems

1. *Without reference to tables* give +, 0, or − for $\Delta_r S$, $\Delta_r H$, and $\Delta_r G$ for each process: (a) $H_2(g) + Cl_2(g) \rightleftharpoons 2HCl(g)$, 25 °C, 1 bar; (b) S(rhombic) = S(monoclinic), 0 K, $\Delta U_\theta < 0$; (c) a dilution process, NaCl(aq, 1 M) = NaCl(aq, 0.1 M). In each case give a brief account of your reasoning, citing algebraic expressions where appropriate.

2. Based on values of $\Delta_r H°_{298}$ and $\Delta_r S°_{298}$, is there any temperature at which graphite can be converted to diamond under a pressure of 1 bar?

3. Show that the conversion of gray tin into its more metallic allotropic modification, white tin, is spontaneous at room temperature. Below what temperature would gray tin be stable and thus cause organ pipes to suffer "tin disease"? (The gray-to-white tin conversion is equivalent to the A-to-B conversion in the countable system analysis of thermal entropy in Chapter 6.)

4. When sulfur is burned with oxygen the product is largely sulfur dioxide. Show that at a flame temperature of 1500 K $\Delta_r G°$ for the reaction $SO_3(g) \rightleftharpoons SO_2(g) + 1/2O_2(g)$ favors the formation of SO_2. What happens to the sign of $\Delta_r G°$ at lower temperatures? (This result shows why SO_2 is the principal product of combustion of sulfur-containing fossil fuels. At lower temperatures, where a catalyst is needed to give a useful rate, SO_3 is favored).

5. *Without reference to tabulated data* give a +, 0, or − for $\Delta_r S°$, $\Delta_r H°$, and $\Delta_r G°$ for each process: (a) $H_2O(l) \rightleftharpoons H_2O(g)$, 100°C; (b) HOAc(aq) +

$H_2O(l) \rightleftharpoons H_3O^+(aq) + OAc^-(aq)$, 25°C, $\Delta U_\theta = 0$. In each case give a brief account of your reasoning, citing algebraic expressions where possible.

6. For the reaction $H_3O^+(aq) + OH^-(aq) \rightleftharpoons 2H_2O(l)$ what is the maximum amount of ordered energy that can be stored in a potential energy reservoir? Ans: $\Delta U_{pot} = -\Delta_r G° = 79.9$ kJ/mol.

7. For the following reactions use qualitative reasoning to predict $\Delta_r S°$ as greater than zero, approximately zero, and less than zero.
$$CO_2(g) + OH^-(aq) \rightleftharpoons HCO_3^-(aq)$$
$$Fe^{3+}(aq) + Cl^-(aq) \rightleftharpoons FeCl^{2+}(aq)$$
$$CO_3^{2-}(aq) + H_3O^+(aq) \rightleftharpoons HCO_3^-(aq) + H_2O(l)$$
$$HCl(aq) \rightleftharpoons H^+(aq) + Cl^-(aq)$$
$$1/2N_2(g) + 1/2O_2(g) \rightleftharpoons NO(g)$$
Ans: two have $\Delta_r S° > 0$, one has $\Delta_r S° \approx 0$, two have $\Delta_r S° < 0$.

8. All of the reactions in problem 7 are spontaneous under standard state conditions. Given your predictions about the signs of $\Delta_r S°$, what can you say about the signs of $\Delta_r H°$? Ans: three reactions must have $\Delta_r H° < 0$.

9. At what temperature is $\Delta_r G°$ for the decomposition of red mercuric oxide, $HgO(c) \rightleftharpoons Hg(g) + 1/2O_2(g)$, equal to zero? N.B.: the gaseous state of mercury is being used. (In a famous experiment in the late 18th century, Priestley prepared pure oxygen gas by focusing the sun's rays on mercuric oxide in a ceramic boat floating on the surface of liquid mercury in an inverted glass tube.)

10. Tables 3.1 and 4.1 give data for the temperature dependence of $\Delta_r H°$ and $\Delta_r S°$ for several reactions. Using the exact values for the two functions at the two temperatures, calculate $\Delta_r G°$ at 298 K and 598 K and the percentage change in $\Delta_r G°$ for the reaction $NO(g) + 1/2O_2(g) \rightleftharpoons NO_2(g)$. Repeat the calculation of $\Delta_r G°_{598}$ using $\Delta_r H°_{298}$ and $\Delta_r S°_{298}$ in the approximate relationship, $\Delta_r G°_T \approx \Delta_r H°_{298} - T\Delta_r S°_{298}$. Ans: $\Delta_r G°_{598} = -12.3$ kJ/mol rxn with the exact values; -13.0 kJ/mol rxn approx.

11. After studying Table 3.2 for general trends in bond dissociation enthalpies and putting it aside, indicate whether or not the following reaction is endothermic or exothermic: $HC\equiv CH(g) + 2H_2(g) \rightleftharpoons H_3C-CH_3(g)$. Also indicate the sign of $\Delta_r S°$. From the signs of $\Delta_r H°$ and $\Delta_r S°$, discuss the spontaneous sense of this reaction as a function of temperature.

12. Apply the analysis of the previous problem to the reaction $H_2(g) + Br_2(g) \rightleftharpoons 2HBr(g)$.

8. CHEMICAL EQUILIBRIUM

In Chapter 7 we encountered the Gibbs free energy as a single, reactive-system-oriented index of change for chemical reactions occurring at constant temperature and constant pressure. We found out how to interpret a negative, a positive, or a zero value of ΔG. The numerical value of the Gibbs free energy gives yet more detailed information about chemical reaction. The change in the standard state Gibbs function is related to the equilibrium constant for a chemical reaction through the important expression $\Delta_r G° = -RT \ln K$. In this expression K is the equilibrium constant, and R is the gas constant. Our principal goal in the present chapter is to derive this relationship and show its uses. A less well known, but more fundamental variant of this relationship is $\Delta S_{tot}° = R \ln K$.

As part of the derivation of the relationship between $\Delta_r G°$ and K, we shall obtain a relationship between $\Delta_r G$ and Q, the reaction quotient, under general, nonequilibrium conditions. In doing so, the basis of the general algebraic form of reaction quotients and equilibrium constant expressions will be seen.

The relationship between $\Delta_r G°$ and K is a powerful connection. It allows the prediction of numerical values of equilibrium constants for chemical reactions from tabulated values of standard Gibbs energies of formation. Thus, the equilibrium constant, which summarizes the outcome of a chemical reaction under all conditions, can be known without a direct study of the particular reaction.

Through an investigation of the dependence of K on temperature, we shall find that $-\Delta_r H°/T = \Delta S_\theta$ is the critical relationship. Thus, as summarized within the LeChâtelier principle, the direction an equilibrium shifts with temperature change depends on the exothermic or endothermic character of the reaction. More fundamentally, we find an interplay between the entropy change in the thermal reservoir and the entropy change in the reactive system.

The presentation in the first part of this chapter involves the most strenuous algebraic argument in this text. With patience and attention to detail you can follow the argument and be rewarded with a deepened understanding of the fundamental concept of chemical equilibrium.

Dependence of Entropy of Reaction on Concentrations of Reactants and Products

As a crucial step in deriving the relationship between the Gibbs energy of reaction and concentrations of reactants and products, we seek the dependence of the reaction entropy, $\Delta_r S$, on concentration. The starting point is the dependence on concentration of the molar entropy of an individual species in solution.

From the discussion of configurational entropy in Chapter 6, we have eq. (6.35), $S_i = -R \ln X_i$, where X_i is the mole fraction of species i. Since species i contributes thermal entropy as well as configurational entropy, the full expression for the molar entropy of species i in an ideal solution is

$$S_i = (S_X{}^\circ)_i - R \ln X_i \qquad (8.1)$$

The subscript X on the standard state thermal entropy term, $(S_X{}^\circ)_i$, designates the standard state as appropriate to mole fraction concentration. $(S_X{}^\circ)_i$ is for pure liquid i, because $R \ln X_i = 0$ when $X_i = 1$.

The next step in the derivation is to recast eq. (8.1) in molar concentrations. Although mole fraction is the natural concentration for the cell model (Chapter 6), molarity is used more commonly for solutions. At low concentrations the mole fraction of species i is proportional to its molarity. Thus,

$$X_i = k_i[i] \qquad (8.2)$$

where $[i]$ is the molar concentration of species i and k_i is a proportionality constant characteristic of species i and the particular solvent. Replacing X_i in eq. (8.1) with X_i from eq. (8.2), we have

$$S_i = (S_X{}^\circ)_i - R \ln k_i[i] = (S_X{}^\circ)_i - R \ln k_i - R \ln [i] \qquad (8.3)$$

which simplifies to

$$\boxed{S_i = S{}^\circ{}_i - R \ln [i]} \qquad (8.4)$$

In writing eq. (8.4) the sum of two terms in eq. (8.3), $(S_X{}^\circ)_i - R \ln k_i$, has been replaced with $S{}^\circ{}_i$. $S{}^\circ{}_i$ is the standard state, thermal molar entropy when concentration in molarity replaces concentration in mole fraction. Eq. (8.4) is true for each solute species in *ideally dilute solutions*. In such solutions the interaction energies between solute species and solvent molecules are independent of concentration, but S_i remains a function of concentration. The standard state has changed from pure species i ($X_i = 1$) to species i at 1 M, since $S_i = S{}^\circ{}_i$ when $[i] = 1$ M. Thus, $S{}^\circ{}_i \neq (S_X{}^\circ)_i$.

When eq. (8.4) is applied to each reactant and each product species in a chemical reaction, $\Delta_r S$ is the outcome. To make the result general, we use a generalized chemical equation,

$$a\text{A} + b\text{B} \rightleftharpoons c\text{C} + d\text{D}.$$

The uppercase letters are reactant and product species. The lowercase letters are stoichiometric coefficients. The corresponding expression for the reaction entropy is

$$\Delta_r S = cS_C + dS_D - aS_A - bS_B \tag{8.5}$$

After insertion of eq. (8.4) for each species, $\Delta_r S$ becomes

$$\Delta_r S = c(S^\circ_C - R \ln [C]) + d(S^\circ_D - R \ln [D]) \tag{8.6}$$

$$-a(S^\circ_A - R \ln [A]) - b(S^\circ_B - R \ln [B]) \tag{8.7}$$

After the collection of similar terms, $\Delta_r S$ becomes

$$\Delta_r S = (cS^\circ_C + dS^\circ_D - aS^\circ_A - bS^\circ_B)$$
$$-R(c \ln [C] + d \ln [D] - a \ln [A] - b \ln [B]) \tag{8.8}$$

The first term in parentheses is simply $\Delta_r S^\circ$. Since the multiplier of a ln term is equivalent to the exponent of the argument of the ln term, $\Delta_r S$ can be reexpressed as

$$\Delta_r S = \Delta_r S^\circ - R(\ln [C]^c + \ln [D]^d - \ln [A]^a - \ln [B]^b) \tag{8.9}$$

Since the sum of ln terms equals a single ln term of the product of the arguments, $\Delta_r S$ becomes

$$\Delta_r S = \Delta_r S^\circ - R \ln \left\{\frac{[C]^c[D]^d}{[A]^a[B]^b}\right\} \tag{8.10}$$

The expression in brackets is called the *reaction quotient*. Thus, the final expression for $\Delta_r S$ is

$$\boxed{\Delta_r S = \Delta_r S^\circ - R \ln Q} \tag{8.11}$$

This expression for the entropy of reaction, which applies to ideally dilute solutions, is the one we sought.

Let us consider the significance of eq. (8.11). Of course, this equation applies to the reactive system only. This equation gives the entropy of reaction per mol rxn over a wide range of concentrations of reactants and products. Equation (8.11) and others that follow in this chapter and Chapter 9 refer to changes that occur in the thermodynamic functions *without the concentrations of reactants or products changing*. To visualize the change under consideration we imagine a very large system in which the change of a moles of A, etc., into c moles of C, etc., does not produce significant changes in concentrations. When the concentration of all reactants *and* all products are 1 M, $Q = 1$ and $\Delta_r S = \Delta_r S^\circ$, the standard state value. For lowered concentrations of products, Q decreases, R ln Q decreases and $\Delta_r S$ increases. Thus, when products are present in high dilution the reaction is favored by a high entropy of reaction. Similar reasoning shows that increased concentrations of reactants also increase $\Delta_r S$ and thereby favor the reaction.

In deriving eq. (8.11), we have shown the generality of the formulation of the reaction quotient. In the numerator of Q are concentrations of reaction products raised to powers of their stoichiometric coefficients. In the denominator are concentrations of reactants raised to powers of their stoichiometric coefficients. The algebraic structure of the reaction quotient is the same as that of the more familiar equilibrium constant expression, as we shall confirm below.

Dependence of the Gibbs Energy of Reaction on Concentrations

With eq. (8.11) in hand for the dependence of the reaction entropy on concentrations of reactants and products in ideally dilute solutions, the derivation of a general expression for $\Delta_r G$ is a simple matter. For ideally dilute solutions the enthalpy of reaction, $\Delta_r H$, is independent of the concentrations of reactants and products. This characterization is another way of saying, as we did above, that the interactions between solute species and solvent molecules are independent of concentration. Thus, $\Delta_r H = \Delta_r H°$. For $\Delta_r G$ at constant temperature for the generalized chemical reaction written above, we have

$$\Delta_r G = \Delta_r H - T\Delta_r S$$

$$= \Delta_r H° - T(\Delta_r S° - R \ln Q) = \Delta_r H° - T\Delta_r S° + RT \ln Q \quad (8.12)$$

Since $\Delta_r G° = \Delta_r H° - T\Delta_r S°$, we have

$$\boxed{\Delta_r G = \Delta_r G° + RT \ln Q} \quad (8.13)$$

Equation (8.13) is an important relationship between the Gibbs energy of reaction and concentrations of reactants and products.

Let us consider the significance of eq. (8.13). $\Delta_r G$ is an intensive quantity with units typically of kJ/mol rxn or simply kJ/mol. The term $\Delta_r G°$ is the standard Gibbs free energy of reaction that is calculable from tabulated standard Gibbs energies of formation. The concentration dependence of $\Delta_r G$ is due to Q in the $RT \ln Q$ term. This concentration dependence is entirely a consequence of configurational entropy effects in the reactive system. Low concentrations of reaction products decrease the $RT \ln Q$ term and thus decrease $\Delta_r G$ algebraically, thereby giving a more favorable reaction as written. Increasing the concentration of reactants also lowers $\Delta_r G$.

Worked Example

Compute $\Delta_r G$ for the reaction of aqueous ammonia with silver ion when the concentration of NH_3 is 0.1 M, the concentration of Ag^+ is 0.01 M, and the concentration of the silver ammonia complex ion is 0.01 M.

$$Ag^+(aq) + 2NH_3(aq) \rightleftharpoons Ag(NH_3)_2{}^+(aq)$$

Gf° (kJ/mol):   77.1   2(–26.5)   –17.1 $\Delta_r G^\circ = -41.2 \text{ kJ/mol}$

$$\Delta_r G = \Delta_r G^\circ + RT \ln \left\{ \frac{[Ag(NH_3)_2{}^+]\, M^2}{[Ag^+][NH_3]^2} \right\}$$

$$= -41{,}200 \text{ J/mol} + (8.314 \text{ J/K mol})(298 \text{ K}) \ln \left\{ \frac{(0.01M)\, M^2}{(0.01M)(0.1M)^2} \right\}$$

$$= -41{,}200 \text{ J/mol} + (2480 \text{ J/mol}) \ln 100 = -29{,}800 \text{ J/mol}$$

See p. 119 for a discussion of the units for Q. The large negative value for $\Delta_r G^\circ$ means that this complexation reaction is highly favored for standard state (1 M) conditions of reactants and products. For the more dilute concentrations of reactants relative to the product given in this example, the reaction is less favored as reflected in the smaller negative value of $\Delta_r G$ than of $\Delta_r G^\circ$.

When the condition for equilibrium, $\Delta_r G = 0$, is applied to eq. (8.13), the equation simplifies and the reaction quotient becomes the *equilibrium constant expression*, K. Thus,

$$0 = \Delta_r G^\circ + RT \ln K \tag{8.14}$$

K has the same algebraic form as the reaction quotient but contains equilibrium concentrations such as $[A]_{eq}$ that satisfy the numerical value of the equilibrium constant. Thus,

$$K = \frac{([C]_{eq})^c ([D]_{eq})^d}{([A]_{eq})^a ([B]_{eq})^b} \tag{8.15}$$

For a given formulation of the chemical equation and for a particular temperature, K has a fixed value. Although the form of the equation relating $\Delta_r G^\circ$ to K given above reflects its derivation, this relationship is usually written

$$\boxed{\Delta_r G^\circ = -RT \ln K} \tag{8.16}$$

If $\Delta_r G^\circ$ is negative, corresponding to a favorable reaction under standard state conditions, $\ln K$ is positive, and $K > 1$. For $K > 1$, the products of the reaction are favored. If $\Delta_r G^\circ > 0$, then $K < 1$. The larger the magnitude of $\Delta_r G^\circ$, the more K differs from one. For a 2 kJ/mol decrease in $\Delta_r G^\circ$ near room temperature, K increases by a factor of 2.2. This result is a good rule of thumb to learn.

Equation (8.16) is very important. It permits calculating the equilibrium constant for a chemical reaction without making a direct study of the reaction. $\Delta_r G°$ comes from tabulated values of standard Gibbs energies of formation or from $\Delta_r H°$ and $\Delta_r S°$ values through the relationship, $\Delta_r G° = \Delta_r H° - T\Delta_r S°$.

There are several reasons that the equilibrium constant for a reaction may not be directly observable. The reaction may be too slow at the temperature of interest. A more favorable, alternative reaction may occur. The equilibrium may lie far on the side of reactants or products thereby making measurement of the concentrations of unfavored species a practical impossibility.

Equation (8.16) also provides $\Delta_r G°$ for a reaction from an observed equilibrium constant. This $\Delta_r G°$ can be applied along with tabulated values of $Gf°$ to compute a missing $Gf°$ for one reactant or one product.

Worked Example

What is the equilibrium constant at 298 K for the formation of the silver ammonia complex ion?

See the previous worked example for the chemical equation and the computation of $\Delta_r G°_{298}$ from tabulated values of $Gf°_{298}$.

$$\Delta_r G° = -RT \ln K = -RT(2.303) \log (K\ M^2)$$

$$\log (K\ M^2) = \frac{-\Delta_r G°}{(2.303)RT} = \frac{-(-41,200\ \text{J/mol})}{(2.303)(8.314\ \text{J/K mol})(298\ \text{K})}$$

$$= 7.22$$

$$K = 10^{7.22}\ M^{-2} = 1.66 \times 10^7\ M^{-2}$$

The units for K have been added as discussed later. We have used the common log of K because we can more quickly interpret the result. The rather large value of K implies favorable formation of $Ag(NH_3)_2^+$ at room temperature.

Although eq. (8.16) is well known, a related equation gives the relationship of the equilibrium constant to the fundamental measure of spontaneity, ΔS_{tot}. Under the constraints of constant temperature and constant pressure,

$$-T\Delta S_{tot} = \Delta G_{T,P} \tag{8.17}$$

as shown early in Chapter 7. Thus,

$$-T\Delta S_{tot}° = \Delta_r G° = -RT \ln K \tag{8.18}$$

where the $^\circ$ on ΔS_{tot}° reminds us that this value is for standard state conditions.[*] Division by $-T$ gives

$$\Delta S_{tot}^\circ = R \ln K \tag{8.19}$$

This equation is a direct relationship between the change in total entropy under standard state conditions and the equilibrium constant. The larger is the increase in the total entropy under these conditions, the more favorable is the reaction as reflected in a large K. For $\Delta S_{tot}^\circ < 0$, $K < 1$.

Equilibrium Constants for Reactions of Substances Other Than in Ideal Solutions

Although a thorough analysis of equilibrium involving nonideal solutions of liquids and solids is beyond the scope of this text, we can take advantage of the thermodynamic treatments for such systems having been modeled on the expressions for ideal solutions. Thus, the equilibrium constant expression has the same form as eq. (8.15), but *activities*, a_i, take the place of concentrations,

$$K_a = \frac{(a_{Ceq})^c (a_{Deq})^d}{(a_{Aeq})^a (a_{Beq})^b} \tag{8.20}$$

The reaction quotient Q_a is also properly expressed in terms of activities. Activities are "generalized concentrations" which take account of the failure of solutions (and real gases) to behave according to the ideal model, in which thermal and configurational effects can be separated. For our purposes it is sufficient to identify activities of various substances under ideally dilute conditions as follows ($a^\circ_i = 1$ for all standard states):

Gases: $a_i = P_i/(1 \text{ bar})$, where P_i is partial pressure of gas i in bar. This approximation is good if the temperature is not too low or the pressure too high.
Pure liquids and solids: $a^\circ_i = 1$, which is exact.
For solvents: $a_i = X_i$ solvent, the mole fraction of the *solvent*, which is almost 1 in dilute solutions.
Solutes: $a_i = [i]/(1 \text{ M})$, where $[i]$ is the molar concentration of solute i. This approximation is good only for very dilute solutions.

For non-ideal systems activities include activity coefficients, symbolized with γ_i. Thus, $a_i = \gamma_i X_i$ and $a_i = \gamma_i [i]/(1 \text{ M})$ for solvents and solutes, respectively.

---

[*] There is an awkwardness in putting the $^\circ$ on ΔS_{tot} since S_{tot} is not a defined function of the reactive system. A function equivalent to ΔS_{tot} was proposed, however, by Planck. He defined $\psi = S - H/T$. Thus, $\Delta S_{tot} = \Delta \psi$.

Equations (8.13) and (8.16) should be written in terms of Q_a and K_a, respectively. Not only do such formulations apply to non-ideal systems, but units are properly handled. In going from eq. (8.3) to eq. (8.4) the ln k_i term in $S°_i$ retained a $(1\ M)^{-1}$. In the activity formulation the $(1\ M)^{-1}$ remains explicitly in the concentration term of eq. (8.4) and carries into Q_a and K_a expressions.

Since activities are unitless, Q_a and K_a are unitless. For dilute solutions, Q_a can be recast as $Q/Q°$, and K_a as $K/K°$ to a good approximation. $Q°$ and $K°$ are the functions expressed in terms of standard values, $P°_i = 1$ bar and $[i]° = 1$ M. $Q°$ and $K°$ are both numerically equal to unity but have units to cancel those in Q and K. For example, for the reaction

$$HOAc(aq) + H_2O(l) \rightleftharpoons H_3O^+(aq) + OAc^-(aq)$$

$$Q_a = \frac{(a_{H_3O^+})(a_{OAc^-})}{(a_{HOAc})(a_{H_2O})} \approx \frac{([H_3O^+]/1\ M)([OAc^-]/1\ M)}{([HOAc]/1\ M)a_{H_2O}}$$

$$= \left\{ \frac{[H_3O^+][OAc^-]}{[HOAc]} \right\} \Big/ \left\{ \frac{(1\ M)(1\ M)}{(1\ M)} \right\} \tag{8.21}$$

Here $Q° = 1$ M with units that cancel the units in Q. The argument of the ln function is unitless. K and $K°$ have the same units as Q and $Q°$, respectively.

The discussion of the general formulation of reaction quotients and equilibrium constant expressions in terms of activities clarifies the *non*role of solvents at low solute concentrations. The activity of the solvent becomes equal to its mole fraction as the concentrations of solutes become small. Consequently, the activity of the solvent approaches 1 under these conditions. Another way to view this result is to learn that mole fraction is retained as the concentration of the solvent when solute concentrations are changed to molarity. One consequence of this treatment of solvents is that they make no numerical or units contribution to equilibrium constant expressions in dilute solutions. Another consequence is that the standard state for the solvent is pure solvent.

Worked Example

For the dissociation of acetic acid in water, the equilibrium constant was found by a titration monitored with a pH meter to be 1.75×10^{-5} M at 298 K. The reaction enthalpy, $\Delta_r H°_{298}$, was found to be -0.25 kJ/mol by calorimetric measurements on the highly favored reverse reaction. Compute $\Delta_r S°_{298}$ for the dissociation of acetic acid in water.

$$HOAc(aq) + H_2O(l) \rightleftharpoons H_3O^+(aq) + OAc^-(aq)$$

$$\Delta_r G°_{298} = -RT\ \ln(K/M) \quad \text{where } K_a = K/K°$$

$$\Delta_r G°_{298} = -(8.314\ J/K\ mol)(298\ K)\ \ln(1.75 \times 10^{-5}\ M/M) = 27{,}100\ J/mol$$

$$\Delta_r G^\circ = \Delta_r H^\circ - T\Delta_r S^\circ$$

$$\Delta_r S^\circ = \frac{\Delta_r H^\circ - \Delta_r G^\circ}{T} = \frac{-250 \text{ J/mol} - 27,100 \text{ J/mol}}{298 \text{ K}} = -91.8 \text{ J/K mol}$$

This substantially negative entropy of reaction is what causes acetic acid to be a weak acid at 25°C. The ions that form "freeze" water molecules around them. $\Delta S_\theta \approx 0$ since $\Delta_r H^\circ \approx 0$. Thus, $\Delta S_{tot} \approx \Delta_r S^\circ$ in this case. This example illustrates how to obtain $\Delta_r S^\circ$, a quantity that is not directly measurable.

Weak Dependence of Enthalpy of Reaction on Concentration

Equation (8.13) shows that the Gibbs energy of reaction, $\Delta_r G$, has a significant dependence on concentration. In contrast, the enthalpy of reaction, $\Delta_r H$, depends weakly on concentration. For reactions involving ideally dilute solutions, $\Delta_r H$ is independent of concentration; thus, $\Delta_r H = \Delta_r H^\circ$. For reactions involving non-ideal solutions, $\Delta_r H \approx \Delta_r H^\circ$. Consequently, comparisons are appropriate between values of $\Delta_r H$ obtained from experimental measurements in solutions of a few tenths molar concentration and $\Delta_r H^\circ$ values as was done without comment in Chapter 3 and thereafter.

Phase Equilibria

Although the discussion up to this point has concentrated on chemical equilibria, the same principles apply to phase equilibria. For the vaporization of water

$$H_2O(l) \rightleftharpoons H_2O(g)$$

has the equilibrium constant expression

$$K_a = \frac{(P_{H_2O}/\text{bar})}{a_{H_2O(l)}} = P_{H_2O}/\text{bar} \tag{8.22}$$

Thus, the equilibrium constant equals the vapor pressure of water, and $\Delta_r G^\circ = -RT \ln (P_{H_2O}/\text{bar})$ since the activity of liquid water is 1. For a solid–liquid phase equilibrium such as that between ice and water

$$H_2O(c) \rightleftharpoons H_2O(l)$$

the equilibrium constant is 1:

$$K_a = \frac{a_{H_2O(l)}}{a_{H_2O(c)}} = 1 \tag{8.23}$$

Thus, $\Delta_r G°_{273} = 0$ for equilibrium between the two pure condensed phases under standard state conditions at a single temperature, 273 K. In many cases phase changes are part of chemical reactions.

Temperature Dependence of Equilibrium Constants

If the enthalpy of a reaction is appreciable, then the equilibrium constant for the reaction has a significant temperature dependence. For an endothermic reaction the equilibrium constant increases with increasing temperature; for an exothermic reaction the equilibrium constant decreases with increasing temperature. These outcomes concur with the LeChâtelier principle applied to the case of thermal stress.

To show the algebraic basis for these relationships, we return to eq. (8.19),

$$\Delta S_{\text{tot}}° = R \ln K \qquad (8.24)$$

and expand $\Delta S_{\text{tot}}°$ to give

$$R \ln K = \Delta S_\theta + \Delta S_\sigma = \frac{-\Delta_r H°}{T} + \Delta_r S° \qquad (8.25)$$

Under the good approximation that $\Delta_r H°$ and $\Delta_r S°$ are temperature independent, the temperature dependence of $R \ln K$ is due to the $-\Delta_r H°/T$ term. For an endothermic reaction with $\Delta_r H°$ positive, the $-\Delta_r H°/T$ term becomes smaller and makes a less negative contribution as T increases. Consequently $R \ln K$ and K increase with increasing temperature. For an exothermic process, the $-\Delta_r H°/T$ term is positive. As T increases, this term becomes smaller and makes a less positive contribution to $R \ln K$. Thus, K decreases with increasing T.

At a more fundamental level, we can apply a full entropy analysis to a rearranged form of eq. (8.25). If all terms are put on the right hand side, we have

$$0 = \frac{-\Delta_r H°}{T} + \Delta_r S° - R \ln K \qquad (8.26)$$

which is an expression for ΔS_{tot} equal to zero for equilibrium. Note that this ΔS_{tot} is not $\Delta S_{\text{tot}}°$, the standard state value. The first term in eq. (8.26) is the change in entropy in the thermal reservoir, that is, a thermal entropy term that depends on temperature. The second term in eq. (8.26) is a fixed thermal entropy term for the reactive system. The third term, $-R \ln K$, is the concentration-dependent, configurational entropy term for the reactive system. To maintain equilibrium ($\Delta S_{\text{tot}} = 0$) as temperature changes, the first and last terms must change in balance. Changes in thermal entropy in the thermal reservoir are compensated by changes in configurational entropy in the reactive system. Thus, with increasing temperature for an endothermic reaction the negative thermal entropy change in the thermal reservoir (first term) gets smaller so the negative configurational entropy change in the reactive system (third term) must get larger. More concentrated products are favored as reflected in a larger K. An equivalent argument applies to the case of an exothermic reaction.

Equation (8.25) can be used in two ways. One way is to compute $\Delta_r H°$ and $\Delta_r S°$ from tabulated data, insert these values in eq. (8.25), and compute K at various temperatures. Another way to use eq. (8.25) is to analyze a series of equilibrium constants measured experimentally for a reaction at various temperatures. To do so, $\ln K$ is plotted versus 1/T. A straight line is fit to the data. The slope of this line is $-\Delta_r H°/R$, and the intercept at zero on the 1/T axis is $\Delta_r S°/R$.

Worked Example

For the dissociation of gaseous I_2, the following data were obtained

T (K)	973	1073	1173	1274
K_P (bar)	0.00176	0.0112	0.0493	0.172

Find $\Delta_r H°$, $\Delta_r S°$, and $\Delta_r G°_{1073}$ for the dissociation of I_2

$$I_2(g) \rightleftharpoons 2I(g) \qquad K_P = \frac{P_I^2}{P_{I_2}}, \text{ in bar}$$

To plot the data, according to eq. (8.25), we need

1/T (10^4/K)	10.3	9.32	8.52	7.85
$\ln (K_P/\text{bar})$	−6.34	−4.49	−3.01	−1.76

The figure shows a plot of $\ln K_P$ versus 1/T.

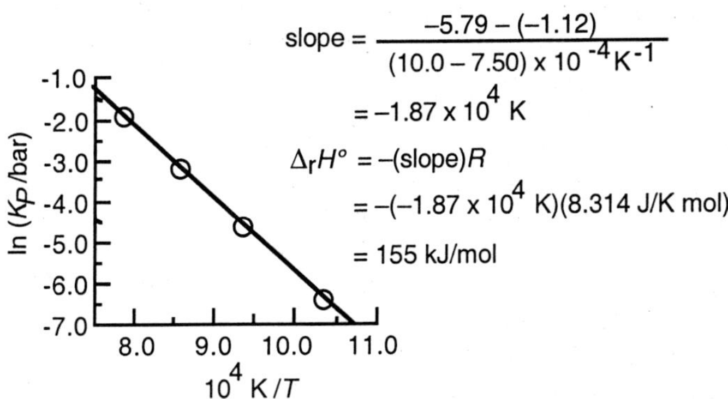

$\Delta_r G°_{1073}$

$$= -RT \ln (K_P/\text{bar}) = -(8.314 \text{ J/K mol})(1073 \text{ K}) \ln (0.0112 \text{ bar/bar})$$

$$= 40,100 \text{ J/mol}$$

$$\Delta_r S° = \frac{\Delta_r H° - \Delta_r G°}{T} = \frac{155,000 - 40,100}{1073 \text{ K}} \text{ J/mol} = 107 \text{ J/K mol}$$

Since the I_2 bond is broken in the reaction, the process is endothermic. Two moles of gas are formed from 1 mol, hence $\Delta_r S° \gg 0$.

Summary

The Gibbs free energy, $\Delta_r G$, gives information about the extent of reaction as well as the direction of spontaneous change. The magnitude of $\Delta_r G$ gives the extent; the sign gives the direction. These relationships are expressed by $\Delta_r G = \Delta_r G° + RT \ln Q$, where Q is the reaction quotient. At equilibrium this expression reduces to $\Delta_r G° = -RT \ln K$, an equation of great importance. The equilibrium constant expression K has the same algebraic form as Q, but a fixed numerical value at a given temperature. The expressions for Q and K always consist of a product of concentrations of reaction product species divided by a product of concentrations of reactant species. Since $\Delta_r G°$ for reactions can be computed from tabulated values of standard Gibbs energies of formation, equilibrium constants can be predicted for many reactions. Direct studies of chemical equilibria are unnecessary.

Underlying the derivation of the relationship between $\Delta_r G$ and Q is the dependence of entropy on the concentration of a single species. For an ideally dilute solution this relationship is $S_i = S°_i - R \ln [i]$, where $[i]$ is the molar concentration of i. This dependence of entropy on the concentration of each species in a reactive system explains the balance that is struck between concentrations of reactants and products at equilibrium.

Although we emphasize applications to ideally dilute solutions, Q and K may be expressed exactly in activities for more concentrated solutions. Activities are effective concentrations that become numerically equal to concentrations in ideally dilute solutions. The algebraic forms of Q and K are unchanged, but activities replace concentrations in these expressions. In dilute solutions the activity of a solvent equals its mole fraction, which becomes 1 at high dilution. Thus, solvents make no numerical or units contribution to equilibrium constant expressions. The principles of formulating equilibrium constant expressions apply to phase equilibria as well as to chemical equilibria.

The dependence of equilibrium constants on temperature is through the sign and magnitude of $\Delta_r H°$. Thus, the direction in which an equilibrium shifts with rising temperature depends on whether the reaction is endothermic or exothermic. For an endothermic reaction K increases as T increases in agreement with the LeChâtelier principle. For an exothermic reaction, K decreases as T increases. The reason for the dependence of K on temperature is the balance that is struck between the thermal entropy change in the thermal reservoir and the configurational entropy change in the reactive system. In the thermal reservoir, the entropy change depends inversely on temperature through $\Delta S_\theta = -\Delta_r H°/T$. Whether ΔS_θ increases algebraically with increasing T or decreases depends on the sign of $\Delta_r H°$. In the reactive system $-R \ln K$ gives the compensatory change in configurational entropy. These relationships are a consequence of maintaining the equilibrium condition, $0 = -\Delta_r H°/T + \Delta_r S° - R \ln K$. From the temperature dependence of observed equilibrium constants for a reaction, $-\Delta_r H°$ and $\Delta_r S°$ may be found for the reaction. These quantities are parameters in the plot of $\ln K$ vs $1/T$.

In contrast to $\Delta_r G$, which is strongly dependent on concentrations, $\Delta_r H$ is independent of concentrations for reactions involving ideally dilute solutions and is weakly dependent on concentration in nonideal solutions of low concentration.

Problems

1. Calculate $\Delta_r G°_{298}$ from tabulated thermodynamic data for the reaction $Zn^{2+}(aq) + 4NH_3(aq) \rightleftharpoons Zn(NH_3)_4{}^{2+}(aq)$. Interpret your value of $\Delta_r G°_{298}$. Compute the equilibrium constant for this reaction. One ans: $K = 3.64 \times 10^8$ M^{-4}.

2. Show that a decrease of 2 kJ/mol rxn in $\Delta_r G°$ corresponds to an increase of a factor of 2.2 in an equilibrium constant at room temperature.

3. Using tabulated thermodynamic functions obtain $\Delta_r G°$ for the dissociation of acetic acid (CH_3COOH) in water and then calculate K, the dissociation constant for this acid. Ans: $K = 1.74 \times 10^{-5}$ M.

4. For the thermodynamic quantities $\Delta_r S°$, ΔS_{tot}, ΔS_θ, ΔS_{mix}, $S°_T$, $\Delta_r H°$, $\Delta_r G°$, and K, indicate the ones that typically depend strongly on temperature.

5. Calculate $\Delta_r G$ at 298 K for the reaction

$$Fe(CN)_6{}^{4-}(aq) + 6H_3O^+(aq) \rightleftharpoons Fe^{2+}(aq) + 6HCN(aq) + 6H_2O(l)$$

when the concentrations of the four species, left to right, are 0.40 M, 1.0 M, 0.25 M, and 0.01 M respectively. Ans: $\Delta_r G = -125.4$ kJ/mol rxn.

6. At 25°C the equilibrium constant for the reaction $NO(g) + 1/2 Br_2(l) \rightleftharpoons$ $NOBr(g)$ has the value 5.6 bar$^{-1/2}$. Calculate $\Delta_r G°$ for the reaction from the equilibrium constant. At 25°C, $Gf° = 86.55$ kJ/mol for gaseous NO. Calculate $Gf°$ for gaseous NOBr without consulting a table. Ans: $Gf°(NOBr) = 82.3$ kJ/mol.

7. Of the two reaction quantities, $\Delta_r H°$ and $\Delta_r S°$, only the first plays a significant role in the temperature dependence of the equilibrium constant. Explain in entropy terms.

8. Calculate $\Delta_r H°$ for the reaction $AgCl(c) \rightleftharpoons Ag^+(aq) + Cl^-(aq)$ and then determine whether or not the solubility of silver chloride increases with increasing temperature. (Notice that this is an equilibrium problem, in which you should consider how K_{sp}, the solubility product, varies with T.) Ans: $\Delta_r H°_{298} = 65.5$ kJ/mol. Solubility increases with increasing temperature.

9. In the famous and commercially important Haber process, ammonia is formed by the reaction $N_2(g) + 3\,H_2(g) \rightleftharpoons 2NH_3(g)$. Assuming $\Delta_r S°$ and $\Delta_r H°$ to be independent of temperature, calculate $\Delta_r G°_{400}$ for this reaction. At what temperature does $\Delta_r G°_T = 0$? What is K at this temperature and at 400 K? Ans: $\Delta_r G°_{400} = -12.7$ kJ/mol; $T_{equil} = 464$ K.

10. Using tabulated thermodynamic data, find the factor by which the solubility of $PbCl_2$ increases between 25°C and 100°C. This increase is used in qualitative analysis in order to separate lead ions from the chlorides of silver and mercury(I).

11. For the dissociation of PCl_5 into PCl_3 and Cl_2 in the gas phase, experimental measurements of the equilibrium constant give

Kp (bar)	0.248	2.02	5.02	9.47
T (K)	485	534	556	574

First, predict the signs and rough magnitudes of $\Delta_r H°$ and $\Delta_r S°$, and then use the data to find the values of these two quantities and of $\Delta_r G°_{534}$. Two ans: $\Delta_r H° = 94.8$ kJ/mol, $\Delta_r S° = 183$ J/K mol.

9. ELECTROCHEMICAL CELLS

In electrochemical cells chemical energy and electrical energy are interconverted. As a consequence, thermodynamics is of much value in analyzing these systems. The voltage of a cell measured under equilibrium (reversible) conditions for the overall electrochemical system is called the electromotive force or emf and is a direct measure of the Gibbs free energy, $\Delta_r G$. Since the change in the Gibbs function is related to the concentrations of reactant and product species, the cell emf is related to the concentrations of electrode-active species. The Nernst equation is the important mathematical relationship between the emf and these concentrations. With the aid of this equation and a measured emf a concentration, including a very tiny one, can be readily found. The pH meter system is a familiar example of this application.

Because electrochemical cell systems include an electrical part that is an additional potential energy reservoir, $\Delta_r G_{T,P}$ alone is no longer an index of spontaneity. Of course, ΔS_{tot} remains a proper index of spontaneity. For these electrochemical systems we will find that $T\Delta S_{tot} = -\Delta_r G - \Delta U_{el} \geq 0$, where ΔU_{el} is the energy change in the electrical part. When the chemical reaction and the electrical system are in balance, the overall system is in a state of electrochemical equilibrium. Then, $\Delta S_{tot} = 0$, and the Nernst equation applies.

In galvanic cells, familiarly called batteries, chemical energy is converted into electrical energy. In electrolytic cells, electrical energy is converted into chemical energy. Under reversible conditions these energy changes balance; $-\Delta G_\sigma = \Delta U_{el}$.

Electrochemical Systems

To discuss the thermodynamics of electrochemical cells we must extend our prototypical overall system (Fig. 2.1) to include an electrical system as well as the familiar reactive system, thermal reservoir, and weight system. Figure 9.1 is a diagram of this augmented overall system. It includes an electrical system (el) which is connected to the reactive system through two wire electrodes. The critical measure of change in energy in the electrical system is the amount of electrical charge, Δq, moved between two electrodes. In Fig. 9.1 the reactive system is divided by a dashed line. The two half-cells which constitute an electrochemical cell must be chemically separated in order for chemical reaction to occur by electron transfer through the external electrical system instead of direct contact in the reactive system. As before, the other critical variables are the n_j's, mole numbers for reactants and products in the chemical reaction; T, temperature for the thermal reservoir; and h, height for the weight system.

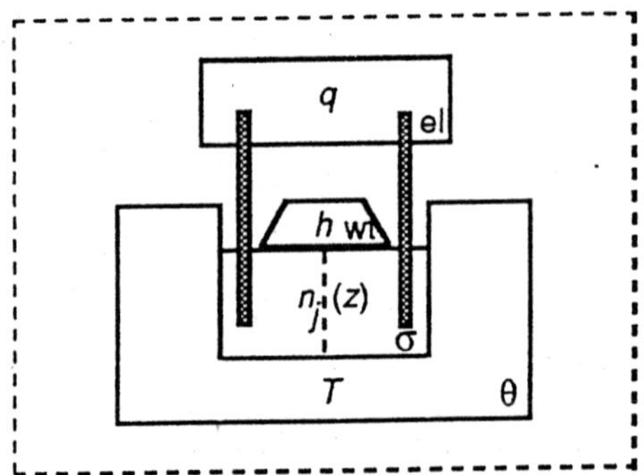

Figure 9.1.   Diagram of a prototypical electrochemical system.   The
electrical system (el) is coupled to the reactive system through
electrode wires.   The dashed dividing line in the reactive system
indicates that the two half-cell reactions must be chemically
separate in electrochemical systems.

In analyzing electrochemical cells a distinction is drawn between *galvanic
cells* and *electrolytic cells*. For galvanic cells the voltage due to the tendency for
the chemical reaction to occur is larger than the voltage in the electrical system.
The chemical reaction occurs in its spontaneous direction. The chemical reaction
is the dominant effect, and chemical energy is converted into electrical energy.
Such systems are commonly called batteries. For electrolytic cells the voltage
of the electrical system is larger than the voltage due to the tendency of the
chemical reaction to occur. If the overall system is wired correctly, then the
chemical reaction goes in reverse. *Electrolysis* occurs, in which electrical energy
is converted into chemical energy. The electrical system is the dominant one in
this case. Although we shall stress the analysis of galvanic cells, our treatment
applies to electrolytic cells as well. Only the signs of various quantities differ.

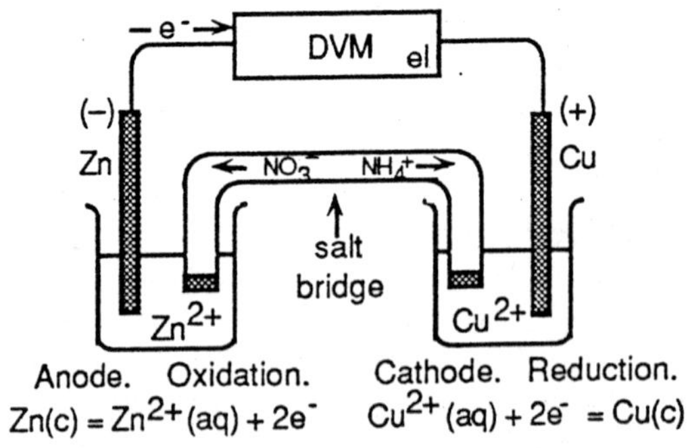

Anode.   Oxidation.   Cathode.   Reduction.
$Zn(c) = Zn^{2+}(aq) + 2e^-$ $Cu^{2+}(aq) + 2e^- = Cu(c)$

Figure 9.2.   Details of a simple galvanic cell, the Daniell cell.

An Example of a Galvanic Cell System; Conventions Used in Describing Cells

To make our discussion concrete consider the galvanic cell shown in Fig. 9.2, which is called the Daniell cell. One *half-cell* consists of a zinc metal electrode and zinc ions in aqueous solution. The other half-cell consists of a copper metal electrode and copper ions in aqueous solution. The two half-cells are ionically coupled but chemically separated by the *salt bridge*, which is filled with an aqueous solution of ions that are chemically inert to the contents of the two half-cells. Ammonium nitrate is often used for this purpose. The two electrodes are wired to an electrical system, which for galvanic cell experiments is typically a very high resistance digital voltmeter (DVM). If the concentrations of the zinc ions and copper ions are 1 M, the standard state values, then the zinc electrode is found to be negative and the copper electrode positive. At a negative electrode in a galvanic cell the spontaneous half-reaction releases electrons in an *oxidation* process. The electrons are released onto the electrode which makes it electron rich. At a positive electrode in a galvanic cell the spontaneous half reaction consumes electrons in a *reduction* process. Here electrons are removed from the electrode, making it electron poor. Whether the overall process is that of a galvanic cell (battery) or an electrolytic cell (electrolysis) the term *anode* is used for the electrode at which oxidation takes place. The term *cathode* is used for the electrode at which reduction takes place. As a memory aid, many people associate the vowels that begin "*a*node" and "*o*xidation" and the consonants that begin "cathode" and "reduction." In electrolytic cells the cathode is negative and the anode is positive, which is opposite to the situation in galvanic cells. (Faraday was doing electrolysis experiments when he named positive ions "cations" because they were attracted to the cathode and negative ions "anions" because they were attracted to the anode.)

Let us now relate the galvanic cell of Fig. 9.2 to the specific chemistry that occurs in it. We can write the two half-reactions and relate them to the standard state emf's, $E°$'s, that we find in standard tables. The emf, which is the voltage of an electrochemical cell measured in the customary way, is defined precisely later. For now, we have

$$
\begin{array}{lll}
 & E° & \\
Zn(c) \rightleftharpoons Zn^{2+}(aq) + 2e^- & 0.76\ V & \text{oxidation; anode } (-) \\
Cu^{2+}(aq) + 2e^- \rightleftharpoons Cu(c) & 0.34\ V & \text{reduction; cathode } (+) \\
\hline
Cu^{2+}(aq) + Zn(c) \rightleftharpoons Cu(c) + Zn^{2+}(aq) & 1.10\ V &
\end{array}
$$

"V" is for volts, the standard unit of voltage. We have written the zinc–zinc ion half-reaction as an oxidation because the zinc electrode is found to be negative. Electrons are left behind on the zinc metal as zinc ions go into solution. We have written the copper–copper ion half-reaction as a reduction. Copper ions join the copper electrode, making it positive and in need of electrons supplied through the electrical circuit. When emf's are taken from tables, we must change the sign if we reverse the sense of the half-reaction. In the present case we find $Zn^{2+}(aq) + 2e^- \rightleftharpoons Zn(c)$ with $E° = -0.76$ V in tables. We changed the sign of the emf when we reversed the sense of this half-reaction. The expected emf for the galvanic cell powered by this reaction under standard state conditions is 1.10 V. Electrons will flow from the negative zinc electrode (anode) through the electrical system to the copper electrode (cathode). Whereas electrons flow through the external circuit, within the cell and the salt bridge the electrical circuit is completed by ion flow. Negative ions migrate toward the negative electrode to compensate for the buildup of positive zinc ions which leave the zinc electrode. Positive ions migrate toward the positive electrode to compensate for the loss of positive copper ions from solution as they are deposited on the copper electrode. The result of these two senses of ion migration is a net negative charge flow that is a continuum of that caused by electron flow externally to the cell. In the salt bridge the NH_4^+ and NO_3^- migrate in proper directions. In the zinc half-cell zinc ions and the accompanying anions move. In the copper half-cell the copper ions and accompanying anions move.

A convention exists for writing the essentials of a galvanic cell. For the cell under consideration the *conventional representation* is

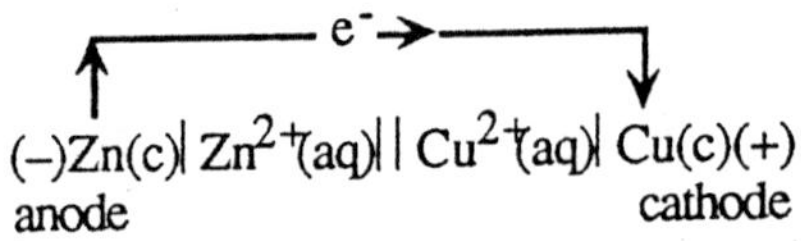

The expected or guessed participants in the anode half-reaction are always written on the left; the participants in the cathode half-reaction are always written on the right. As a consequence, *the electrode that is written on the left is expected to be negative*, and the one that is written on the right is expected to be positive. Expected electron flow in the external electrical circuit as written on paper is clockwise as is the net negative ion flow in the internal circuit. If the signs of the electrodes of the actual cell in the laboratory are found to be as expected, then the emf is taken as positive. If the electrode signs are opposite to the expected ones, the emf is taken as negative. Thus, a negative emf means that a reaction is spontaneous in the opposite sense to which it is written. A single vertical bar signifies a phase boundary such as between the zinc metal electrode and the aqueous solution across which charged particles, zinc ions in this case, are transferred. The double bar means a salt bridge, because it consists of two phase boundaries between the solution in the salt bridge and the different solutions in the two half-cell compartments. As a memory aid, note that the expected reduction reaction, which occurs at the cathode, is written on the *right*. Also, the expected negative charge flow of electrons and negative ions is clockwise.

Electrical Energy

For a thermodynamic analysis of the electrochemical system that is shown in Fig. 9.1, we must expand our expression for the first law to include a term for the change in energy in the electrical system, ΔU_{el}. Thus, we have

$$\Delta U_{tot} = \Delta U_\sigma + \Delta U_{wt} + \Delta U_\theta + \Delta U_{el} = 0 \qquad (9.1)$$

Since all of our applications will be under the commonly used condition of constant pressure, we replace $\Delta U_\sigma + \Delta U_{wt}$ with ΔH_σ and have

$$\Delta H_\sigma + \Delta U_\theta + \Delta U_{el} = 0 \qquad (9.2)$$

To use this first-law expression we must have an experimentally well-defined way of evaluating ΔU_{el}. ΔU_{el} is given by the product of the electrical potential difference, V_{el}, between the electrodes and the charge Δq, which moves through this potential difference. Thus,

$$\Delta U_{el} = V_{el}\Delta q \qquad (9.3)$$

where the units of potential difference are volts (V) and the units of charge are coulombs (C). One volt-coulomb equals one joule (1 V C = 1 J). Measurement of the potential difference between the electrodes and of the charge moved between the electrodes permits evaluation of ΔU_{el}.

For electrochemical systems it is desirable to reexpress ΔU_{el} in terms of reactive-system-oriented variables. In doing so we are applying the same change-of-view strategy that we employed in developing the enthalpy and Gibbs energy functions. We express the change in electrical charge Δq in terms of the Faraday constant, which is the charge on a mole of electrons. The symbol for this constant is F, and the value is 96,500 C/mol e$^-$. For moles of electrons we use the symbol z. Thus,

$$\Delta q = F\Delta z \text{ and } \Delta U_{el} = V_{el}F\Delta z \qquad (9.4)$$

The numbers of moles of electrons transferred per mole of reaction in a particular galvanic cell process or electrolysis is Δz. Δz is always taken as positive for the chemical reaction of an electrochemical cell as the reaction is arbitrarily written. The spontaneous sense of the reaction may be in the opposite direction, as would be reflected in a negative emf. The units of Δz are moles of electrons per mole reaction or mol e$^-$/mol rxn.

As we noted at the beginning of our discussion of electrochemical systems, the voltage of a galvanic cell is normally measured under near-reversible conditions and is called the *electromotive force* or emf. This special value of the voltage is denoted with E, and it is the maximum voltage that can be measured for a galvanic cell. In practice, such measurements are made with very high resistance devices so that the current flow is negligible. High-resistance DVM's have this property, as do the classical devices called potentiometers. Observing and recording the physical signs of the electrodes in a galvanic cell is just as important as measuring the magnitude of the emf. The sign of an electrode is the same as the sign of the lead of the DVM when a positive voltage reading is obtained. From the sign of an electrode we can deduce the spontaneous sense of the half-reaction occurring at the electrode. In galvanic cells an oxidation process occurs at a negative electrode; a reduction process at a positive one. When the emf is measured, $V_{el} = E$ and

$$\boxed{\Delta U_{el} = EF\Delta z} \tag{9.5}$$

Thus, the experimental condition for what we shall call *electrochemical equilibrium* is $V_{el} = E$. This condition is comparable to $T_\theta = T_\sigma$ for thermal equilibrium between a thermal reservoir and the reactive system or to $P_{atm} = P_\sigma$ for mechanical equilibrium between the atmosphere and the reactive system.

The condition of electrochemical equilibrium is equivalent to the condition of reversibility. In thermodynamics a reversible process is one that runs in the *exact reverse* when a tiny change is made in a constraint on the system. When the voltage applied by the electrical system is slightly less than E, the current flows in the galvanic cell sense. If the applied voltage is slightly larger than the emf, the current flows in the opposite sense and electrolysis occurs. Thus, in a reversible process the direction of change in the overall system reverses smoothly as we go from $V_{el} < E$ to $V_{el} = E$ to $|V_{el}| > |E|$.

Relationship Between Electrical Energy and the Gibbs Free Energy

An important relationship exists between the energy change in an electrical system and the change in Gibbs energy function for a chemical reaction. We shall develop this. At constant pressure the first-law expression is given by eq. (9.2),

$$\Delta_r H_\sigma + \Delta U_\theta + \Delta U_{el} = 0 \tag{9.6}$$

The second-law expression is

$$\Delta S_{tot} = \Delta_r S_\sigma + \Delta S_\theta \geq 0 \tag{9.7}$$

or, at constant temperature,

$$\Delta S_{tot} = \Delta_r S_\sigma + \frac{\Delta U_\theta}{T} \geq 0 \tag{9.8}$$

where we have used $\Delta S_\theta = \Delta U_\theta/T$. Since electrical energy is ordered energy, like the energy of a weight system, no entropy change is associated with it. When

ΔU_θ is eliminated between eqs. (9.6) and (9.8), we have a combined first- and second-law expression

$$\Delta_r S_\sigma - \frac{\Delta_r H_\sigma}{T} - \frac{\Delta U_{el}}{T} \geq 0 \tag{9.10}$$

or

$$-(\Delta_r H - T\Delta_r S) - \Delta U_{el} = -\Delta_r G - \Delta U_{el} \geq 0 \tag{9.11}$$

$$-\Delta_r G \geq \Delta U_{el} = V_{el}F\Delta z \tag{9.12}$$

where we have recalled that $\Delta_r G = \Delta_r H - T\Delta_r S$ and have dropped the σ subscripts for the obvious reactive-system functions. The constraints of constant pressure and constant temperature apply. For the important condition of overall equilibrium the equality sign applies and $\Delta U_{el} = EF\Delta z$. This overall equilibrium is what we have called *electrochemical equilibrium*, because, taken together, the electrical and chemical systems are at equilibrium. The opposing electrical tendencies of the chemical system and the electrical system are in balance. ΔS_{tot} for a process occurring under these conditions equals zero and, as we noted above, $V_{el} = E$.

$\Delta_r G$ alone is not a measure of spontaneity for an overall electrochemical system. The chemical system (reactive system) is typically far from equilibrium, and $\Delta_r G$ is far from being zero. As we noted in an earlier section, $\Delta_r G$ is a measure of the spontaneity of a chemical reaction at constant temperature and pressure when the only potential energy reservoir is a weight system. At electrochemical equilibrium the electrical system is connected, and the tendency for the chemical reaction to occur by electron flow through the electrical system is balanced by the voltage of the electrical system.

Returning to our equations, we have for *electrochemical equilibrium*,

$$\boxed{EF\Delta z = -\Delta_r G} \tag{9.13}$$

This important relationship shows that the emf of a galvanic cell is directly proportional to $\Delta_r G$. However, note the negative sign. Thus, a spontaneous chemical reaction, for which $\Delta_r G$ is negative, is associated with a positive emf in a galvanic cell. In the absence of electrochemical equilibrium

$$V_{el}F\Delta z = \Delta U_{el} \leq -\Delta_r G \tag{9.14}$$

where $V_{el} < E$. The overall expression shows that the maximum amount of electrical energy that can be produced by a chemical reaction is given by $-\Delta_r G$ for the reaction.

Let us apply eq. (9.13) to the calculation of the Gibbs function for the example of the Daniell galvanic cell, which was presented above. Under standard state conditions eq. (9.13) becomes

$$\Delta_r G^\circ = -E^\circ F \Delta z$$

$$= -(1.10 \text{ V})\left(96{,}500\,\frac{\text{C}}{\text{mol e}^-}\right)\left(\frac{2 \text{ mol e}^-}{\text{mol rxn}}\right)\left(1\,\frac{\text{J}}{\text{V C}}\right)$$

$$= -212{,}000 \text{ J/mol rxn or } -212 \text{ kJ/mol} \tag{9.15}$$

This amount of energy can be obtained from this chemical reaction and converted into ordered electrical energy if the galvanic cell is operated at the reversible limit. This result is consistent with calling the change in the Gibbs function free energy. As we showed in a general analysis in Chapter 7, of which the present case is a specific example, for any process at constant T and P, $-\Delta_r G$ is the *maximum* amount of energy from a chemical reaction that can be converted into ordered energy other than $\Delta U_{wt} = P \Delta V$. Note that $\Delta_r H$ is not alone a measure of the amount of ordered energy that can be obtained from a chemical reaction. $\Delta_r G$ is the proper measure for a chemical reaction. We shall develop this distinction for another example of a cell reaction in a later section.

Nernst Equation

The Nernst equation is the relationship between the emf of a galvanic cell and the concentrations of reactants and products. This equation is of central importance in the applications of thermodynamics to electrochemical systems. We obtain the Nernst equation by combining eqs. (8.13) and (9.13). The constraint of electrochemical equilibrium as well as the constraints of constant pressure and constant temperature apply. Thus,

$$EF\Delta z = -\Delta_r G = -\Delta_r G^\circ - RT \ln Q = E^\circ F \Delta z - RT \ln Q \tag{9.16}$$

where Q is the familiar reaction quotient. Dividing through by $F\Delta z$ we have

$$E = E^\circ - \frac{RT}{F\Delta z} \ln Q \tag{9.17}$$

which is the famous Nernst equation. Since our applications will be at room temperature and since we are more at home with the log function than the ln function, we reexpress the Nernst equation with the numerical constant,

$$\frac{RT(2.303)}{F} = \frac{(8.314 \text{ J/K mol})(298 \text{ K})(2.303)(1 \text{ V C/J})}{(96{,}500 \text{ C/mol e}^-)}$$

$$= 0.0592 \text{ V mol e}^-/\text{mol} \tag{9.18}$$

Under these conditions the Nernst equation becomes

$$E = E° - \frac{(0.0592 \text{ V mol e}^-)}{\Delta z} \log Q \qquad (9.19)$$

Note that log not ln is used.

Let us consider the Nernst equation and the conditions under which it applies. Not only are the customary constraints of constant pressure and constant temperature involved, but so is the condition of electrochemical equilibrium. The presence of E's in the Nernst equation reminds us of the latter constraint, since $E = V_{el}$ under this condition. Thus, the Nernst equation applies when the chemical reaction system is balanced by the electrical system. Negligible current flows in the electrical system; negligible reaction occurs in the chemical system. Through the role of Q, the emf depends on the concentration of reactants and products. Increased concentrations of reactants decrease Q thereby making the ln Q term smaller and E larger. An increased E reflects a greater tendency for the reaction to occur. An equivalent argument shows that increased concentrations of products lower E. Try it. For standard state conditions for reactants and products, $Q° = 1$ and $E = E°$. Q and Δz depend on how the chemical reaction is written, but E does not. If the stoichiometric coefficients for a reaction are doubled, Q is squared and Δz is doubled. Since $(1/2\Delta z) \ln Q^2 = (1/2\Delta z)2 \ln Q$, the effect cancels. E is an intensive variable that does not depend on the extent of reaction. The only change that occurs in E or $E°$ when a different equation is written for a chemical reaction is the sign when the sense of the reaction is reversed.

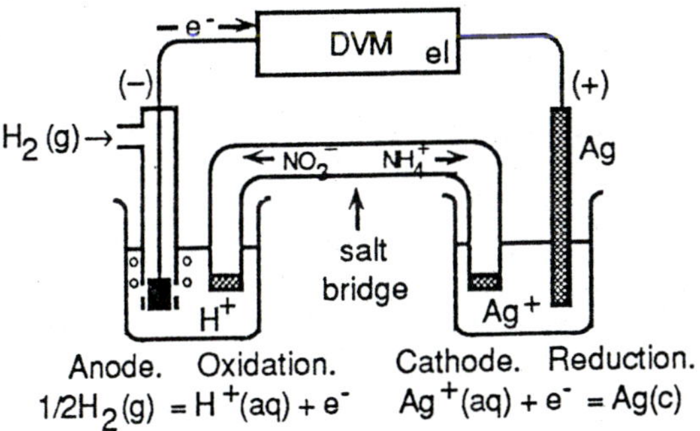

Figure 9.3. Essentials of an electrochemical cell in which one electrode is the standard hydrogen electrode. Shown in operation as a galvanic cell.

Applications of the Nernst Equation

To illustrate the use of the Nernst equation we consider the cell depicted in Fig. 9.3. This cell uses the fundamentally important gaseous hydrogen electrode. For this electrode hydrogen gas and a hydronium ion solution bathe a platinum electrode that is plated with finely divided "platinum black." This surface is catalytically active for the reaction

$$H_2(g) \rightleftharpoons 2H(adsorbed)$$

and the platinum is a metallic electron conductor. We use H^+ as a simplification of H_3O^+ in these electrochemical systems. The signs of the electrodes at standard state concentrations are as given. We write the half-reaction equations and the overall equation.

$$
\begin{array}{ll}
 & E^\circ \\
H_2(g) \rightleftharpoons 2H^+(aq) + 2e^- & \text{0.00 V oxidation; anode } (-) \\
2Ag^+(aq) + 2e^- \rightleftharpoons 2Ag(c) & \text{0.80 V reduction; cathode } (+) \\
\hline
2Ag^+(aq) + H_2(g) \rightleftharpoons 2Ag(c) + 2H^+(aq) & \text{0.80 V}
\end{array}
$$

Note that even though we doubled the silver-silver ion half-reaction we did not change the magnitude of the tabulated E°. The conventional representation of this galvanic cell is

$$(-)Pt \mid H_2(g),H^+(aq) \mid\mid Ag^+(aq) \mid Ag(c)(+)$$

Because hydrogen gas and hydronium ion are dissolved in a single phase, water, they are separated by a comma. It is the phase boundary between the platinum metal surface and solution across which charged species move that is indicated with the vertical bar.

For the galvanic cell just described, the Nernst equation at 25°C is

$$E = 0.80 \text{ V} - \left(\frac{0.0592 \text{ V mol } e^-/\text{mol}}{2 \text{ mol } e^-/\text{mol}}\right) \log\left\{\frac{[H^+]^2 \text{ bar}}{[Ag^+]^2 P_{H_2}}\right\} \tag{9.20}$$

The reaction quotient has been written out for this reaction, and the appropriate cancelling unit of bar has been introduced into the argument of the log function. The mole fraction (activity) of crystalline silver is unity and does not appear. If we know $[H^+]$, $[Ag^+]$, and P_{H_2}, that is, Q, we can calculate the emf of this cell. If all the species are in standard states, then $Q = 1$ and $E = E^\circ = 0.80$ V, as expected. If, for example, $[H^+] = 1.0 \times 10^{-5}$ M, while $[Ag^+]$ and P_{H_2} retain their standard state values,

$$E = 0.80 \text{ V} - \frac{0.0592 \text{ V mol e}^-/\text{mol}}{2 \text{ mol e}^-/\text{mol}} \log\left[\frac{(1.0 \times 10^{-5} \text{ M})^2 \text{ bar}}{(1.0 \text{ M})^2 (1.0 \text{ bar})}\right]$$

$$= 0.80 \text{ V} - \frac{(0.0592 \text{ V})(2)}{2} \log\left[\frac{1.0 \times 10^{-5}}{1.0}\right]$$

$$= 0.80 \text{ V} - (0.0592 \text{ V})(-5) = 1.10 \text{ V} \tag{9.21}$$

Thus, lowering the concentration of the product, H^+, increases the tendency for the reaction to occur and thus increases E, which reflects this tendency.

A very important application of the Nernst equation is in the measurement of low concentrations of electrode-active species. Let us use a modification of the foregoing example to calculate the pH of a solution which is in the anode half cell. Suppose $E = 1.30$ V when the $[Ag^+]$ and P_{H_2} have standard state values. What is the pH?

$$1.30 \text{ V} = 0.80 \text{ V} - \frac{(0.0592 \text{ V})}{2} \log\left[\frac{(H^+)^2 \text{ bar}}{(1 \text{ M})^2(1.0 \text{ bar})}\right] \tag{9.22}$$

$$1.30 \text{ V} - 0.80 \text{ V} = \frac{(0.0592 \text{ V})(2)}{2} (-\log [H^+] \text{ M}^{-1})$$

$$0.50 \text{ V} = (0.0592 \text{ V}) \text{ pH}$$

$$\text{pH} = 8.4, \text{ since pH} \equiv -\log([H^+] \text{ M}^{-1}) \tag{9.23}$$

From this illustration of the calculation of the pH from the emf of a cell with an electrode sensitive to H^+, we can see why electrochemical pH meter systems are so useful. For the Nernst equation when all the concentrations of electrode-active species except H^+ are fixed and the only variables are E and pH, we can write

$$E = E° + a\text{pH} \tag{9.24}$$

where a is a constant in the Nernst equation and $E°$ depends on the nature of the other or *reference electrode*. We see that the emf of such a cell is a linear function of pH. The simplicity of the relationship between pH, rather than $[H^+]$, and the measurable E shows one reason why pH is such an important concept. For pH meter systems a glass electrode is used, which is a glass membrane that responds in the same mathematical way as the standard hydrogen gas electrode. A glass electrode is much simpler to use than a standard gaseous hydrogen electrode.

The example of measuring $[H^+]$ or, more directly, pH shows the power of the electrochemical method. Not only has a low concentration of a species, H^+, been measured, but this concentration has been found without causing a significant chemical change. By contrast, if we attempted to measure $[H^+]$ by a titration reaction with OH^-, for example, we would continuously change $[H^+]$.

The reason that $[H^+]$ remains fixed during the measurement is the constraint of electrochemical equilibrium. The chemical reaction is frozen by the balance between the chemical reaction and the electrical system. In addition to being sensitive to concentration over a wide range and to being nonreactive, the electrochemical method is selective. Thus, with an appropriate electrode system, the concentration of H^+ can be measured selectively in the presence of many other ionic and nonionic species. Selective electrodes are known for many other species.

If the chemical reaction that powers a galvanic cell is allowed to run until chemical equilibrium is reached, the emf becomes zero. Also, the reaction quotient Q becomes the equilibrium constant. At *chemical equilibrium* the Nernst equation reduces to

$$0 = E^\circ - \frac{RT}{F\Delta z}\ln K \qquad\qquad (9.25)$$

Thus, chemical equilibrium constants may be calculated from E° values. This method of calculating equilibrium constants is not limited to oxidation-reduction reactions. It can be applied to any reaction type for which E° can be calculated.

Worked Example

For the acid–base equilibrium

$$2H_2O(l) \;\rightleftharpoons\; H_3O^+(aq) + OH^-(aq)$$

for which we would write

$$K_w = [H_3O^+][OH^-]$$

compute K_w from E° values.

Two half reactions that sum to this acid–base process are

	E°
$1/2H_2(g) + H_2O(l) \rightleftharpoons H_3O^+(aq) + e^-$	0.00 V
$H_2O(l) + e^- \rightleftharpoons 1/2H_2(g) + OH^-(aq)$	-0.828 V
$2H_2O(l) \rightleftharpoons H_3O^+(aq) + OH^-(aq)$	-0.828 V

The first half reaction is for the standard state of $[H_3O^+] = 1$ M. The second is, however, for $[OH^-] = 1$ M, which implies $[H_3O^+] = 1 \times 10^{-14}$ M. In both cases $P_{H_2} = 1$ bar and $X_{H_2O} = 1$. The inclusion of water and hydronium ion in the first half reaction makes no difference in E° for this reaction. From eq. (9.25) under room temperature conditions [cf. eq. (9.19)], we have

$$E^\circ = \frac{0.0592 \text{ V mol } e^-/\text{mol}}{\Delta z}\;\log\,(K_w\, M^{-2})$$

$$\log (K_w \ M^{-2}) = \frac{(-0.828 \ V)(1 \ mol \ e^-/mol)}{(0.0592 \ V \ mol \ e^-/mol)} = -14.0$$

$$K_w = 1.0 \times 10^{-14} \ M^2$$

Standard Electrode Potentials. The standard hydrogen electrode, the $H_2(g)/H^+(aq)$ half-cell under standard state conditions, plays a pivotal role in the development of tables of $E°$ values. There is no way to measure the $E°$ of a single half-cell. Only $E°$ for two coupled half-cells can be measured. Thus, to build a table of $E°$ values for individual half reactions it is necessary to designate a value for one half-cell. *$E°$ for the standard hydrogen electrode is set equal to zero.* All other half-cell $E°$'s are relative to this choice. When two half-cell $E°$'s are combined to give the $E°$ for an overall reaction, the arbitrariness associated with $E° = 0$ for the H_2/H^+ half-cell cancels out. This process is completely analogous to our designating zero enthalpies of formation and of zero Gibbs energies of formation for the reference forms of elements in their standard states.

Returning to the example of the silver–hydrogen galvanic cell considered above, we can see the consequence of assigning a zero value to the emf of the standard hydrogen half cell. The observed $E°$ of 0.80 V for the overall cell reaction becomes the $E°$ for the silver–silver ion electrode.

Worked Example

A galvanic cell consisting of a silver–silver ion electrode and a zinc–zinc ion electrode is used to measure the equilibrium constant for dissociation of the tetraamminezinc ion, $Zn(NH_3)_4^{2+}$, at 25°C. The concentration of Ag^+ is 0.10 M. The concentration of Zn^{2+} is 0.10 M before an equal volume of 7.0 M NH_3 water is added to the zinc half-cell. The final emf is 1.86 V, and the zinc electrode is negative.

In the zinc half cell the *chemical* equilibrium process of interest is

$$Zn(NH_3)_4^{2+}(aq) \ \rightleftharpoons \ Zn^{2+}(aq) + 4NH_3(aq)$$

for which

$$K = \frac{[Zn^{2+}][NH_3]^4}{[Zn(NH_3)_4^{2+}]}$$

To compute K we need values for the concentrations, $[Zn^{2+}]$, $[NH_3]$, and $[Zn(NH_3)_4^{2+}]$, at equilibrium. The value for $[Zn^{2+}]$ comes from a measurement of E and the Nernst equation.

$$
\begin{array}{ll}
 & E° \\
Zn(c) \rightleftharpoons Zn^{2+}(aq) + 2e^- & 0.76 \ V \ \text{negative electrode} \\
2Ag^+(aq) + 2e^- \rightleftharpoons 2Ag(c) & 0.80 \ V \ \text{positive electrode} \\
\hline
2Ag^+(aq) + Zn(c) \rightleftharpoons Zn^{2+}(aq) + 2Ag(c) & 1.56 \ V
\end{array}
$$

$$E = 1.56 \text{ V} - \frac{(0.0592 \text{ V mol e}^-/\text{mol})}{2 \text{ mol e}^-/\text{mol}} \log \left\{ \frac{[Zn^{2+}] \text{ M}}{[Ag^+]^2} \right\}$$

$$\log \left\{ \frac{[Zn^{2+}] \text{ M}}{(0.10 \text{ M})^2} \right\} = \frac{1.56 \text{ V} - 1.86 \text{ V}}{0.0296 \text{ V}} = -10.0$$

$$\frac{[Zn^{2+}] \text{ M}}{0.010 \text{ M}^2} = 1.0 \times 10^{-10.0}$$

$$[Zn^{2+}] = 1.0 \times 10^{-12} \text{ M}$$

To obtain equilibrium concentrations of NH_3 and $Zn(NH_3)_4^{2+}$, we consider the stoichiometry of the complex-forming reaction in the zinc half-cell.

	Before mixing	After mixing; before reaction	After reaction
$[Zn^{2+}]$	0.10 M	0.050 M	small
$[NH_3]$	7.0 M	3.5 M	3.3 M
$[Zn(NH_3)_4^{2+}]$	- - -	- - -	0.050 M

4×0.050 M of the after-mixing NH_3 concentration is used to form $Zn(NH_3)_4^{2+}$. Thus, the final $[NH_3] = (3.5 - 4 \times 0.050 \text{ M}) = 3.3$ M.

Now we can compute K by substituting the three concentration values in the expression for K.

$$K = \frac{(1.0 \times 10^{-12} \text{ M})(3.3 \text{ M})^4}{(0.050 \text{ M})} = 2.4 \times 10^{-9} \text{ M}^4$$

The result is an experimental value that has some error.

In the example we see how a *chemical* equilibrium in one half-cell can be studied under the umbrella of *electrochemical* equilibrium for the overall cell reaction. Through the Nernst equation the measured E is selectively sensitive to $[Zn^{2+}]$ in the presence of the zinc metal electrode and the $Zn(NH_3)_4^{2+}$ ion. The complexation reaction determines the equilibrium concentration of Zn^{2+}. The emf measurement reports on but does not disturb the small concentration.

Sign Conventions in Electrochemical Cells

Because signs play an important and potentially confusing role in discussions of electrochemical cells, we shall review them here. The *physical* sign of a metal electrode is a consequence of an excess or deficiency of electrons. The electrode with an excess of electrons is negative, whether this condition is a consequence of the dominance of the chemical reaction in a galvanic cell or the dominance of the electrical system in electrolysis. A negative electrode in a *galvanic* cell is the site of an oxidation half-reaction, which is supplying the electrons. On the other hand, the negative electrode in *electrolysis* is the site of a reduction half-reaction, which is being "forced" by the excess of electrons that the electrical system has helped pump from the other electrode.

Of completely different significance is the sign of the emf of a cell. The sign of the emf is an *algebraic* sign, and it tells whether or not the chemical reaction in the cell goes as written on paper and whether or not the conventional cell representation has the proper anode reaction on the left. A negative sign for the emf means that the reaction is spontaneous in the opposite sense to which it is written or that the right-hand electrode in the cell diagram is really the anode. Let us consider a cell that might have the following reaction under standard state conditions.

$$2Ag(c) + Zn^{2+}(aq) \rightleftharpoons 2Ag^+(aq) + Zn(c)$$

The half-reactions and corresponding $E°$'s would be

$$
\begin{array}{ll}
 & E° \\
2Ag(c) \rightleftharpoons 2Ag^+(aq) + 2e^- & -0.80 \text{ V} \\
Zn^{2+}(aq) + 2e^- \rightleftharpoons Zn(c) & -0.76 \text{ V} \\
\hline
2Ag(c) + Zn^{2+}(aq) \rightleftharpoons 2Ag^+(aq) + Zn(c) & -1.56 \text{ V}
\end{array}
$$

The negative sign for $E°$ means that this reaction is spontaneous in reverse under standard state conditions. For a galvanic cell the reaction will occur in reverse, and the zinc electrode will be the anode, which is then the site of oxidation. The reaction as written above would be the spontaneous sense of an electrolysis process in which the electrical system is dominant. *For either sense of this reaction, Δz, the moles of electrons transferred, has a positive sign*. The conventional cell diagram is

$$(-)Ag(c)|\,Ag^+\,||\,Zn^{2+}(aq)|\,Zn(c)(+)$$

The silver ion–silver electrode is, however, actually positive, which implies a negative $E°$ for the cell reaction *as written*.

Interconversion of Chemical and Electrical Energy; Relationship Between Electrolytic Cells and Galvanic Cells

If the galvanic cell shown in Fig. 9.3 is converted into an electrolytic cell by supplying a slightly superior voltage from the electrical system, the signs on the electrodes are unchanged, but the processes are reversed. In electrolysis the electrical system is helping electrons move from the positive electrode of the cell to the negative electrode of the cell. The negative electrode is the cathode, where electrons are being supplied to hydronium ions to reduce them to hydrogen gas. The positive electrode is the anode, where electrons are removed from silver atoms to oxidize them to silver ions. The electron flow in the wires and net negative ion flow through the solutions are in the opposite sense of those shown in Fig. 9.3. Electrical energy is being converted into chemical energy. $\Delta_r G = -EF\Delta z = -\Delta U_{el}$. E is negative, $\Delta_r G$ is positive, Δz is positive, and ΔU_{el} is negative.

In the following table we consider the sign relationships for a chemical reaction run alone, which is equivalent to a perfect shortcircuit between the electrodes ($V_{el} = 0$ and $\Delta U_{el} = 0$). We also consider the same chemical reaction powering a galvanic cell near the reversible limit and then under rather irreversible conditions. Also, we consider this cell reaction undergoing electrolysis under standard state conditions near the reversible limit and then under rather irreversible conditions. You should be able to confirm these sign relationships. Multiple signs indicate greater magnitudes.

	$\Delta_r G°$	$V_{el}/E°$	ΔU_{el}	$T\Delta S_{tot}$
Chemical reaction only	$--$	$V_{el} = 0$	0	$++$
Galvanic cell, reversible	$--$	$V_{el} = E°$	$++$	0
Galvanic cell, irreversible	$--$	$V_{el} < E°$	$+$	$+$
Electrolytic cell, reversible	$++$	$V_{el} = E°$	$--$	0
Electrolytic cell, irreversible	$++$	$V_{el} < E°$	$---$	$+$

The maximum amount of chemical energy $\Delta_r G$ that can be stored in electrolysis is the full change in electrical energy ($-\Delta U_{el}$). Conversely, the maximum of chemical energy that can be converted into electrical energy is $-\Delta_r G$.

Can the Electrical Energy Obtained from a Galvanic Cell Exceed $\Delta_r H$ in Magnitude? We have already noted that $\Delta_r G$ is the measure of the amount of energy a chemical reaction can supply as ordered energy to an electrical system. $\Delta_r G$ can exceed $\Delta_r H$ for the reaction, if $\Delta_r S$ is positive. To see this consider the following example.

$$H^+(aq) + OH^-(aq) \rightleftharpoons H_2O(l)$$

$S°_{298}$ (J/K mol):	0	-10.8	69.9	$\Delta_r S° = 80.7$ J/K mol
$Hf°_{298}$ (kJ/mol):	0	-230.0	-285.8	$\Delta_r H° = -55.8$ kJ/mol
$Gf°_{298}$ (kJ/mol):	0	-157.2	-237.1	$\Delta_r G° = -79.9$ kJ/mol

The positive $\Delta_r S°$ for this reaction is an expected consequence of the consumption of ions, which releases "frozen" water of solvation. We have

$$\Delta U_{el} = -\Delta_r G° = \underset{-(-)}{-\Delta_r H°} + \underset{(+)}{T\Delta_r S°} > -\Delta H° \qquad (9.26)$$

In such reactions under near-reversible conditions ($E \approx V_{el}$ and $\Delta S_{tot} = \Delta S_\sigma + \Delta S_\theta \approx 0$), the cell draws

$$-\Delta U_\theta = -T\Delta S_\theta = T\Delta S_\sigma \qquad (9.27)$$

of energy from the thermal reservoir to augment $\Delta_r H^\circ$. The increase in entropy in the reactive system compensates for the decrease in entropy that occurs as energy is withdrawn from the thermal reservoir.

Additional Examples of Galvanic Cells

Three examples of galvanic cells of particular importance and interest are the common dry cell, the rechargeable lead–acid storage battery, and the fuel cell.

The most familiar galvanic cell in general use is the "dry" cell or "battery," which produces about 1.5 V and is used in flashlights and other common devices. The cell is typically composed of a zinc case, which serves as the negative electrode; a chemically inert but electrically conducting carbon rod, which serves as the positive electrode; and moist, porous solid material containing other reactants, which is packed between the electrodes. These reactants are manganese dioxide and ammonium chloride. The chemical processes that occur in the dry cell remain open to question, but the reaction

$$Zn(c) + 2MnO_2(c) + 2NH_4^+ \rightleftharpoons Zn^{2+}(aq) + 2MnOOH(c) + 2NH_3(aq)$$

seems to be consistent with most of the known facts. The product ammonia is absorbed in water, which is present in the porous contents of the cell, where it also reacts with zinc ions to form zinc ammonia complex ions. The actual reaction may vary somewhat with conditions of operation of the cell.

An alkaline form of the "dry" cell, which has a longer lifetime and a higher price, has gained acceptance in recent years. Along with manganese dioxide the alkaline cell contains aqueous potassium hydroxide instead of ammonium chloride. The overall reaction can be written as

$$2Zn(c) + 3MnO_2(c) + 4OH^-(aq) + 2H_2O(l) \rightleftharpoons 2Zn(OH)_4^{2-}(aq) + Mn_3O_4(c)$$

Since the manganese oxide undergoes a larger oxidation state change in the alkaline cell ($+4 \rightarrow +2.67$ instead of $+4 \rightarrow +3$), an alkaline cell with a given amount of MnO_2 delivers more electrical energy. Reaction of NH_4^+ with zinc metal and so-called polarization effects also reduce the efficiency of the standard, nonalkaline cell.

The rechargeable lead–acid storage battery is found in virtually every vehicle on the highways. It is based on the reaction

$$Pb(c) + PbO_2(c) + 2H^+(aq) + 2HSO_4^-(aq) \underset{\substack{\text{charge}\\ \text{electrolysis}}}{\overset{\substack{\text{discharge}\\ \text{galvanic cell}}}{\rightleftharpoons}} 2PbSO_4(c) + 2H_2O(l)$$

One electrode is made of lead metal. The other electrode is also made of lead metal with lead dioxide embedded in a lattice work on the surface. Note that $PbSO_4$ is the product of both the oxidation of lead and the reduction of PbO_2. This cell produces about 2.0 V, and six of them are connected in series to obtain about 12 V in the battery in common use. The lead–acid cell is capable of delivering very high currents and of being discharged and recharged many, many times.

The fuel cell operates like conventional galvanic cells, which have been previously discussed, except that the gaseous materials that react at the electrodes are stored outside the cell and fed into it. Fuel cells are compact, and they can be much more efficient and less polluting than the usual sources of power which convert chemical energy into thermal energy and then into electrical energy. They have been employed to meet electrical requirements on spacecraft, and it is possible that they may become nonpolluting sources of energy for transportation. The hydrogen–oxygen fuel cell with an emf of 1.2 V is based on the reaction

$$H_2(g) + 1/2O_2(g) \rightleftharpoons H_2O(l)$$

It utilizes a cell configuration that is shown schematically in Fig. 9.4. The electrolyte is concentrated (80%) aqueous potassium hydroxide or a special solid electrolyte in the form of membranes. The electrodes are porous nickel metal.

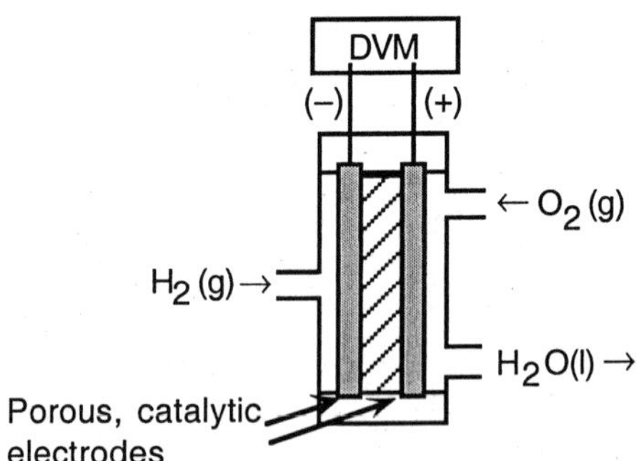

Figure 9.4.   Schematic diagram of a fuel cell to produce electrical energy from the reaction of hydrogen and oxygen.

Summary

In electrochemical cells an electrical system is coupled through wire electrodes to a chemical reaction system. When the dominant partner is the chemical reaction, the electrochemical cell is a galvanic cell. Chemical energy is converted into electrical energy. When the dominant partner is the electrical system, electrolysis occurs and the electrochemical cell is an electrolytic cell. Electrical energy is converted into chemical energy.

The change in energy in the electrical system, ΔU_{el}, is given by $\Delta U_{el} = V_{el}F\Delta z$, where V_{el} is the voltage between the two electrodes. For electrochemical systems this ΔU_{el} term must be included in the first-law expression. In the laboratory the standard measurement of V_{el} gives the emf, because the chemical reaction tendency is balanced by the electrical system. This condition is called electrochemical equilibrium.

The conventional representation of a galvanic cell *on paper* shows the species involved in the two half-reactions and places the oxidation half-reaction on the left. For example,

$$(-)Zn(c)|\ Zn^{2+}(aq)|\ |\ Cu^{2+}(aq)|\ Cu(c)(+)$$

A single vertical bar denotes a phase boundary across which ions transfer and contribute to the emf of the cell. The double vertical bar denotes a salt bridge. For the spontaneous sense of reaction, the left-hand electrode is negative. Tabulated $E°$ values for half-reactions are added to give $E°$ for the overall reaction. These tabulated $E°$ values for half-reactions are a consequence of setting $E° = 0$ for the standard H_2/H^+ electrode.

When the general condition for spontaneity, $\Delta S_{tot} \geq 0$, is applied to electrochemical cells, we find that $T\Delta S_{tot} = -\Delta_r G_{T,P} - \Delta U_{el} \geq 0$. Thus, $\Delta_r G_{T,P}$ is not alone a condition for spontaneity in electrochemical systems as it is in simpler chemical systems. At electrochemical equilibrium, where, $\Delta S_{tot} = 0$, an important relationship exists between $\Delta_r G_{T,P}$ and ΔU_{el} or E, namely $\Delta_r G_{T,P} = -\Delta U_{el} = -EF\Delta z$. Thus, the emf of a cell is directly proportional to the Gibbs free energy of reaction.

The Nernst equation, which applies under the condition of electrochemical equilibrium, is the key equation for the relationship between concentrations of reactants and products and the emf of a galvanic cell. This equation is $E = E° - (RT/F\Delta z)\ \ln Q$, where Q is the reaction quotient. If all concentrations of reactants and products in a galvanic cell except the concentration of one electrode-active species are known, then the concentration of that one species can be found from the observed E, the known $E°$, and the Nernst equation. Thus, through applied electrochemistry we have a powerful way to measure the concentration of a species such as H^+ over a wide range of concentrations. From such measurements of the concentration of a species or from $E°$ values alone, equilibrium constants for chemical reactions can be found.

The same thermodynamic expressions apply to electrolytic cells and to galvanic cells. For electrolytic cells, however, the signs of the electrodes and various quantities are opposite to those of corresponding galvanic cells. Although the process occurring at the anode is oxidation in both types of cells, the anode in an electrolytic cell is positive and the anode in a galvanic cell is negative. The emf, E, is negative for the electrolysis process and positive for the galvanic cell. For the electrolysis process, ΔU_{el} is negative and $\Delta_r G_{T,P}$ is positive. The signs of these two quantities are exchanged in galvanic cells. From a global point of view, an electrolytic cell process or a galvanic cell process can be spontaneous with $\Delta S_{tot} > 0$. The sense of the process depends on whether the $\Delta_r G_{T,P}$ or the ΔU_{el} term dominates.

Three galvanic cell systems of practical importance are the dry cell, the lead–acid storage battery, and the fuel cell. The chemistry and construction of these cells are discussed.

Problems

A good table of $E°$ values is needed for these problems.

1. For a galvanic cell with the reaction $2Ag^+(aq) + Cu(c) \rightleftharpoons 2Ag(c) + Cu^{2+}(aq)$.
    (a) Write the half-reactions involved.
    (b) Calculate $E°$ and indicate the direction of spontaneous change under standard state conditions.
    (c) Give the sign of the silver–silver ion electrode.
    Ans: $E° = 0.46$ V; silver electrode is (+)

2. For the cell in problem 1, compute the value of ΔU_{el} that accompanies production of 2 mol of silver metal under (near) reversible conditions, i.e., when $\Delta_r G° + \Delta U_{el} = 0$. Ans: $\Delta U_{el} = 88.8$ kJ/mol.

3. For each of the following cell reactions make: (a) a sketch of the essential parts of the cells; (b) a conventional diagram of the cell. Platinum is commonly used as an inert electrode that conducts electrons. Indicate on each sketch the anode, the cathode, the signs of the electrodes, the directions in which the anions and cations migrate through the cell (and salt bridge, if any), and the direction in which electrons migrate through the external circuit. Calculate $E°$ for each cell.
    (a) $5Fe^{2+}(aq) + 8H^+(aq) + MnO_4^-(aq) \rightleftharpoons 5Fe^{3+}(aq) + Mn^{2+}(aq) + 4H_2O(l)$
    (b) $AgCl(c) \rightleftharpoons Ag(c) + 1/2Cl_2(g)$
    Ans: (a) $E° = 0.74$ V; (b) $E° = -1.14$ V for reaction as written; silver electrode (–) for spontaneous sense of reaction.

4. (a) What are the signs of ΔU_{el} and V_{el} in a galvanic cell system?
    (b) What are the signs of ΔU_{el} and V_{el} in an electrolytic cell system?
    (c) In a galvanic cell system, is V_{el} or E larger when the cell is working?

5. For the reactions in problem 3 compute the values of $\Delta_r G^\circ$ from your E° values. Compare these values of $\Delta_r G^\circ$ with the ones computed from tabulated Gibbs energies. Ans: (a) $\Delta_r G^\circ = -358$ kJ/mol; (b) $\Delta_r G^\circ = 110$ kJ/mol.

6. Write Nernst equations at 25°C for the two galvanic cell reaction systems in problem 3.

7. For a reversible (near electrochemical equilibrium) galvanic cell process in which $\Delta V_\sigma = (+)$, i.e., the volume change is positive, give the signs for ΔU_{el}, $\Delta_r G_{T,P}$, E, ΔU_{el}, Δz, and ΔU_{wt}. Ans: Since the chemical reaction is spontaneous in a galvanic cell, $\Delta_r G_{T,P} = (-)$; $\Delta U_{el} = -\Delta_r G_{T,P} = (-)(-) = (+)$; $\Delta U_{el} = EF\Delta z$, hence $E = (+)$; $\Delta z = (+)$ always; $\Delta U_{wt} = P_\sigma \Delta V_\sigma = (+)$.

8. Consider a cell in which one-half cell consists of a zinc electrode in 0.1 M zinc ion solution and the other half-cell consists of a silver electrode in a solution made from 0.1 M silver nitrate and ammonia water. The emf is 1.20 V. The zinc electrode is negative. What is the silver ion concentration? What additional information would you need in order to calculate an equilibrium constant for the formation of the silver ammonia complex? One ans: $[Ag^+] = 2.5 \times 10^{-7}$ M.

9. Does electrochemical equilibrium exist for the system in question 8? If so, for what parts? Does chemical equilibrium exist for this system? If so, in what part?

10. A pH meter system at 25°C is adjusted to give an emf of 0.0 V at pH 7.00. What will be the emf for a solution of pH 4.0? Of pH 9.5? Ans: pH 4.0, $E = -0.177$ V; pH 9.5, $E = 0.148$ V.

11. Show that a change of one pH unit ($[H^+]$ changes by a factor of 10) corresponds to a change in emf of 0.059 V.

12. Write two half-reactions that sum to the overall reaction $AgCl(c) \rightleftharpoons Ag^+(aq) + Cl^-(aq)$. Calculate E° for the overall reaction and then K_{sp}. Ans: $E^\circ = -0.58$ V; $K_{sp} = 1.5 \times 10^{-10}$ M^2.

13. Consider the cell in problem 1 being subjected to electrolysis. Make a sketch of the system. Indicate the anode, the cathode, the signs of the electrodes, the directions in which the anions and cations migrate through the

cell, and the direction in which electrons migrate through the external circuit. Ans: silver electrode is made positive.

14. What is the minimum voltage that would have to be applied to a single cell of a lead–acid storage battery in order to charge it? To which electrode would you attach the negative lead of the charger? (Hint: find $E°$ for the lead-acid storage cell reaction.) Ans: $V_{el} > 2.04$ V.

15. What is $E°$ for the reaction $Hg(l) + Cu^{2+}(aq) \rightleftharpoons Hg^{2+}(aq) + Cu(c)$? Is the reaction spontaneous under standard state conditions as written? What would be the sign of the copper electrode? What would happen to the emf of this cell if ammonia water were added to the copper half cell? Two ans: $E° = -0.51$ V; copper electrode (–) for spontaneous direction; E increases when NH_3 is added.

16. The cell reaction, $2Ag^+(aq) + Zn(s) \rightleftharpoons 2Ag(s) + Zn^{2+}(aq)$ is used to measure the solubility product constant for silver chloride. In doing so, a measured excess of hydrochloric acid is added to the silver half cell. Find $E°$ and write the Nernst equation for this cell. Would the observed E be larger or smaller than $E°$? Why? Ans: $E° = 1.56$ V; E decreases when Cl^- is added.

17. What is the maximum amount of available chemical energy that is stored as a consequence of electrolysis? Ans: $\Delta G_{T,P} = -\Delta U_{el}$. The decrease in electrical energy corresponds to an increase in ΔG, the available chemical energy. This answer presumes a reversible, near-equilibrium process. Under irreversible conditions, $\Delta G_{T,P} < -\Delta U_{el}$, and excess thermal energy is produced.

18. How does *electrochemical* equilibrium differ from chemical equilibrium? Ans: In electrochemical equilibrium the cell's chemical reaction is typically far from chemical equilibrium. The electrical system and the chemical system are in balance. $\Delta S_{tot} = 0$, $E \neq 0$, $\Delta_r G_{T,P} \neq 0$. At chemical equilibrium, $E = 0$, $\Delta_r G_{T,P} = 0$, and $\Delta S_{tot} = 0$.

10. ENERGY CONVERSIONS

We began our presentation of thermodynamics by describing it as the science of energy transactions and of energy quality. Considerations of possible energy transactions as conditioned by energy quality have been dominant themes throughout our development of the subject. The emphasis has been, however, on assessing spontaneity in chemical reactions and on finding the state of chemical equilibrium. Our purpose in this final chapter is to refocus attention on energy conversions as such and to extend our analysis into the important area of coupled chemical reactions.

The Scope of Energy Conversions

Chapter 2 on the first law (energy principle) opened with a review of a number of familiar energy conversions. Among these were mechanical $\rightleftarrows$ electrical, electrical $\rightleftarrows$ chemical, chemical $\rightleftarrows$ light, and chemical $\rightleftarrows$ mechanical. Familiar circumstances under which these various conversions take place were named. We noted that, in principle, energy conversions among these forms of energy, subsequently characterized as ordered forms, were complete and reversible. Thus, for example, mechanical energy can be converted wholly into electrical energy with a frictionless generator, and electrical energy can be converted wholly into mechanical energy with a frictionless motor. At the beginning of Chapter 2 we also recognized that when thermal energy is involved at a single temperature there is a one-wayness about energy conversions. Ordered forms of energy can be converted into thermal energy, but thermal energy cannot be converted into ordered energy in a single temperature process. Subsequently, from the microscopic discussion of entropy in Chapter 6, we recognized that the disorder associated with thermal energy is the reason for this one-wayness. Thus, energy transactions are conditioned by energy quality.

Entropy Change as a Measure of the Quality of Energy

The entropy function was introduced in Chapter 4 and was seen as an index of the quality of energy. The atomic–molecular basis of the entropy function was developed with the aid of the harmonic oscillator and cell models in Chapter 6. When a change in energy occurs in a potential energy reservoir such as a weight system or an electrical system, the accompanying entropy change is zero. Energy changes of this type involve ordered energy of high quality that can be converted fully into any other form of energy. On the other hand, thermal energy dispersed over the motions of molecules, ions, and atoms is disordered energy of low quality. The energy change in a thermal reservoir, ΔU_θ, is accompanied by an entropy change that depends inversely on temperature through $\Delta S_\theta = \Delta U_\theta / T$. For energy to leave a thermal reservoir, the process must be accompanied by a compensatory entropy increase either in another thermal reservoir or in a chemical reaction. Because of the inverse temperature dependence of ΔS_θ, however, a high-temperature thermal reservoir provides energy at a smaller entropy price than does a low-temperature one.

Interconversion of Ordered and Disordered Energy at the Microscopic Level

As shown in the microscopic view of entropy in Chapter 6, spontaneous processes, in which disordered energy becomes temporarily ordered, occur all the time at the atomic–molecular level and in somewhat larger, Brownian motion events. Since energy increases in quality in such processes, $\Delta S_{tot} < 0$ locally. Thus, a number of molecules with different tiny amounts of motional energy may strike a small particle in such a way as to give the particle a temporary boost of mechanical energy. For a moment, an entropy decrease has occurred in this tiny, local thermal reservoir. Such a process is called a *fluctuation*. The increase in mechanical energy of the small particle itself is accompanied by $\Delta S_{wt} = 0$. Thus, $\Delta S_{tot} < 0$ locally. Soon, however, the small particle loses its extra mechanical energy which becomes thermal energy again through collisions with surrounding molecules. $\Delta S_{tot} > 0$ locally for this undoing process. Over time, $\Delta S_{tot} = 0$ in the system as $\Delta S_{tot} < 0$ and $\Delta S_{tot} > 0$ events cancel out.

Enthalpy of Reaction and Thermal Energy

Chapter 3 was devoted to the enthalpy function. This function is useful in characterizing the energy change in a chemical reaction when the reaction occurs at constant pressure and in contact with a large thermal reservoir. Under these conditions, $\Delta H_\sigma + \Delta U_\theta = 0$. Thus, the enthalpy change in a chemical reaction, which is almost entirely a consequence of changes in the ordered energy associated with bonding in molecules and ions, is converted into thermal energy. This conversion of enthalpy of reaction into thermal energy at constant temperature is a one-way process. The thermal energy produced cannot be converted back into electronic energy of chemical bonds in a single-temperature process.

Under other reaction conditions, such as in electrochemical cells, the enthalpy of reaction may be converted largely into ordered electrical energy. We shall return to this more favorable circumstance of energy conversion later.

Interconversion of Thermal and Mechanical Energies; Coupled Processes

Chapter 5 was devoted to heat engines and refrigerators. In such devices, energy leaves thermal reservoirs but not in single-temperature processes. In a heat engine a partial conversion of disordered thermal energy into ordered mechanical energy occurs. Such a conversion is possible because of the compensatory entropy increase that occurs when part of the thermal energy that left the high-temperature thermal reservoir flows into a low-temperature thermal reservoir.

We may view the energy conversion in a heat engine as the consequence of coupling a nonspontaneous energy conversion to a spontaneous one. The spontaneous effect, $\Delta S_{tot} > 0$, that accompanies the direct transfer of thermal energy from a high-temperature thermal reservoir to a low-temperature thermal reservoir is coupled to the nonspontaneous process, $\Delta S_{tot} < 0$, of converting thermal energy into mechanical energy. The overall coupled process is spontaneous. Some thermal energy has been converted to mechanical energy by virtue of some other thermal energy flowing from high temperature to low temperature.

A similar analysis in terms of coupled processes applies to the energy conversions in a refrigerator. In the refrigerator, energy leaves a low-temperature thermal reservoir, where $\Delta S_{\theta c} < 0$, and flows into a high-temperature thermal reservoir augmented by energy supplied by a mechanical system for which $\Delta S_{wt} = 0$. As a consequence of the energy supplied to the high-temperature reservoir, $\Delta S_{\theta h} > 0$ to an extent large enough to offset $\Delta S_{\theta c} < 0$. The impossible process of energy flowing directly from a cold thermal reservoir to a hot thermal reservoir, for which $\Delta S_{tot} < 0$, is coupled to the spontaneous conversion of mechanical energy into thermal energy in the high-temperature thermal reservoir, for which $\Delta S_{tot} > 0$. The overall coupled process is spontaneous. Energy has moved from a low-temperature thermal reservoir to a high-temperature thermal reservoir by virtue of some mechanical energy being converted to thermal energy.

Gibbs Free Energy and Chemical Energy

Chapter 7 introduced the Gibbs energy of reaction, $\Delta_r G_{T,P}$, as the amount of ordered energy available from a chemical reaction at constant temperature and constant pressure. Thus, $\Delta_r G_{T,P}$ is regarded as the *chemical energy* associated with a chemical reaction and as the free energy of the process. $\Delta_r G_{T,P}$ plays this role despite $\Delta_r H$ being essentially the change in ordered electronic energy as reactants become products. Why is this so?

The reason lies in the entropy change, $\Delta_r S$, that accompanies chemical reactions. This $\Delta_r S$ is due to changes in the distribution of energy over the molecular motions of reactants and products and to changes in concentration between reactants and products. As a consequence, $\Delta_r H$ is not alone a measure of the amount of ordered energy available from a chemical reaction. Properly harnessed, as in a galvanic cell, or a physiological process in a living system, a chemical reaction delivers a maximum of $-\Delta_r G_{T,P}$ of ordered energy. At constant temperature, $\Delta_r G = \Delta_r H - T\Delta_r S$. Thus, $\Delta_r G_{T,P}$ becomes more negative when $\Delta_r S > 0$ for the chemical reaction. Under this circumstance energy is drawn from the thermal reservoir to augment $\Delta_r H$ in $\Delta_r G$. The entropy decrease in the thermal reservoir is offset by the entropy increase in the reactive system. On the other hand, if $\Delta_r S < 0$, $\Delta_r G_{T,P}$ is smaller in magnitude than $\Delta_r H$. Thus, the amount of ordered energy available from a chemical reaction may be larger or smaller in magnitude than $\Delta_r H$. Under conditions of constant temperature and constant pressure, the correct maximum amount is $-\Delta_r G_{T,P}$.

The energy conversions associated with chemical reactions lie between the extremes of energy changes in potential energy reservoirs on the one hand and thermal reservoirs on the other. Accompanying energy changes in potential energy reservoirs, $\Delta S_{pot} = 0$. The energy provided is ordered and thus can be converted into any other type of energy. Accompanying energy changes in thermal reservoirs, $\Delta S_\theta \neq 0$. Thus, there is always an entropy consequence of energy changes in thermal reservoirs. Specifically, energy does not leave a thermal energy reservoir without a compensating entropy increase somewhere else in the overall system. Since $\Delta S_\theta = \Delta U_\theta / T_\theta$, this entropy decrease in the thermal reservoir is proportional to ΔU_θ and decreases with increasing T. Chemical reactions are characterized by a near-ordered energy component, reflected in $\Delta_r H$, and by an entropy change, $\Delta_r S$, that conditions energy transactions with the thermal reservoir. In the previous paragraph, we reviewed how the sign of $\Delta_r S$ determines whether $\Delta_r H_\sigma$ is augmented by thermal energy drawn from the thermal reservoir or diminished by thermal energy supplied necessarily to the thermal reservoir. The outcome of this inbetween character of chemical reactions is summarized by $\Delta_r G_{T,P} = \Delta_r H - T\Delta_r S$ under conditions of constant temperature and constant pressure. This $-\Delta_r G_{T,P}$ compromise is what is commonly called chemical energy.

$T\Delta S_{tot}$ Measures Excess Thermal Energy Production, the Amount of Ordered Energy Wasted

As part of the thermodynamic analysis of electrochemical systems in Chapter 9, we showed that

$$T\Delta S_{tot} = -\Delta_r G_{T,P} - \Delta U_{el} \geq 0 \qquad (10.1)$$

For an overall reversible process, electrochemical equilibrium in this case, $-\Delta_r G_{T,P} - \Delta U_{el} = 0$ or $-\Delta_r G_{T,P} = \Delta U_{el}$. Thus, we confirmed with the example of an added electrical energy reservoir that $-\Delta_r G_{T,P}$ is the ordered energy made available, the free energy, from the chemical reaction. Not only can the free energy from a chemical reaction be converted into electrical energy, but $-\Delta_r G_{T,P}$

of chemical energy from a favored chemical reaction may be converted into chemical energy of an otherwise unfavored reaction.

Before considering coupled chemical reactions, we investigate the proposition that $T\Delta S_{tot}$ measures *excess* conversion of ordered energy into thermal energy. Thus, $T\Delta S_{tot}$ is the ordered energy wasted in a particular, irreversible process. This interpretation of $T\Delta S_{tot}$ was given in Chapter 7 based on a qualitative argument. We now demonstrate this relationship algebraically.

To show the relationship of $T\Delta S_{tot}$ to excess thermal energy production, we must first define this quantity. Excess thermal energy, $\Delta U_{\theta,exc}$, is equal to the difference between the thermal energy produced in an irreversible process, $\Delta U_{\theta,irr}$, and the unavoidable thermal energy production in a reversible process, $\Delta U_{\theta,rev}$. Thus,

$$\Delta U_{\theta,exc} = \Delta U_{\theta,irr} - \Delta U_{\theta,rev} \tag{10.2}$$

Although $\Delta U_{\theta,irr}$ depends on the manner in which the process occurs, the quantities $\Delta_r G_{T,P}$, $\Delta_r H$, and $\Delta_r S$ are fixed for a given chemical reaction. When the reaction occurs as part of a process that is overall reversible, such as at electrochemical equilibrium,

$$T\Delta S_{tot} = T\Delta_r S + T\Delta S_\theta = T\Delta_r S + \Delta U_{\theta,rev} = 0 \tag{10.3}$$

Thus,

$$\Delta U_{\theta,rev} = -T\Delta_r S \tag{10.4}$$

We obtain an expression for $\Delta U_{\theta,irr}$ from the first-law relationship,

$$\Delta U_{\theta,irr} + \Delta_r H + \Delta U_{el} = 0 \tag{10.5}$$

where we have used ΔU_{el} as an example of a potential energy reservoir in which ordered energy is stored. When we substitute eq. (10.4) and eq. (10.5) into eq. (10.2), we obtain

$$\begin{aligned} \Delta U_{\theta,exc} &= -\Delta_r H_\sigma - \Delta U_{el} - \Delta U_{\theta,rev} \\ &= -\Delta_r H - \Delta U_{el} + T\Delta_r S \end{aligned} \tag{10.6}$$

Then, after recognizing $\Delta_r G_{T,P}$ in this expression, we have

$$\Delta U_{\theta,exc} = -\Delta_r G_{T,P} - \Delta U_{el} \tag{10.7}$$

Comparison of eqs. (10.1) and (10.7) shows the result

$$T\Delta S_{tot} = \Delta U_{\theta,exc} \tag{10.8}$$

as asserted.

We consider the implications of eq. (10.8). When the overall process is reversible, $T\Delta S_{tot} = 0$ and $\Delta U_{\theta,exc} = 0$. No excess thermal energy is produced. All of the ordered energy available from the chemical reaction is converted into ordered electrical energy as reflected in the equations, $-\Delta_r G_{T,P} - \Delta U_{el} = 0$ or $-\Delta_r G_{T,P} = \Delta U_{el}$. If the process is irreversible, $T\Delta S_{tot} > 0$. Furthermore,

$$T\Delta S_{tot} = -\Delta_r G_{T,P} - \Delta U_{el} > 0 \tag{10.9}$$

Since $-\Delta_r G_{T,P}$ is unchanged, ΔU_{el} is less than optimal. Some ordered energy available from the chemical reaction is wasted by conversion to thermal energy, $\Delta U_{\theta,exc}$, beyond that required by the limiting reversible process. When no electrical energy is obtained, $\Delta U_\theta = -\Delta_r H$. Once formed, this amount of thermal energy cannot be converted back to ordered energy in a constant temperature process.

Coupled Chemical Reactions

We have recognized the role of coupled thermodynamic processes in several instances. The coupling of chemical reactions and electrical systems in electrochemical processes permits the direct conversion of chemical energy into electrical energy (galvanic cell) or the direct conversion of electrical energy into chemical energy (electrolysis). In a galvanic cell the spontaneous chemical reaction causes the nonspontaneous accumulation of electrical energy to occur. In electrolysis the spontaneous and nonspontaneous roles are exchanged. Heat engines can be regarded as the coupling of a spontaneous process of energy flow from a high-temperature thermal reservoir to a low-temperature thermal reservoir with the nonspontaneous process of conversion of thermal energy into mechanical energy at a single temperature. A refrigerator or heat pump can be regarded as the coupling of the spontaneous process of converting mechanical energy into thermal energy with the nonspontaneous process of transferring thermal energy from a low-temperature reservoir to a high-temperature one.

In coupled chemical reactions, a reaction that is favored thermodynamically causes a second reaction to take place that, by itself, is unfavored. For processes occurring at constant temperature and constant pressure, we can express the coupling relationship in terms of Gibbs free energies as

$$T\Delta S_{tot} = -\Delta_r G_1 - \Delta_r G_2 > 0 \tag{10.10}$$

Thus, if one of the $\Delta_r G_{T,P}$ values is negative and of larger magnitude than the other, positive one, the overall coupled process is spontaneous. The difference in the sum $-\Delta_r G_1 - \Delta_r G_2$ appears as excess thermal energy production in the thermal reservoir. Because the coupling of chemical reactions plays a large role in biological processes, reaction coupling has been of great interest to biochemists. Coupling of chemical reactions is, however, of wider significance than biochemistry. Furthermore, nonbiological examples are simpler. Consequently, we shall begin with an example drawn from a geological application.

As a simple example of coupled chemical reactions, consider the rather insoluble substance, $CaCO_3$, dissolving in water due to the action of acid. This process is the geologist's time-honored field test for limestone rock. The unfavorable reaction, dissolution of $CaCO_3$ in water, is caused to occur by coupling to the favorable chemical reaction, the action of hydronium ion on carbonate ion. Thus,

$$CaCO_3(c) \rightleftharpoons Ca^{2+}(aq) + CO_3^{2-}(aq)$$

Gf°_{298} (kJ/mol): -1128.8 -553.6 -527.8 $\Delta_r G^{\circ}_1 = 47.4$ kJ/mol

$$2H^+(aq) + CO_3^{2-}(aq) \rightleftharpoons CO_2(g) + H_2O(l)$$

Gf°_{298} (kJ/mol): 0 -527.8 -394.4 -237.1
$$\Delta_r G^{\circ}_2 = -103.7 \text{ kJ/mol}$$

Taken together, the two reactions give

$$2H^+(aq) + CaCO_3(c) \rightleftharpoons Ca^{2+}(aq) + CO_2(g) + H_2O(l)$$

for which $\Delta_r G^{\circ} = \Delta_r G^{\circ}_1 + \Delta_r G^{\circ}_2 = -56.3$ kJ/mol. The larger, negative free energy of the second reaction overcomes the positive free energy of the first. In terms of mechanism, the CO_3^{2-} ion provides the linkage between the two reactions. For the overall coupled process

$$T\Delta S_{tot} = -\Delta_r G^{\circ}_1 - \Delta_r G^{\circ}_2 = 56.3 \text{ kJ/mol} \qquad (10.11)$$

This amount of energy appears as excess thermal energy in the thermal energy reservoir. It is chemical energy that has been wasted.

Often a pair of inorganic reactions of the type under consideration are regarded as coupled equilibria rather than coupled reactions. Such a description is simply an alternative description since eq.(8.16) is $\Delta_r G^{\circ} = -RT \ln K$. Hence,

$$-\Delta_r G^{\circ}_1 - \Delta_r G^{\circ}_2 = RT \ln K_1 + RT \ln K_2 = RT \ln K_1 K_2 \qquad (10.12)$$

The equilibrium constant for the overall reaction is $K = K_1 K_2$.

As a biochemical example we consider the conversion of glucose into glucose 6-phosphate coupled to the hydrolysis of adenosine triphosphate (ATP). The glucose reaction, which has a positive $\Delta_r G^{\circ}$, is not spontaneous alone. The ATP hydrolysis reaction is spontaneous. For these reactions occurring in living systems it is preferable to use $\Delta_r G^{\circ\prime}$ values adjusted to a reference state of pH 7. The prime designates this pH condition. For the two reactions we have

$$\text{glucose(aq)} + \text{phosphate(aq)} \;\rightleftharpoons\; \text{glucose 6-phosphate(aq)} + H_2O(l)$$
$$\Delta_r G^{\circ\prime}{}_1 = 13.8 \text{ kJ/mol}$$

$$\text{ATP(aq)} + H_2O(l) \;\rightleftharpoons\; \text{ADP(aq)} + \text{phosphate(aq)}$$
$$\Delta_r G^{\circ\prime}{}_2 = -30.5 \text{ kJ/mol}$$

ADP is adenosine diphosphate. The overall free energy change for the coupled reaction is

$$\Delta_r G^{\circ\prime}{}_1 + \Delta_r G^{\circ\prime}{}_2 = -16.7 \text{ kJ/mol} \qquad (10.13)$$

The net reaction is

$$\text{glucose(aq)} + \text{ATP(aq)} \;\rightleftharpoons\; \text{glucose 6-phosphate(aq)} + \text{ADP(aq)}$$

Thus, glucose is converted to glucose 6-phosphate at the expense of the hydrolysis of ATP. The enzyme hexokinase directs this coupled process. Through various enzymes ATP hydrolysis is also coupled to many other non-spontaneous reactions in living systems.

The mechanisms of coupling through enzyme-containing intermediates are not known in detail in most cases. Nonetheless, the principles are the same as those in the transparent example of coupling of the dissolution of $CaCO_3$ to the acid–base reaction of CO_3^{2-} and H_3O^+. A product species in one step is a reactant species in another, and thus such species cancel out in the overall reaction, whatever the coupling species are. The only difference is that the enzyme may speed one of several alternative reactions that may occur in the given reaction medium. Of course, enzymes cannot cause reactions to occur that are not thermodynamically favored. Enzymes change rates only.

Returning to the simple $CaCO_3/H_3O^+$ reaction, we see a characteristic of coupled reactions that deserves consideration. The net consequence of coupling the two reactions is not the expected outcome of the nonspontaneous reaction. Thus, $CaCO_3$ has not gone into solution as Ca^{2+} and CO_3^{2-} without further change. The CO_3^{2-} had been consumed in the second reaction. The essential outcome is that the useful process of dissolving the $CaCO_3$ reactant in water occurred.

In the biochemical example a similar observation applies. Glucose has been converted into the useful product glucose 6-phosphate even though the first reaction itself is not the final result. The needed inorganic phosphate is a product of the other reaction, and the product water is consumed in the other reaction. Often, in considerations of biochemical processes the reactant and product roles of water and also of H_3O^+ ion are overlooked. Nonetheless, such species as well as enzyme intermediates and other species such as inorganic phosphate may serve as couplers between two reactions.

Summary

In this chapter we have pulled together and expanded prior discussions of energy conversions encountered throughout the text. Crucial to feasible energy conversions are the accompanying entropy changes that quantify the quality of each energy change that occurs in the interacting systems. Energy changes in potential energy reservoirs, such as electrical systems, have $\Delta S_{pot} = 0$, whereas energy changes in thermal reservoirs have $\Delta S_\theta = \Delta U_\theta / T_\theta$. For chemical reactions the enthalpy change, $\Delta_r H$, can be regarded as being almost entropy-change neutral. The $\Delta_r S$ for the reaction has consequences, however, that place chemical reactions intermediate between potential energy reservoirs and thermal reservoirs. The Gibbs free energy, $\Delta_r G_{T,P}$, reflects the compromise for chemical reactions.

Although energy conversions at the macroscopic level must always have $\Delta S_{tot} > 0$, energy conversions at the atomic–molecular or even the intermediate Brownian motion level can have momentary, local energy transactions for which $\Delta S_{tot} < 0$. Such processes are called fluctuations.

We have shown that $T\Delta S_{tot}$ for a process is the amount of excess thermal energy produced, that is, the amount of ordered energy capability that has been lost. In a reversible process, $T\Delta S_{tot} = 0$. No excess thermal energy is produced, and all of the ordered energy released by a chemical reaction appears as ordered energy elsewhere, for example, in an electrical system.

Many energy conversions can be usefully regarded as coupled processes. Heat engines and refrigerators involve the coupling of thermal–mechanical energy conversions and the flow of energy between thermal reservoirs at two temperatures. Through coupling by means of one or more shared reaction species, a favorable chemical reaction can cause an unfavorable chemical reaction to occur. Such reaction coupling is of great importance in understanding biological processing in which enzymes help direct reaction outcomes.

Important energy conversions that have not been considered in this text are ones involving the consumption or production of light. The principles we have developed apply, however, to such systems. Try them for yourself.

Problems

1. Light energy and various other energies can be interconverted. All of the following coupled processes involve light. Tell what other type of energy is involved: (a) a light-emitting diode (LED); (b) a photovoltaic silicon cell; (c) the formation of O_3 from O_2 in the stratosphere; (d) a fluorescent light; (e) a cathode ray tube.

2. Cite examples of actual chemical reactions for which: (a) $|\Delta_r G_{T,P}| > |\Delta_r H|$ and (b) $|\Delta_r G_{T,P}| < |\Delta_r H|$.

3. Silver chloride dissolves in water with the aid of aqueous ammonia. What are the two reactions that can be viewed as coupled in this process? What is $\Delta_r G^\circ$ for each of these reactions? What is $\Delta_r G^\circ$ for the overall coupled process? How much excess thermal energy is produced in the overall reaction?

4. When ADP is reconverted to ATP in biological systems, what thermodynamic characteristic must the reactions have that cause this conversion?

5. Can fluctuations in concentration occur in solutions at the microscopic level? If so, what are the entropic consequences of such events?

6. If the weak acid, acetic acid, is to be converted completely into acetate ion in an acid–base reaction, about how negative must $\Delta_r G^\circ$ be for the coupled reaction?

7. For a spontaneous endothermic reaction what relationship must hold between $\Delta_r G$, $\Delta_r H$, and $\Delta_r S$?

8. What energy conversions are involved in the following processes: (a) a liquid crystal display (LCD); (b) nerve impulse; (c) a thermocouple; (d) a thermoelectric cooler.

9. In aqueous solution the diamminesilver(I) complex ion $[Ag(NH_3)_2{}^+]$ decomposes when treated with nitric acid. The overall process can be viewed as two coupled chemical reactions. The breakup of the complex ion has a positive $\Delta_r G^\circ$, which is offset by the large negative $\Delta_r G^\circ$ of the reaction of aqueous ammonia with hydronium ion. Compute the $\Delta_r G^\circ$ values separately for the two coupled reactions and for the overall reaction, which is

$$Ag(NH_3)_2{}^+(aq) + 2H_3O^+(aq) \rightleftharpoons Ag^+(aq) + 2NH_4{}^+(aq) + 2H_2O(l)$$

10. The reaction $Zn(c) + Cu^{2+}(aq) \rightleftharpoons Zn^{2+}(aq) + Cu(c)$ is used to power an electrochemical cell. What is $\Delta_r G^\circ{}_{298}$ for this process? Suppose 200 kJ/mol is stored as energy in the electrical system, what is $T\Delta S_{tot}$? Thus, what fraction of the available, ordered energy is dissipated unnecessarily as thermal energy? Ans: $\Delta_r G^\circ{}_{298} = -212.6$ kJ/mol; fraction wasted = 0.53.

11. Room temperature is a *very* low temperature for a nuclear chemical reaction such as the decay of radon-200 by alpha-particle emission.

$$^{220}Rn \rightarrow {}^{216}Po + {}^{4}\alpha + 6.40 \text{ MeV}$$

Compute ΔS_θ per mole for this reaction. (1 eV/particle $\Rightarrow 9.6 \times 10^4$ J/mol; 1 MeV = one million electron volts) ΔS_σ for this reaction would be about 130 J/K mol, the entropy change accompanying the formation of one net mole of gas. What is ΔS_{tot}? What do you conclude about the reversibility of nuclear reactions at room temperature? One ans: $\Delta S_\theta = 2.0 \times 10^9$ J/K mol. It is possible to reverse spontaneous nuclear reactions with the aid of beams of particles raised to high energies in accelerators. The particle beams are essentially ordered energy and thus make a $\Delta S_{particle} \approx 0$ contribution to the reverse reaction. If these particles carry a bit of energy in excess of the ΔU_σ of the forward reaction, then a positive ΔS_θ for the reverse reaction makes the reverse reaction spontaneous.

12. What is the maximum amount of useful (ordered) energy available from a chemical reaction at constant T, P? Ans: The Gibbs free energy reflects the maximum amount of ordered energy available from a chemical reaction, i.e., $-\Delta_r G_{T,P}$ is this energy. Also, $-\Delta_r G_{T,P} = T\Delta S_{tot}$, for the chemical reaction considered alone. Note that this maximum amount of available energy is not $-\Delta_r H$. $\Delta_r G = \Delta_r H - T\Delta_r S$. Thus, $\Delta_r G_{T,P}$ differs from $\Delta_r H$ by the $T\Delta_r S$ term, which reflects the consequence of the entropy change in the reactive system. The useful (ordered) energy available from a chemical reaction may be converted into electrical energy, ΔU_{el}, or into available chemical energy of another chemical reaction, $\Delta_r G_2$.

13. Consider the figure summarizing energy conversions on p. 3 of Chapter 2. Do the missing arrows suggest opportunities for inventions of practical energy conversion processes?

APPENDIX A

Reconciliation of the Global Formulation of the First and Second Laws with the System-Oriented One

First Law. Usually the first law is expressed by

$$\Delta U = Q + W \tag{A.1}$$

where the change in energy, ΔU, of *the system* is equal to the difference between the heat, Q, absorbed by the system *from* the surroundings and the work, W, done *by* the surroundings *on* the system. The use of Δ with U means that U is a state function for the (reactive) system, whereas the absence of Δ with Q and W means they are not state functions. In differential form, $dU = DQ + DW$. dU is an exact differential, whereas DQ and DW are inexact differentials. The change in U depends only on the initial and final states of the (reactive) system even though the values of Q and W depend on the particular path followed in the transformation. Another way of saying this is that ΔU is well defined in terms of the variables (e.g., temperature and volume) that characterize the (reactive) system, whereas Q and W are not well defined in terms of these variables. In fact, values for Q and W can only be obtained in general by measuring changes in the surroundings.

If we rearrange the customary statement of the first law to give

$$\Delta U - Q - W = 0 \tag{A.2}$$

and compare the result with our statement

$$\Delta U_\sigma + \Delta U_\theta + \Delta U_{wt} = 0 \tag{A.3}$$

we immediately recognize equivalent terms. The change in energy that we have been associating with the "reactive system" is what is usually associated with "the system." We also have $\Delta U_\theta = -Q$, and $\Delta U_{wt} = -W$. At first glance, it appears that changes in state functions are being equated with path-dependent quantities. Not so. Q and W are path dependent only from the point of view of *the system.* These energy transactions are well defined, however, in terms of state functions in each of two principal parts (θ, wt) of the overall system. Else, how would we ever be able to measure these energy changes?

The customary statement of the first law is implicitly reactive-system or *local* in orientation. The beginner rarely comprehends this fully, however. The statement we have employed in this text is *global* in point of view. As a consequence, we do not have to contend with inexact differentials or with confusion about how Q and W are measured and how their signs are understood. Also, problems attending the elusive "heat" concept are avoided. Energy *transfer* terms, Q and W, are replaced with changes in energy *contents* in well-defined systems. Beginners find it more concrete to think in terms of energy contents than in terms of incompletely defined energy transfers, and they are less subject to confusion about algebraic signs. This global formulation of the first law anticipates the formulation of the second law, which is naturally global. Furthermore, the conservation aspect of the first law stands in clearer contrast to the growth principle aspect of the second law.

Second Law. From a classical statement of the second law concerning heat engines or related energy transfers, usually the one of Kelvin and Planck, one shows that $1/T$ is an integrating factor for DQ_{rev} for a reversible Carnot cycle. Thus, the differential of a new function S, the entropy, is exact if defined by

$$dS \equiv DQ_{rev}/T \tag{A.4}$$

One then shows that this expression for dS applies to *all reversible* (rev) *processes*. Also, from a consideration of heat engines, the Clausius inequality,

$$dS > DQ_{irrev}/T \tag{A.5}$$

is derived for irreversible (irrev) or spontaneous processes.

Equations (A.4) and (A.5) are applied to a general *irreversible* change occurring in an *overall* system, for which $DQ = 0$, i. e., the overall process is adiabatic. This overall (global) system is divided into two parts: a (reactive) system, sys, in which the irreversible process occurs and a (thermal) surroundings (surr) in which thermal energy is gained or lost reversibly. We have

$$dS_{total} = dS_{sys} + dS_{surr} \tag{A.6}$$

For the irreversible process in the system (sys), DQ_{irrev} is accompanied by a reversible energy decrease in surr, for which $dS_{surr} = -DQ_{irrev}/T$. Thus,

$$dS_{total} = dS_{sys} - DQ_{irrev}/T > 0 \tag{A.7}$$

since eq. (A.5) gives $dS_{sys} > DQ_{irrev}/T$ for the irreversible process in sys. Reinserting dS_{surr} into this equation, we have

$$dS_{total} = dS_{sys} + dS_{surr} \geq 0 \tag{A.8}$$

where the inequality sign refers to an irreversible process and the equals sign refers to a reversible process. To calculate dS_{sys} one must find a reversible path between the same initial and final states in sys. For this alternative, reversible path $dS_{sys} = DQ_{rev}/T$.

Turning to the second law as stated in this text we see that our global treatment has anticipated eq. (A.8). From the global formulation of the first law we had recognized the importance of changes in the thermal reservoir as well as those in the reactive system. The relationship

$$dS_{total} = dS_\sigma + dS_\theta > 0 \qquad (A.9)$$

is the equivalent of eq. (A.8), differing only in the use of the more specific subscripts. For finite differences, as used throughout this text, eq. (A.9) becomes

$$\Delta S_{tot} = \Delta S_\sigma + \Delta S_\theta \geq 0 \qquad (A.10)$$

The restriction of the expression used for calculating entropy changes, namely $\Delta S_\theta = \Delta U_\theta/T$, to thermal reservoirs, ensures equivalence to $dS \equiv DQ_{rev}/T$. Our conception of the thermal reservoir, which conforms to our experience with such systems, is such that energy change occurs within it reversibly. The thermal reservoir is large and changes temperature by only a small amount. Under these circumstances the finite difference form, $\Delta S_\theta = \Delta U_\theta/T$, suffices. Furthermore, the thermal reservoir is understood to be at internal equilibrium with respect to chemical reactions and phase changes. In fact, the same properties are assumed for the thermal reservoir as for the surroundings that are used in the customary derivation, as reviewed in the previous paragraph.

A thermal reservoir in which a phase change, such as the melting of ice, occurs has a heat (thermal energy) capacity which changes very rapidly with temperature. A chemical reaction may have the same effect on heat (thermal energy) capacity. In practice such thermal reservoirs are to be avoided unless temperature change is replaced with some other measurable quantity, such as volume change. An ice calorimeter is an example of using volume change instead of temperature change to measure ΔU_θ.

In the formulation of the second law in this text, we have used $\Delta S_\theta = \Delta U_\theta/T$ in all cases. We have done so even though most thermal reservoirs will be constant-pressure systems for which $\Delta S_\theta = \Delta H_\theta/T$. Little error is made by using ΔU_θ because ΔU_θ is very nearly equal to ΔH_θ for a water bath, or the like, under 1 bar pressure. To distinguish ΔH_θ from ΔU_θ in calculations of ΔS_θ, we would have to introduce a $P_\theta \Delta V_\theta$ term into the expression for ΔU_{tot} and thereby lose the simplicity of the first law expressed with single terms for ΔU_σ, ΔU_θ, and ΔU_{wt}. In sample calculations, we recommend using constant-pressure heat capacities to calculate ΔU_θ and thus actually calculate ΔH_θ.

APPENDIX B

Primitive Chemical Reaction at the Microscopic Level with the Temperature Constant

As part of our general consideration of the entropy function at the microscopic level, we analyzed a simple model for the interconversion of solid A and solid B. The diagram on p. 79 depicts the energy level schemes for these two solids.

Solid A has the lower ground-state energy and the wider spacing of oscillator energy levels in accordance with it being the more strongly bonded form. Solid B has the higher ground-state energy and the closer spacing of oscillator energy levels because B is the more weakly bonded form. Each form of the solid is modeled with four harmonic oscillators. For simplicity the reaction was discussed under the constraint of constant energy. In this appendix we investigate our microscopic model under the more widely applicable constraint of constant temperature. The "low-energy case" discussed in Chapter 6 is an approximation to a low-temperature case if, in a B $\rightarrow$ A conversion, we transfer $4 \cdot 4hv = 16hv$ of energy from the B form of the solid to a thermal reservoir and leave only $2hv$ in the A form of the solid. It is necessary to so reduce the amount of energy in A if A is to be at nearly the same temperature as B. The overall B $\rightarrow$ A reaction may be summarized by the following equation

$$
\begin{pmatrix} U_B = 18hv \\ n_B = 2 \\ \Omega_B = 10 \\ \frac{1}{T} \propto \log 2 \end{pmatrix} \begin{array}{c} \text{more likely} \\ \rightarrow \\ \leftarrow \\ \text{less likely} \end{array} \begin{pmatrix} U_A = 2hv \\ n_A = 1 \\ \Omega_A = 4 \\ \frac{1}{T} \propto \log 2 \end{pmatrix} + \begin{pmatrix} \Delta U_\theta = 16hv \\ \Delta S_\theta = \dfrac{16hv}{T} \\ \frac{1}{T} \propto \log 2 \end{pmatrix} \quad \text{(B.1)}
$$

$$\text{B form } (\sigma) \qquad\qquad \text{A form } (\sigma) \qquad\qquad \text{thermal reservoir } (\theta)$$

where T has been "measured" separately for B and A by the change that occurs when an increment of energy (hv) is added. Thus, temperature can be obtained from $T = \Delta U_\theta / \Delta S_\theta$ when $\Delta U_\theta = hv$ as a probe. Adding one unit of energy (hv) to B increases Ω_B from 10 to 20, hence by log 2. Adding one unit of energy (hv) to A increases Ω_A from 4 to ~7, which is log 1.8 $\approx$ log 2. For present purposes, the reciprocal of temperature, as given by $1/T = \Delta S_\theta / \Delta U_\theta$, is more useful.

$$
\frac{1}{T} = \frac{\Delta S_\theta}{\Delta U_\theta} = \frac{k(2.303) \log \Omega}{hv} \quad \text{(B.2)}
$$

Since A has the larger energy spacing, it has the smaller Ω (or S) at a given temperature (Appendix C). The same $1/T$ value applies to the thermal reservoir as to the B and A forms. For the B $\rightarrow$ A reaction we have

$$\frac{\Delta S_{tot}}{2.303k} = \frac{\Delta S_\theta + S_A - S_B}{2.303k} = \frac{16h\nu}{h\nu}\log 2 + \log\frac{4}{10}$$

$$= 16\log 2 - \log 2.5 = 4.8 - 0.40 > 0 \qquad\qquad (B.3)$$

Thus, the B $\rightarrow$ A transformation is favored at low temperatures. The entropy decrease in the reactive system (crystal) is offset by a larger entropy increase in the thermal reservoir. The energy that is released to the thermal reservoir is the difference in ground-state electronic energies (ΔU_0) of A and B.

The "high-energy case" discussed in Chapter 6 proves to be an approximation to the high-temperature case if, as before, $16h\nu$ of energy comes from a thermal reservoir with the balance of $34h\nu$ coming from A. Under these conditions the temperature of A and B are essentially the same. We summarize the A $\rightarrow$ B reaction with the equation,

$$\begin{pmatrix} \Delta U_\theta = -16h\nu \\ \\ \Delta S_\theta = \dfrac{-16h\nu}{T} \end{pmatrix} + \begin{pmatrix} U_A = 34h\nu \\ n_A = 17 \\ \Omega_A = 1140 \\ \dfrac{1}{T} \propto \log 1.1 \end{pmatrix} \xrightarrow[\substack{\longleftarrow \\ \text{less likely}}]{\substack{\text{more likely} \\ \longrightarrow}} \begin{pmatrix} U_B = 50h\nu \\ n_B = 34 \\ \Omega_B = 7760 \\ \dfrac{1}{T} \propto \log 1.1 \end{pmatrix} \qquad (B.4)$$

$$\;\;\text{thermal reservoir } (\theta) \qquad \text{A form } (\sigma) \qquad\qquad\quad \text{B form } (\sigma)$$

where, as before, a probe with an energy increment of $h\nu$ has been used to measure the temperature. Since A has the larger energy spacings, it has the smaller Ω (or S) at a given temperature. For the A $\rightarrow$ B reaction we have

$$\frac{\Delta S_{tot}}{2.303k} = \frac{\Delta S_\theta + S_B - S_A}{2.303k} = \frac{-16h\nu}{h\nu}\log 1.1 + \log\frac{7760}{1140}$$

$$= -16\log 1.1 + \log 6.8 = -0.64 + 0.83 > 0 \qquad\qquad (B.5)$$

At this higher temperature the reaction A $\rightarrow$ B is favored. The principal reason is the diminished entropy change in the thermal reservoir at the higher temperature. Also, a somewhat larger entropy change occurs in the reactive system. This latter effect is a consequence of entropy increasing more rapidly with temperature for a distribution over a manifold of closely spaced energy states than for a manifold of more widely spaced states. All of the energy drawn from the thermal reservoir is used to supply the higher ground-state energy ($\Delta U_0 = 16h\nu$) of the B crystal.

APPENDIX C

Effect of a Change in Energy-Level Spacing on Energy and Entropy

In Chapter 6 we asserted that decreasing the spacing of energy levels accessible to an atomic–molecular system increases the entropy. In this appendix we examine the effect of changes in energy spacing on energy content and entropy more quantitatively with the aid of two four-oscillator models.

To do this analysis we choose harmonic oscillator systems that are related in a simple way. Oscillator system 1 has an energy level spacing of hv, and oscillator system 2 has spacing of $2hv$. Table C.1 compares the two systems as increments of energy are added.

We shall be interested in comparing the two-oscillator systems at *the same temperature*. Temperature can be obtained from

$$T_\theta = \frac{\Delta U_\theta}{\Delta S_\theta} = \frac{2hv}{k \ln (\Omega_f/\Omega_i)} = \frac{2hv}{k(2.303) \log (\Omega_f/\Omega_i)}$$

$$\propto \frac{1}{\log (\Omega_f/\Omega_i)} = "T" \tag{C.1}$$

For our present purpose it is simpler and sufficient to use "T," which is proportional to temperature. For system 1 ratios of Ω's are taken for $2hv$ increments in order to be comparable with the only increments possible for system 2. "Temperatures" corresponding to each increment are tabulated for the two systems. As seen in two different rows in the table, the two systems have essentially the same temperature ("T" ≈ 4.2) when $U_1 = 9hv$ and $U_2 = 7hv$. Furthermore, $\Omega_1 = 220$ and $\Omega_2 \approx 28$ at this temperature. Thus, we conclude that the system with the more closely spaced energy levels has the larger thermal energy and the larger entropy (larger Ω) at a given temperature. Furthermore, the system with the more closely spaced energy levels has the larger heat (thermal energy) capacity. More energy was absorbed to reach a given temperature.

We may also use the table to compare the two systems at constant *thermal energy* instead of constant temperature. We do so by reading a single line of the table. From the last line in the table we see that system 1 with the more closely spaced levels has the larger entropy at constant thermal energy. We find that at constant temperature *or* constant energy the system with the more closely spaced energy levels has the larger entropy.

The conclusions of the analysis are not limited to the equal spacing of energy levels of the harmonic oscillator. Closer, but not equal energy spacing of heavier atoms undergoing translational motion will cause a higher entropy. For example, $S°_{298}[Ne(g)] = 146.2$ J/K mol, whereas $S°_{298}[He(g)] = 126.0$ J/K mol. (The heat capacities of these two substances are the same because the spacing of translational levels is so close that quantization of these levels does not matter at room temperature.) A change in energy level spacing due to a change in bond strength (strictly, a force constant) would have the same effect.

In the discussion in this appendix we have compared two oscillator systems having different energy level spacings but the same energy zero. In practice, as shown in the microscopic analysis of the primitive chemical reaction in Chapter 6, the two oscillator systems would have different energy zeroes. The oscillators with closer energy spacings (weaker bonds) would have the higher energy zero. Two oscillator systems that differ in this more realistic way are considered in Appendix B.

Table C.1. **Comparison of Two Four-Oscillator Solids That Differ in Energy Level Spacing***

System 1				System 2			
$n_1(=U/h\nu_1)$	Ω_1	$\Omega_{1,f}/\Omega_{1,i}$	"T_1"	$n_1(=U/2h\nu_2)$	Ω_2	$\Omega_{2,f}/\Omega_{2,f}$	"T_2"
0	1			0	1		
1	4	10	1.0			4	0.6
2	10			1	4		
3	20	3.5	1.8			2.5	2.5
4	35			2	10		
5	56	2.4	2.6			2.0	3.3
6	84			3	20		
7	120	1.96	3.4			1.75	4.1
8	165			4	35		
9	220	1.73	4.2			1.6	4.9
10	286			5	56		

*The energy-level spacing in system 2 is twice the energy-level spacing in system 1.

APPENDIX D

STANDARD STATE THERMODYNAMIC PROPERTIES AT 298.15 K (25°C)

All data are for species in their standard states at 298.15 K (25°C) unless otherwise noted. For all substances the standard state is 1 bar pressure (1 bar = 10^5 Pa = 1 N/m^2 = 0.9869 atm); however, gases are in an ideal gas state. For solutions the standard state is typically an ideal solution of unit activity (molal $\approx$ molar scale), which is approximately 1 M. Abbreviations for states are: c, crystalline solid; l, liquid; g, gaseous; aq, aqueous; Gf° and Hf° are the Gibbs energy of formation and the enthalpy of formation, respectively, relative to elements in their reference states. Other than for ions, S° and Cp°, the entropy and the constant-pressure heat capacity, are "absolute" values. For ions the computation of S° (and Gf°) incorporates a value of 65.34 J/K mol for electrons, which is $S^\circ[1/2H_2(g)]$. In converting data in the literature in calories to data in joules, the relationship 1 cal = 4.184 J was used.

The order of the elements in the table is that used by the National Institute of Standards and Technology (formerly the National Bureau of Standards), which is based on the arrangement of the elements in the periodic table (Fig. D.1). This arrangement starts with oxygen, goes to hydrogen, then generally down each column from right to left in the table. As each element is added to the table, compounds of this element with all preceding elements are introduced. Thus, compounds consisting of nonmetals alone are found early in the table. Compounds containing alkaline earth and alkali metals are near the end of the table. In the table, entries for the most stable form of each element are at the top of the section for each element.

Formulas for many species have been written out structurally for ease of recognition. In some places names or abbreviations for names are given in order to remove ambiguity and to define these abbreviations for use elsewhere, such as in writing complex ions. In organic formulas the symbol "c" has been used frequently to distinguish cyclic compounds.

Values in parentheses were either deemed insecure by the original source or are in doubt due to use of different sources for the several values for that one species. Data of intermediate quality are given without decimal significance. For some substances that we deemed desirable for this table we did not find data in the standard sources or readily in the original literature. However, we decided that keeping the species in the table would make it easier to insert data as they are found and also would draw attention to needed data.

In order of decreasing frequency of use the principal references were:

D. D. Wagman, W. H. Evans, V. B. Parker, R. H. Schumm, I. Halow, S. M. Bailey, K. L. Churney, R. L. Nutall, *The NBS tables of chemical thermodynamic properties. Selected values for inorganic and C_1 and C_2 organic substances in SI units. J. Phys. Chem. Ref. Data* **1982**, *11*, Supplement No. 2

M. W. Chase, Jr., C. A. Davies, J. R. Downey, Jr., D. J. Frurip, R. A. McDonald, A. N. Syverud, *JANAF Thermochemical Tables*, Third Ed., Parts I-II, *J. Phys. Chem. Ref. Data* **1985**, *14*, Supplement No. 1.

D. R. Stull, E. F. Westrum, Jr., and G. C. Sinke, *The Chemical Thermodynamics of Organic Compounds*, John Wiley and Sons, New York, 1969.

W. M. Latimer, *Oxidation Potentials*, Second Ed., Prentice-Hall, New York, 1952.

Selected Values of Properties of Chemical Compounds, Thermodynamics Research Center Data Project, College Station, Texas, 1980.

Selected Values of Properties of Hydrocarbons and Related Compounds, Thermodynamics Research Center Hydrocarbon Project (formerly API Research Project 44), College Station, Texas, 1980.

J. D. Cox, D. D. Wagman, and V. A. Medvedev, *Codata Key Values for Thermodynamics* Hemisphere Publ. Co., New York, 1989.

J. D. Cox and G. Pilcher, *Thermochemistry of Organic and Organometallic Compounds*, Academic Press, 1970.

S. Sunner and M. Månsson, eds., *Combusion Calorimetry. Experimental Chemical Thermodynamics*, vol. 2, IUPAC, Pergamon Press, Oxford, 1979.

H. D. Brown, *Experimental Microcalorimetry*, Academic Press, New York, 1969.

STANDARD ARRANGEMENT

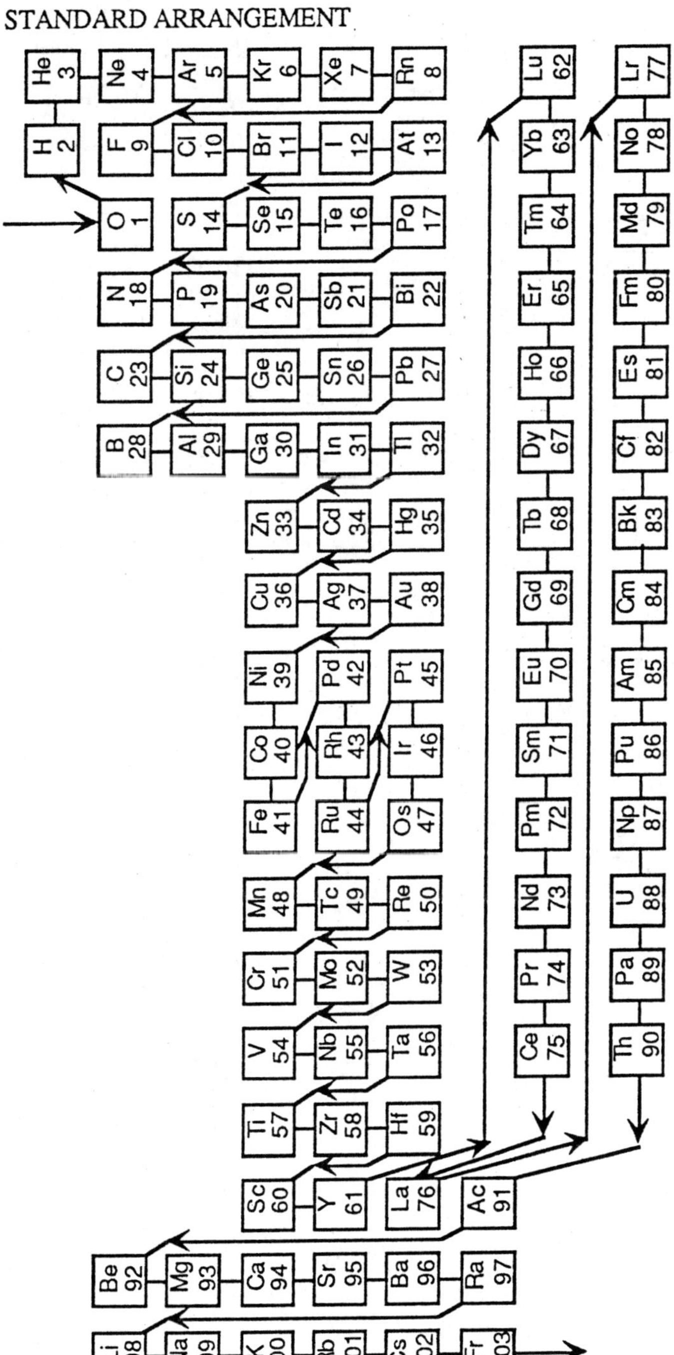

Figure D.1. Standard order of the elements and compounds based on the Periodic Classification.

	H_f° (kJ/mol)	G_f° (kJ/mol)	S° (J/K mol)	C_P° (J/K mol)
OXYGEN				
$O_2(g)$	0.0	0.0	205.14	29.36
$O(g)$	249.17	231.73	161.05	21.91
$O_3(g)$	142.17	163.2	238.93	39.20
HYDROGEN				
$H_2(g)$	0.0	0.0	130.68	28.82
$H(g)$	217.96	203.25	114.71	20.78
$D(g)$	221.67	206.51	123.35	20.79
$H^+(aq)$	0.0	0.0	0.0	0.0
$H^-(g)$	138.99	132.12	108.96	20.79
$H_2^+(g)$	1488.42	.	.	.
$OH(g)$	38.95	34.23	183.74	29.89
$OH^-(aq)$	−229.99	−157.24	−10.75	−148.5
$H_2O(g)$	−241.82	−228.57	188.82	33.58
$H_2O(l, 298\ K)$	−285.83	−237.13	69.91	75.29
$H_2O(c, 298\ K)$	(−292.8)	.	(44.6)	(37.8)
$H_2O(l, 273\ K;\ ref\ 298\ K)$	−287.72	.	63.34	76.17
$H_2O(c, 273K;\ ref\ 298\ K)$	−293.73	.	41.34	37.78
$H_3O^+(aq)$	−285.83	−237.13	69.91	75.29
$HO_2^-(aq)$	−160.33	−67.3	23.8	.
$H_2O_2(l)$	−187.78	−120.35	109.6	89.1
$H_2O_2(aq)$	−191.17	−134.03	143.9	.
NOBLE GASES				
$He(g)$	0.0	0.0	126.15	20.79
$He(aq)$	−1.7	19.7	54.4	.
$He^+(g)$	2378.50	.	.	.
$Ne(g)$	0.0	0.0	146.33	20.79
$Ne(aq)$	−4.6	19.3	66.1	.
$Ne^+(g)$	2086.95	.	.	.
$Ar(g)$	0.0	0.0	154.84	20.79
$Ar(aq)$	−12.1	16.4	59.4	.
$Ar^+(g)$	1526.76	.	.	.
$Kr(g)$	0.0	0.0	164.08	20.79
$Kr(aq)$	−15.5	15.1	61.5	.
$Kr^+(g)$	1357.0	.	.	.
$Xe(g)$	0.0	0.0	169.68	20.79
$Xe(aq)$	−17.6	13.4	65.7	.
$Xe^+(g)$	1176.54	.	.	.
$XeO_3(c)$	402.	.	.	.
$HXeO_6^{3-}(aq)$	.	.	.	.
$H_2XeO_6^{2-}(aq)$	.	.	.	.

	$H_f°$ (kJ/mol)	$G_f°$ (kJ/mol)	$S°$ (J/K mol)	$C_P°$ (J/K mol)
FLUORINE				
$F_2(g)$	0.0	0.0	202.78	31.30
$F(g)$	79.99	61.91	158.75	22.74
$F^-(aq)$	−332.63	−278.79	−13.8	−106.7
$F_2O(g)$	24.7	41.9	247.43	43.30
$HF(g)$	−271.1	−273.2	173.78	29.13
$HF(l)$	−299.78	.	75.4	51.67
$HF(aq)$	−320.08	−296.8	88.7	.
$HF_2^-(aq)$	−649.94	−578.08	92.5	.
$HOF(g)$	−98.89	−85.64	226.77	35.93
$XeF_2(c)$	−162.8	−86.18	.	.
$XeF_4(c)$	−267.1	−145.6	.	(118.6)
$XeF_6(c)$	−338.2	−169.13	.	.
CHLORINE				
$Cl_2(g)$	0.0	0.0	223.07	33.91
$Cl(g)$	121.68	105.68	165.20	21.84
$Cl^-(aq)$	−167.16	−131.23	56.75	−136.4
$ClO^-(aq)$	−107.1	−36.8	42.	.
$ClO_2(g)$	102.5	120.5	256.84	41.97
$ClO_2^-(aq)$	−66.5	17.2	101.3	.
$ClO_3^-(aq)$	−103.97	−7.95	162.3	−75.3
$ClO_4^-(aq)$	−129.33	−8.52	182.0	.
$Cl_2O(g)$	80.3	97.9	266.21	45.40
$HCl(g)$	−92.13	−95.31	186.91	29.12
$HOCl(aq)$	−120.9	−79.9	142.	.
$HClO_4(l)$	−40.58	.	.	.
$ClF_3(g)$	−163.2	−123.0	281.61	63.85
BROMINE				
$Br_2(l)$	0.0	0.0	152.23	75.69
$Br(g)$	111.88	82.40	175.02	20.79
$Br^-(aq)$	−121.55	−103.96	82.4	−141.8
$Br_2(g)$	30.91	3.11	245.46	36.02
$Br_3^-(aq)$	−130.42	−107.05	215.5	.
$BrO^-(aq)$	−94.1	−33.4	42.	.
$BrO_3^-(aq)$	−67.07	18.60	161.71	(−79.5)
$BrO_4^-(aq)$	13.0	118.1	199.6	.
$HBr(g)$	−36.40	−53.45	198.70	29.14
$HBr(aq)$	−121.55	−103.96	82.4	−141.8
$BrF_3(g)$	−255.60	−229.43	292.53	66.61
$BrCl(g)$	14.64	−0.98	240.10	34.98

	$H_f°$ (kJ/mol)	$G_f°$ (kJ/mol)	$S°$ (J/K mol)	$C_P°$ (J/K mol)
IODINE				
$I_2(c)$	0.0	0.0	116.14	54.44
$I(g)$	106.84	70.25	180.79	20.79
$I^-(aq)$	−55.19	−51.57	111.3	−142.3
$I_2(g)$	62.44	19.33	260.69	36.90
$I_2(aq)$	22.6	16.40	137.2	.
$I_2(cyclohexane)$	24.3	11.7	158.2	.
$I_3^-(aq)$	−51.5	−51.4	239.3	.
$IO^-(aq)$	−107.5	−38.5	−5.4	.
$IO_3^-(aq)$	−221.3	−128.0	118.4	.
$I_2O_5(c)$	−158.07	.	.	.
$HI(g)$	26.48	1.70	206.59	29.16
$HOI(aq)$	−138.1	−99.1	95.4	.
$IF_5(g)$	−822.49	−751.73	327.7	99.2
$ICl(g)$	17.78	−5.46	247.55	35.56
$ICl_3(c)$	−89.5	−22.29	167.4	.
$IBr(g)$	40.84	3.69	258.77	36.44
SULFUR				
$S(c, rhombic)$	0.0	0.0	31.80	22.64
$S(c, monoclinic)$	0.36	0.07	33.03	23.22
$S(g)$	278.80	238.25	167.82	23.67
$S^{2-}(aq)$	33.1	85.8	−14.6	.
$S_2(g)$	128.37	79.30	228.18	32.47
$SO_2(g)$	−296.83	−300.19	248.22	39.87
$SO_2(aq)$	−322.98	−300.68	161.9	.
$SO_3(g)$	−395.72	−371.06	256.76	50.67
$SO_3(l)$	−441.04	−373.75	113.8	.
$SO_3^{2-}(aq)$	−635.5	−486.5	−29.	.
$SO_4^{2-}(aq)$	−909.27	−744.53	20.1	−293.
$S_2O_3^{2-}(aq)$	−648.5	−522.5	67.	.
$S_2O_8^{2-}(aq)$	−1344.7	−1114.9	244.3	.
$S_4O_6^{2-}(aq)$	−1224.2	−1040.4	257.3	−67.8
$HS^-(aq)$	−17.6	12.08	62.8	.
$H_2S(g)$	−20.63	−33.56	205.79	34.23
$H_2S(aq)$	−39.7	−27.83	121.	.
$HSO_3^-(aq)$	−626.22	−527.73	139.7	.
$HSO_4^-(aq)$	−887.34	−755.91	131.8	−84.
$H_2SO_3(aq)$	−608.81	−537.81	232.2	.
$H_2SO_4(l)$	−813.99	−690.00	156.90	138.9
$SF_4(g)$	−774.9	−731.3	292.03	73.01
$SF_6(g)$	−1209.	−1105.3	291.82	97.28
$SOCl_2(g)$	−212.5	−198.3	309.77	66.5
$SO_2Cl_2(g)$	−364.0	−320.0	311.94	77.0

	$Hf°$ (kJ/mol)	$Gf°$ (kJ/mol)	$S°$ (J/K mol)	$Cp°$ (J/K mol)
SELENIUM				
Se(c, hex)	0.0	0.0	42.44	25.36
Se(g)	227.07	187.03	176.62	20.82
SeO_3^{2-}(aq)	−509.2	−369.8	13.	.
SeO_4^{2-}(aq)	−599.1	−441.3	54.0	.
HSe^-(aq)	15.9	44.0	79.	.
H_2Se(g)	29.7	15.9	219.02	34.73
H_2Se(aq)	19.2	22.2	163.6	.
$HSeO_3^-$(aq)	−514.55	−411.46	135.1	.
$HSeO_4^-$(aq)	−581.6	−452.2	149.4	.
H_2SeO_3(aq)	−507.48	−426.14	207.9	.
SeF_6(g)	−1117.	−1017.	313.87	110.5
$SeCl_2$(g)	−31.8	.	.	.
TELLURIUM				
Te(c)	0.0	0.0	49.71	25.73
Te(g)	196.73	157.08	182.74	20.79
TeO_2(c)	−322.6	−270.3	79.5	(66.5)
H_2Te(g)	99.6	.	(234.)	.
H_2TeO_3(aq, ionic)	.	−476.1	.	.
TeF_6(g)	−1318.	.	340.	117.5
$TeCl_4$(c)	−326.4	.	(209.)	138.5
NITROGEN				
N_2(g)	0.0	0.0	191.61	29.12
N(g)	472.70	455.56	153.30	20.79
N_3^-(aq)	275.14	348.2	107.9	.
NO(g)	90.25	86.55	210.76	29.84
NO_2(g)	33.18	51.31	240.06	37.20
NO_2^-(aq)	−104.6	−32.2	123.0	−97.5
NO_3^-(aq)	−207.36	−111.25	146.4	−86.6
N_2O(g)	82.05	104.20	219.85	38.45
N_2O_2(g)	170.4	202.9	287.6	63.51
N_2O_3(g)	84.72	139.46	312.28	65.61
N_2O_4(g)	9.16	97.89	304.29	77.28
N_2O_5(c)	−43.1	113.9	178.2	143.1
NH_3(g)	−46.11	−16.45	192.45	35.06
NH_3(aq)	−80.29	−26.50	111.3	.
NH_4^+(aq)	−133.51	−79.31	113.4	79.9
N_2H_4(g)	95.40	159.35	238.47	49.58
N_2H_4(l)	50.63	149.34	121.21	98.87
N_2H_4(aq)	34.31	128.1	138.	.
$N_2H_5^+$(aq)	−7.5	82.5	151.	70.3

	$Hf°$ (kJ/mol)	$Gf°$ (kJ/mol)	$S°$ (J/K mol)	$Cp°$ (J/K mol)
$HN_3(g)$	294.1	328.1	238.97	43.68
$HN_3(aq)$	260.08	321.8	146.0	.
$HNO_2(aq)$	−119.2	−50.6	135.6	.
$HNO_3(l)$	−174.10	−80.71	155.60	109.87
$NH_2OH(aq)$	−98.3	.	.	.
$NH_4NO_3(c, IV)$	−365.56	−183.87	151.08	139.3
$NF_2(g)$	43.1	57.8	249.94	41.00
$NF_3(g)$	−124.7	−83.2	260.73	53.1
$cis\text{-}N_2F_2(g)$	68.61	108.74	259.81	49.96
$trans\text{-}N_2F_2(g)$	81.17	120.45	262.86	53.47
$N_2F_4(g)$	−7.1	81.2	301.19	79.1
$NOCl(g)$	51.71	66.08	261.69	44.69
$NH_4Cl(c)$	−314.43	−202.87	94.6	84.1
$NOBr(g)$	82.17	82.42	273.66	45.48
$(NH_4)_2SO_4(c)$	−1180.85	−901.67	220.1	187.49

PHOSPHORUS

	$Hf°$ (kJ/mol)	$Gf°$ (kJ/mol)	$S°$ (J/K mol)	$Cp°$ (J/K mol)
$P(c, white)$	0.0	0.0	41.09	23.84
$P(c, red)$	−17.6	−12.1	22.80	21.21
$P(g)$	314.64	278.25	163.93	20.79
$P_2(g)$	144.03	103.7	218.13	32.05
$P_4(g)$	58.91	24.44	279.98	67.15
$PO_4^{3-}(aq)$	−1277.4	−1018.7	222.	.
$P_2O_7^{4-}(aq)$	−2271.1	−1919.0	−117.	.
$P_4O_6(c)$	−1640.1	.	(346.)	(144.)
$P_4O_{10}(c)$	−2984.0	−2697.7	228.86	211.71
$PH_3(g)$	5.4	13.4	210.3	37.11
$PH_3(aq)$	−9.50	25.36	120.1	.
$PH_4^+(aq)$	.	92.1	.	.
$HPO_3^{2-}(aq)$	−969.0	(−811.7)	.	.
$HPO_4^{2-}(aq)$	−1292.14	−1089.15	−33.5	.
$H_2PO_3^-(aq)$	−969.4	.	(79.5)	.
$H_2PO_4^-(aq)$	−1296.29	−1130.28	90.4	.
$H_3PO_3(aq)$	−964.8	.	(167.)	.
$H_3PO_4(c)$	−1279.0	−1119.1	110.50	106.06
$H_3PO_4(aq)$	−1288.34	−1142.54	158.2	.
$H_4P_2O_7(aq)$	−2268.6	−2032.0	268.	.
$PF_3(g)$	−918.8	−892.5	273.24	58.70
$PF_5(g)$	−1594.41	−1520.70	300.81	84.84
$PF_6^-(aq)$	.	.	.	.
$PCl_3(g)$	−287.0	−267.8	311.78	71.84
$PCl_5(g)$	−374.9	−305.0	364.58	112.80
$POCl_3(g)$	−558.48	−512.93	325.47	84.94
$PBr_3(g)$	−139.3	−162.8	348.09	75.98

	$H_f°$ (kJ/mol)	$G_f°$ (kJ/mol)	$S°$ (J/K mol)	$C_P°$ (J/K mol)
ARSENIC				
As(c, gray metal)	0.0	0.0	35.1	24.64
As(g)	302.5	261.0	174.21	20.79
As_4(g)	143.9	92.4	314.	.
AsO^+(aq)	.	−163.80	.	.
AsO_4^{3-}(aq)	−888.14	−648.41	−162.8	.
AsH_3(g)	66.44	68.93	222.78	38.07
$HAsO_4^{2-}$(aq)	−906.34	−714.60	−1.7	.
$H_2AsO_4^-$(aq)	−909.56	−753.17	117.	.
H_3AsO_3(aq)	−742.2	−639.80	195.0	.
H_3AsO_4(aq)	−902.5	−766.0	184.	.
AsF_3(g)	−785.76	−770.76	289.10	65.51
AsF_3(l)	−821.3	−774.16	181.21	126.57
AsF_5(g)	−1236.7	−1172.5	326.5	.
AsF_6^-(aq)	.	.	.	.
$AsCl_3$(l)	−305.0	−259.4	216.3	.
As_2S_3(c)	−169.0	−168.6	163.6	116.3
ANTIMONY				
Sb(c, metal)	0.0	0.0	45.69	25.23
Sb(g)	262.3	222.1	180.27	20.79
SbO^+(aq)	.	−177.11	.	.
Sb_2O_5(c)	−971.9	−829.2	125.1	.
Sb_4O_6(c, orthorhombic)	−1417.1	−1253.0	246.0	202.76
SbH_3(g)	145.10	147.75	232.78	41.05
SbF_3(c)	−915.5	(−836.0)	(105.)	.
SbF_5(l)	−1337.	.	.	.
SbF_6^-(aq)	.	.	.	.
$SbCl_3$(c)	−382.17	−323.67	184.1	107.9
$SbCl_5$(g)	−394.34	−334.29	401.94	121.13
$SbCl_5$(l)	−440.2	−350.1	301.	.
$SbCl_6^-$(aq)	.	.	.	.
SbOCl(c)	−374.0	.	.	.
Sb_2S_3(c, black)	−174.9	−173.6	182.0	119.87
BISMUTH				
Bi(c)	0.0	0.0	56.74	25.52
Bi(g)	207.1	168.2	187.00	20.79
BiO^+(aq)	.	−146.4	(105.9)	.
Bi_2O_3(c)	−573.88	−493.7	151.5	113.51
BiF_3(c)	(−904.)	(−837.)	.	.
$BiCl_3$(c)	−379.1	−315.0	177.0	105.
BiOCl(c)	−366.9	−322.1	120.5	.
Bi_2S_3(c)	−143.1	−140.6	200.4	122.2

	$Hf°$ (kJ/mol)	$Gf°$ (kJ/mol)	$S°$ (J/K mol)	$Cp°$ (J/K mol)
CARBON				
C(c, graphite)	0.0	0.0	5.74	8.53
C(c, diamond)	1.90	2.90	2.38	6.13
C(g)	716.68	671.26	158.10	20.84
C_2(g)	831.90	775.89	199.42	43.21
C_3(g)	820.06	754.46	237.25	37.74
C_4(g)	970.69	909.46	228.32	50.18
CO(g)	−110.52	−137.17	197.67	29.14
CO_2(g)	−393.51	−394.36	213.74	37.11
CO_2(l)	−403.6	−387.0	155.2	.
CO_2(aq)	−413.80	−385.98	117.6	.
CO_3^{2-}(aq)	−677.14	−527.81	−56.9	.
C_3O_2(g)	−93.64	−109.65	276.07	66.99
CH_2(g)	390.37	372.92	194.87	33.76
CH_3(g)	145.69	147.92	194.02	38.70
CH_4(g)	−74.81	−50.72	186.26	35.31
$HCOO^-$(aq)	−425.55	−351.0	92.	−87.9
HCO_3^-(aq)	−691.99	−586.77	91.2	.
HCHO(g)	−108.57	−102.53	218.77	35.40
HCHO(aq)	−141.8	.	.	.
HCOOH(l)	−424.72	−361.35	128.95	99.04
HCOOH(aq)	−425.43	−372.3	163.	.
H_2CO_3(aq)	−699.65	−623.08	187.4	.
CH_3OH(l)	−238.66	−166.27	126.8	81.6
CH_3OH(g)	−200.66	−161.96	239.81	43.89
CH_3OH(aq)	−245.93	−175.31	133.1	.
CF_2(g)	−182.00	−191.64	240.83	38.95
CF_4(g)	−933.20	−888.51	261.42	61.05
CH_3F(g)	−234.30	−210.36	222.84	37.50
CH_2F_2(g)	−446.9	−419.2	246.71	42.89
CHF_3(g)	−688.3	−653.9	259.68	51.04
CCl_4(l)	−135.44	−65.21	216.40	131.75
CCl_4(g)	−102.9	−60.59	309.85	83.30
$COCl_2$(g)	−218.8	−204.6	283.53	57.66
CH_3Clg)	−80.83	−57.37	234.58	40.75
CH_2Cl_2(g)	−92.47	−65.87	270.23	50.96
CF_2Cl_2(g)	−477.	−439.	300.77	72.26
$CHCl_2F$	−283.26	−252.76	293.26	61.00
$CFCl_3$(g)	−276.	−238.	309.93	78.07
$CHCl_3$(l)	−134.47	−73.66	201.7	113.8
$CHCl_3$(g)	−103.14	−70.34	295.71	65.69
CBr_4(c)	18.8	47.7	212.5	144.3
CBr_4(g)	79.	67.	358.05	91.17
CH_3Br(g)	−35.1	−25.9	246.38	42.43

	$H_f°$ (kJ/mol)	$G_f°$ (kJ/mol)	$S°$ (J/K mol)	$C_P°$ (J/K mol)
$CH_3I(l)$	−15.5	13.4	163.2	126.1
$CS_2(l)$	89.70	65.27	151.34	75.7
$CS_2(g)$	117.36	67.12	237.84	45.40
$COS(g)$	−142.09	−169.34	231.57	41.51
$CH_3SH(g)$	−22.34	−9.30	255.17	50.25
$CN(g)$	437.6	407.5	202.61	29.16
$CN^-(aq)$	150.6	172.4	94.1	.
$CNO^-(aq)$	−146.0	−97.4	106.7	.
$HCN(l)$	108.87	124.97	112.84	70.63
$HCN(g)$	135.1	124.7	201.78	35.86
$HCN(aq)$	107.1	119.7	124.7	.
$CH_3NH_2(g)$	−22.97	32.16	243.41	53.1
$CH_3NH_2(aq)$	−70.17	20.77	123.4	.
$CH_3NH_3^+(aq)$	−124.93	−39.86	142.7	.
$H_2CN_2(g)$ diazomethane	192.	217.8	242.87	52.51
$HCNO(aq)$ cyanic acid	−154.39	−117.1	144.8	.
$NH_4HCO_3(c)$	−849.4	−665.9	120.9	.
$CO(NH_2)_2(c)$	−333.51	−197.33	104.60	93.14
$NCCl(g)$	137.95	131.04	236.17	44.98
$NCBr(g)$	186.2	165.3	248.30	46.94
$SCN^-(aq)$	76.44	92.71	144.3	−40.2
$HSCN(aq)$ thiocyanic acid	.	97.56	.	.
$HNCS(g)$ isothiocyanic acid	127.6	113.0	247.8	46.9
$NH_4SCN(c)$	−78.7	.	.	.
$C_2O_4^{2-}(aq)$	−825.1	−673.9	45.6	.
$C_2H_2(g)$	226.73	209.20	200.94	43.93
$1/n(C_2H_4)_n(c)$ polyethylene	.	.	.	.
$C_2H_4(g)$	52.26	68.15	219.56	43.56
$C_2H_6(g)$	−84.68	−32.82	229.60	52.63
$HC_2O_4^-(aq)$	−818.4	−698.34	149.4	.
$CH_2CO(g)$ ketene	−47.7	−48.5	247.63	51.76
$(COOH)_2(c)$	−827.2	(−701.2)	(120.1)	117.
$(COOH)_2(aq)$	−825.1	−673.9	45.6	.
$CH_3COO^-(aq)$ OAc$^-$	−486.01	−369.31	86.6	−6.3
$NH_4OAc(aq)$	−618.52	−488.61	200.0	73.6
$c\text{-}C_2H_4O(g)$	−52.63	−13.01	242.53	47.91
$CH_3CHO(l)$	−192.30	−128.12	160.2	.
$CH_3CHO(g)$	−166.19	−128.86	250.3	57.3
$CH_3COOH(l)$	−484.5	−389.9	159.8	124.3
$CH_3COOH(g)$	−432.25	−374.0	282.5	66.5
$CH_3COOH(aq)$ HOAc	−485.76	−396.46	178.7	.
$C_2H_5OH(l)$	−277.69	−174.78	160.7	111.46
$C_2H_5OH(g)$	−235.10	−168.49	282.70	65.44
$C_2H_5OH(aq)$	−288.3	−181.64	148.5	.
$CF_3COOH(l)$	−1068.	.	.	.

	$Hf°$ (kJ/mol)	$Gf°$ (kJ/mol)	$S°$ (J/K mol)	$Cp°$ (J/K mol)
$CH_2ClCOOH$(aq)	−496.40	.	.	.
CH_2ClCOO^-(aq)	−501.30	.	.	.
$CHCl_2COOH$(aq)	−503.8	.	.	.
$CHCl_2COO^-$(aq)	−512.1	.	.	.
CCl_3COOH(c)	−505.0	.	.	.
CCl_3COO^-(aq)	−516.3	.	.	.
$(CH_3)_2O$(l)	−203.	−109.	188.	110.
$(CH_3)_2O$(g)	−184.05	−112.59	266.38	64.39
$1/n(C_2F_4)_n$(c) teflon	−820.5	.	.	.
C_2F_4(g)	−650.6	−615.9	300.06	80.46
C_2F_6(g)	−1297.	−1213.	332.3	106.7
C_2Cl_4(g)	−12.1	22.6	341.1	94.93
C_2Cl_6(g)	−141.8	−57.7	398.8	136.8
$1/n(CH_2CHCl)_n$(c) polyv. chl.	−94.1	.	.	59.4
CH_2CHCl(l)	14.6	.	.	.
$C_2H_2Cl_4$(g) sym	−149.4	−81.9	362.82	100.79
C_2H_5Br(g)	−64.52	−26.48	286.71	64.52
C_2H_5I(g)	−7.70	19.17	306.0	66.9
$(CN)_2$(g)	308.95	297.36	241.90	56.82
CH_3CN(g)	65.23	82.58	245.12	52.22
CH_3NC(g)	155.44	149.0	246.92	52.93
CH_2NH_2COOH(c)	−528.10	−368.44	103.51	99.20
$NH_2CH_2CH_2NH_2$(l) en	(24.35)	.	.	(209.)
$NH_2CH_2CH_2NH_2$(200 H_2O)	−155.73	.	.	.
C_3H_4(g) allene	192.1	202.4	244.0	.
c-C_3H_4(g)	276.	286.3	244.3	.
$(CH_3)_2SO$(l)	−203.	−99.2	188.	147.
$(CH_3)_2SO_2$(g)	−371.	−273.	310.	100.
c-C_3H_6(g)	20.41	62.72	266.9	63.89
$(CH_3)_2CO$(l)	−248.	−155.4	200.	.
C_3H_8(g)	−103.8	−23.5	269.9	73.51
$CH_2OHCHOHCH_2OH$(l)	−670.7	−479.5	205.	217.
C_4H_6(g) 1,3-butadiene	110.2	150.7	278.7	.
c-C_4H_6(g)	129.7	174.7	263.5	.
c-C_4H_8(g)	27.2	110.7	265.4	72.22
n-C_4H_{10}(g)	−126.1	−17.2	310.1	.
i-C_4H_{10}(g)	−134.5	−20.9	294.6	.
$(C_2H_5)_2O$(g)	−252.1	−121.8	341.	117.
$(C_2H_5)_2O$(l)	−279.6	−122.7	252.	173.1
c-C_5H_6(g)	133.9	179.3	267.8	.
c-C_5H_{10}(g)	−77.03	38.9	292.9	82.93
c-$C_5H_5N_5$(g)	140.37	190.48	282.8	78.12
c-C_5H_5N(l)	100.	181.3	177.9	.

	$H_f°$ (kJ/mol)	$G_f°$ (kJ/mol)	$S°$ (J/K mol)	$C_P°$ (J/K mol)
c-C_6H_6(l)	49.04	124.3	173.3	.
c-C_6H_6(g)	82.93	129.66	269.2	81.67
$C_6H_8O_7$(aq) citric acid	1525.9	–1244.2	329.	320.
$C_6H_7O_7^-$(aq)	–1521.	–1226.3	286.	188.
$C_6H_6O_7^{2-}$(aq)	–1518.5	–1199.2	203.	0.84
$C_6H_5O_7^{3-}$(aq)	–1515.1	–1162.7	92.0	–255.
c-C_6H_{10}(l)	–38.8	101.6	216.2	.
c-C_6H_{10}(g)	–5.36	106.9	310.7	.
c-C_6H_{12}(l)	_156.2	26.7	204.3	.
c-C_6H_{12}(g)	–123.1	31.8	298.2	106.3
c-C_6H_5OH(c)	–166.65	–51.80	143.45	126.77
$C_6H_{12}O_6$(c) d-glucose	–1274.4	–910.56	212.	.
$C_6H_{12}O_6$(c) d-galactose	1285.4	–919.43	205.	.
n-C_8H_{18}(l)	–250.3	6.12	361.1	254.1
$C_{10}H_{16}O_8N_2$(c) EDTA	–1759.	.	.	
$C_{12}H_{22}O_{11}$(c) sucrose	–2222.	–1544.	360.	.

SILICON				
Si(c)	0.0	0.0	18.83	20.00
Si(g)	455.6	411.3	167.97	22.25
SiO(g)	–99.6	–126.4	211.61	29.92
SiO_2(c)quartz	–910.94	–854.64	41.84	44.43
SiH_4(g)	34.3	56.9	204.62	42.84
Si_2H_6(g)	80.3	127.3	272.66	80.79
H_4SiO_4(c)	–1481.1	–1332.9	192.	.
SiF_4(g)	–1614.94	–1572.65	282.49	63.64
SiF_6^{2-}(aq)	–2389.1	–2199.4	122.2	.
$SiCl_4$(l)	–687.0	–619.84	239.7	145.31
$SiCl_4$(g)	–657.01	–616.98	330.73	90.25
SiC(c, hexagonal, alpha)	–62.8	–60.2	16.48	26.69
SiC(c, cubic, beta)	–65.3	–62.8	16.61	26.86
$(CH_3)_4Si$(l) TMS	–264.	–100.	277.27	204.10
$(CH_3)_3SiCl$(l)	–382.8	–246.40	278.2	.

GERMANIUM				
Ge(c)	0.0	0.0	31.09	23.47
Ge(g)	276.6	335.9	167.90	30.73
GeO(g)	–46.19	–73.19	224.29	30.92
GeO_2(c, hexagonal)	–551.0	–497.0	55.27	52.09
GeO_2(c, tetragonal)	–580.2	.	39.71	.
GeH_4(g)	90.8	113.4	217.13	45.02
Ge_2H_6(l)	137.32	.	.	.
GeF_4(g)	–1190.15	.	302.86	81.84
$GeCl_4$(l)	–531.8	–462.7	245.6	.

	Hf° (kJ/mol)	Gf° (kJ/mol)	S° (J/K mol)	Cp° (J/K mol)
TIN				
Sn(c, white, metallic)	0.0	0.0	51.55	26.99
Sn(c,gray)	−2.09	0.13	44.14	25.77
Sn(g)	302.1	267.3	168.49	21.59
Sn^{2+}(aq)	−8.8	−27.2	−17.	.
SnO(c)	−285.8	−256.9	56.5	44.31
SnO_2(c)	−580.7	−519.6	52.3	52.59
$Sn(OH)_2$(c)	−561.1	−491.6	155.	.
$Sn(OH)_6^{2-}$(aq)	.	(−1299.)	.	.
SnF_4(c)	.	.	.	.
SnF_6^{2-}(aq)	−1986.	−1757.	(0.)	.
$SnCl_2$(c)	−325.1	.	(123.)	.
$SnCl_4$(l)	−511.3	−440.1	258.6	165.3
$SnCl_6^{2-}$(aq)	−970.3	.	.	.
SnS(c)	−100.	−98.3	77.0	49.25
SnS_2(c)	.	.	87.4	70.12
LEAD				
Pb(c)	0.0	0.0	64.81	26.44
Pb(g)	195.0	161.9	175.37	20.86
Pb^{2+}(aq)	−1.7	−24.43	10.5	.
PbO(c, yellow)	−217.32	−187.89	68.70	45.77
PbO(c, red)	−218.99	−189.93	66.5	45.81
PbO_2(c)	−277.4	−217.33	68.6	64.64
$HPbO_2^-$(aq)	.	−338.42	.	.
$Pb(OH)_2$(c)	.	−452.2	.	.
Pb_3O_4(c)	−718.4	−601.2	211.3	146.9
PbF_2(c, alpha)	−676.97	−630.88	112.97	72.26
PbF_2(c, beta)	−675.99	−630.32	114.40	74.27
$PbCl^+$(aq)	.	−164.81	.	.
$PbCl_2$(c)	−359.41	−314.10	136.0	77.07
$PbCl_3^-$(aq)	.	−426.3	.	.
$PbCl_4$(l)	−329.3	.	.	.
$PbBr_2$(c)	−278.7	−261.92	161.5	80.12
PbI_2(c)	−175.48	−173.64	174.85	77.36
PbS(c)	−100.4	−98.7	91.2	49.50
$PbSO_4$(c)	−919.94	−813.14	148.57	103.07
$Pb(NO_3)_2$(c)	−451.9	.	.	.
$PbCO_3$(c)	−699.1	−625.5	131.0	87.40
PbC_2O_4(c)	−851.4	−750.1	146.0	105.4
$Pb(CH_3)_4$(l)	97.9	.	.	.
$Pb(C_2H_5)_4$(l)	52.7	.	.	.

	$H_f°$ (kJ/mol)	$G_f°$ (kJ/mol)	$S°$ (J/K mol)	$C_P°$ (J/K mol)
BORON				
B(c)	0.0	0.0	5.86	11.09
B(g)	562.7	518.8	153.45	20.80
B_2O_3(c)	−1272.7	−1193.65	53.97	62.93
BO_2^-(aq)	−772.37	−678.89	−37.2	·
BH_3(g)	100.	·	·	·
BH_4^-(aq)	48.16	114.35	110.5	·
B_2H_6(g)	35.6	86.7	232.11	56.90
B_4H_{10}(g)	66.1	·	·	·
B_5H_9(g)	73.2	175.0	275.92	96.78
HBO_2(c, monoclinic)	−794.25	−723.4	38.	54.4
HBO_2(c, orthorhombic)	−788.77	−721.7	50.	54.4
H_3BO_3(aq)	−1072.32	−968.75	162.3	·
H_3BO_3(c)	−1094.33	−968.92	88.83	81.38
$B(OH)_4^-$(aq)	−1344.03	−1153.17	102.5	·
BF_3(g)	−1137.00	−1120.33	254.12	50.46
BF_4^-(aq)	−1574.9	−1486.9	180.	·
BCl_3(l)	−427.2	−387.4	206.3	106.7
BCl_3(g)	−403.76	−388.72	290.10	62.72
BCl_4^-(aq)	·	·	·	·
B_2Cl_4(l)	−523.0	−464.8	262.3	137.7
BBr_3(l)	−239.7	−238.5	229.7	128.
BBr_3(g)	−205.64	−232.50	324.24	67.78
BN(c)	−254.4	−228.4	14.81	19.71
ALUMINUM				
Al(c)	0.0	0.0	28.33	24.35
Al(g)	326.4	285.7	164.54	21.38
Al^{3+}(aq)	−531.	−485.	−321.7	·
AlO_2^-(aq)	−930.9	−830.9	−36.8	·
Al_2O_3(c, alpha)	−1675.7	−1582.3	50.92	79.04
$Al(OH)_3$(amorphous)	−1276.	·	·	·
$Al(OH)_4^-$(aq)	−1502.5	−1305.3	102.9	·
AlF_3(c)	−1504.1	−1425.0	66.44	75.10
AlF_6^{3-}(aq)	−2522.5	·	(−167.)	·
$AlCl_3$(c)	−784.2	−628.8	110.67	91.84
Al_2Cl_6(g)	−1290.8	−1220.4	490.	·
$AlCl_4^-$(aq)	·	·	·	·
$AlBr_3$(c)	−511.28	−488.52	180.22	100.56
$Al_2(SO_4)_3$(c)	−3440.84	−3099.94	239.3	259.41
$Al_2(SO_4)_3·6H_2O$(c)	−5311.71	−4622.08	469.0	492.9
$Al(NO_3)_3·6H_2O$(c)	−2850.48	−2203.39	467.8	433.0
$(NH_4)Al(SO_4)_2·12H_2O$(c)	−5941.37	−4937.20	697.1	683.2
Al_4C_3(c)	−208.8	−196.2	88.95	116.78

	$Hf°$ (kJ/mol)	$Gf°$ (kJ/mol)	$S°$ (J/K mol)	$Cp°$ (J/K mol)
GALLIUM				
Ga(c)	0.0	0.0	40.88	25.86
Ga(l)	5.56	.	.	.
Ga(g)	277.0	238.9	169.06	25.36
Ga^{3+}(aq)	–211.7	–159.0	–331.	.
GaO(g)	279.5	253.5	231.1	32.05
Ga_2O_3(c, rhombic)	–1089.1	–998.3	84.98	92.05
GaF_3(c)	–1163.	–1085.3	84.	.
$GaCl_3$(c)	–524.7	–454.8	142.	.
GaN(c)	–110.5	.	.	.
GaAs(c)	–71.	–67.8	64.18	46.23
INDIUM				
In(c)	0.0	0.0	57.82	26.74
In(g)	243.30	208.71	173.79	20.84
In^{3+}(aq)	–105.	–98.0	–151.	.
InO(g)	387.0	364.4	236.5	32.55
In_2O_3(c)	–925.79	–830.68	104.2	92.
InF(g)	–203.38	.	.	.
InF_3(c)	.	.	.	.
$InCl_3$(c)	–537.2	.	(138.)	.
THALLIUM				
Tl(c)	0.0	0.0	64.18	26.32
Tl(g)	182.21	147.41	180.96	20.86
Tl^+(aq)	5.36	–32.40	125.5	.
Tl^{3+}(aq)	196.6	214.6	–192.	.
Tl_2O(c)	–178.7	–147.3	126.	.
Tl_2O_3(c)	.	–311.7	.	.
Tl(OH)(c)	–238.9	–195.8	88.	.
$Tl(OH)_3$(c)	.	–507.0	.	.
TlF(c)	–324.7	.	.	.
TlF_3(c)	(–732.)	(–665.)	.	.
TlCl(c)	–204.14	–184.92	111.25	50.92
TlCl(g)	–67.8	.	(256.)	(36.2)
$TlCl_3$(aq, undissoc.)	–351.5	–274.4	134.	.
TlBr(c)	–173.2	–167.36	120.5	.
TlBr(g)	–37.7	.	(267.)	(36.9)
TlI(c)	–123.8	–125.39	127.6	.
TlI(g)	7.1	.	(274.)	(37.1)

	$H_f°$ (kJ/mol)	$G_f°$ (kJ/mol)	$S°$ (J/K mol)	$C_P°$ (J/K mol)
ZINC				
$Zn(c)$	0.0	0.0	41.63	25.40
$Zn(g)$	130.73	95.14	160.98	20.86
$Zn^{2+}(aq)$	−153.89	−147.06	−112.1	46.
$ZnO(c)$	−348.28	−318.30	43.64	40.25
$Zn(OH)_2(c,beta)$	−641.91	−553.52	81.2	(72.4)
$Zn(OH)_4^{2-}(aq)$	.	−858.52	.	.
$ZnF_2(c)$	−764.4	−713.3	73.68	65.65
$ZnCl_2(c)$	−415.05	−369.40	111.46	71.34
$ZnCl_4^{2-}(aq)$	.	−666.0	.	.
$ZnBr_2(c)$	−328.65	−312.13	138.5	.
$ZnS(c, wurtzite)$	−192.63	.	.	.
$ZnS(c, sphalerite)$	−205.98	−201.29	57.7	46.0
$ZnSO_4(c)$	−982.8	−871.5	110.5	99.2
$ZnSO_4 \cdot 7H_2O(c)$	−3077.75	−2562.07	388.7	383.42
$Zn(NO_3)_2(c)$	−483.7	.	.	.
$Zn(NH_3)_4^{2+}(aq)$	−533.5	−301.9	301.	.
$ZnCO_3(c)$	−812.78	−731.52	82.4	79.71
$Zn(CN)_2(c)$	95.8	.	(95.8)	.
$Zn(CN)_4^{2-}(aq)$	342.3	446.9	226.	.
$Zn(en)^{2+}(aq)$	237.7	.	.	.
$Zn(en)_2^{2+}(aq)$	−323.0	.	.	.
$Zn(en)_3^{2+}(aq)$	−407.5	.	.	.
CADMIUM				
$Cd(c, gamma)$	0.0	0.0	51.76	25.98
$Cd(g)$	112.1	77.41	167.75	20.86
$Cd^{2+}(aq)$	−75.90	−77.61	−73.2	.
$CdO(c)$	−258.2	−228.4	54.8	43.43
$Cd(OH)_2(c)$	−560.7	−473.6	96.	.
$CdF_2(c)$	−700.4	−647.7	77.4	.
$CdCl^+(aq)$	−240.6	−224.39	43.5	.
$CdCl_2(c)$	−391.5	−343.93	115.27	74.68
$CdCl_2(aq, undissoc.)$	−405.0	−359.29	121.8	.
$CdCl_3^-(aq)$	−561.1	−487.0	202.9	.
$CdS(c)$	−162.	−156.	64.9	.
$CdSO_4(c)$	−933.28	−822.72	123.39	99.58
$CdSO_4 \cdot H_2O(c)$	−1239.55	−1068.73	154.03	134.56
$CdSO_4 \cdot 8/3H_2O(c)$	−1729.4	−1465.14	229.63	213.26
$Cd(NO_3)_2 \cdot 4H_2O(c)$	−1648.96	.	.	.
$Cd(NH_3)_4^{2+}(aq)$	−450.2	−226.1	336.4	.
$Cd(CN)_2(c)$	162.3	.	(104.)	.
$Cd(CN)_4^{2-}(aq)$	428.0	507.6	322.	.
$Cd(en)_2^{2+}(aq)$	−243.5	.	.	.

	$Hf°$ (kJ/mol)	$Gf°$ (kJ/mol)	$S°$ (J/K mol)	$Cp°$ (J/K mol)
MERCURY				
$Hg(l)$	0.0	0.0	76.02	27.98
$Hg(g)$	61.32	31.82	174.96	20.79
$Hg^{2+}(aq)$	171.1	163.40	−32.2	·
$Hg_2^{2+}(aq)$	172.4	153.52	84.5	·
$HgO(c, red)$	−90.83	−58.54	70.29	44.06
$HgO(c, yellow)$	−90.85	−58.41	71.1	44.06
$HgF(g)$	4.2	−17.2	248.56	34.56
$HgCl_2(c)$	−224.3	−178.6	146.0	·
$HgCl_4^{2-}(aq)$	−554.0	−446.8	293.	·
$Hg_2Cl_2(c)$	−265.22	−210.74	192.5	(102.)
$Hg_2Br_2(c)$	−206.90	−181.75	218.	·
$HgI^+(aq)$	43.1	39.7	79.	·
$HgI_2(c, red)$	−105.4	101.7	180.	77.75
$HgI_2(c, yellow)$	−102.9	·	·	·
$HgI_4^{2-}(aq)$	−235.1	−211.7	360.	·
$Hg_2I_2(c)$	−121.34	−111.00	233.5	106.
$HgS(c, red)$	−58.2	−50.6	82.4	48.41
$HgS(c, black)$	−53.6	−47.7	88.3	·
$HgSO_4(c)$	−707.5	·	·	·
$Hg_2SO_4(c)$	−743.12	−625.15	200.66	131.96
$Hg(NO_3)_2·1/2H_2O(c)$	−392.5	·	·	·
$Hg_2(NO_3)_2·2H_2O(c)$	−868.2	·	·	·
$Hg(CH_3)_2(l)$	59.8	140.3	209.	·
$Hg(CN)_2(c)$	263.6	(311.)	(115.)	·
$Hg(CN)_4^{2-}(aq)$	526.3	618.5	305.	·
COPPER				
$Cu(c)$	0.0	0.0	33.15	24.44
$Cu(g)$	338.32	298.58	166.38	20.86
$Cu^+(aq)$	71.67	49.98	40.6	·
$Cu^{2+}(aq)$	64.77	65.49	−99.6	·
$CuO(c)$	−157.3	−129.7	42.63	42.30
$Cu_2O(c)$	−168.6	−146.0	93.14	63.64
$Cu(OH)_2(c)$	−450.37	−372.66	108.37	95.19
$CuF_2(c)$	−542.7	·	·	·
$CuCl(c)$	−137.2	−119.86	86.2	48.5
$CuCl_2(c)$	−220.1	−175.7	108.07	71.88
$CuCl_2^-(aq)$	·	−240.1	·	·
$CuI(c)$	−67.8	−69.5	96.7	54.06
$CuS(c)$	−53.1	−53.6	66.5	47.82
$Cu_2S(c)$	−79.5	−86.2	120.9	76.32
$CuSO_4(c)$	−771.36	−661.8	109.2	100.0

	$Hf°$ (kJ/mol)	$Gf°$ (kJ/mol)	$S°$ (J/K mol)	$Cp°$ (J/K mol)
$CuSO_4 \cdot H_2O(c)$	−1085.8	−918.11	146.0	134.
$CuSO_4 \cdot 3H_2O(c)$	−1684.31	−1399.96	221.3	205.
$CuSO_4 \cdot 5H_2O(c)$	−2279.65	−1879.45	300.4	280.
$Cu(NO_3)_2(c)$	−302.9	.	.	.
$Cu(NH_3)_4^{2+}(aq)$	−348.5	−111.07	273.6	.
$CuCN(c)$	96.2	111.3	84.5	.
$Cu(CN)_2^{-}(aq)$	.	257.8	.	.
$Cu(en)^{2+}(aq)$	−44.4	.	.	.
$Cu(en)_2^{2+}(aq)$	−151.9	.	.	.

SILVER

	$Hf°$ (kJ/mol)	$Gf°$ (kJ/mol)	$S°$ (J/K mol)	$Cp°$ (J/K mol)
$Ag(c)$	0.0	0.0	42.55	25.35
$Ag(g)$	284.55	245.65	173.00	20.86
$Ag^+(aq)$	105.58	77.07	72.68	21.8
$Ag^{2+}(aq)$	268.6	269.0	−88.	.
$Ag_2O(c)$	−31.05	−11.20	121.3	65.86
$Ag_2O_3(c)$	33.9	121.4	100.	.
$AgF(c)$	−204.6	.	.	.
$AgF_2(c)$	−360.	.	.	.
$AgCl(c)$	−127.07	−109.79	96.2	50.79
$AgCl(aq, undissoc.)$	−72.8	−72.8	154.0	.
$AgCl_2^{-}(aq)$	−245.2	−215.4	231.4	.
$AgClO_3(c)$	−30.29	64.5	142.	.
$AgClO_4(c)$	31.13	.	.	.
$AgBr(c)$	−100.37	−96.90	107.1	52.38
$AgBrO_3(c)$	−10.5	71.34	151.9	.
$AgI(c)$	−61.84	−66.19	115.5	56.82
$AgIO_3(c)$	−171.1	−93.7	149.4	102.93
$Ag_2S(c, ortho. rhomb., alpha)$	−32.59	−40.67	144.01	76.53
$Ag_2S(c, beta)$	−29.41	−39.46	150.6	.
$Ag(S_2O_3)_2^{3-}(aq)$	−1285.7	.	.	.
$Ag_2SO_4(c)$	−715.88	−618.41	200.4	131.38
$AgN_3(c)$	308.8	376.2	104.2	.
$AgNO_2(c)$	−45.06	19.13	128.20	80.21
$AgNO_3(c)$	−124.39	−33.41	140.92	93.05
$Ag(NH_3)_2^{+}(aq)$	−111.29	−17.12	245.2	.
$Ag_2CO_3(c)$	−505.8	−436.8	167.4	112.26
$Ag_2C_2O_4(c)$	−673.2	−584.0	209.	.
$AgOAc(c)$	−398.7	−307.69	149.8	.
$AgCN(c)$	146.0	156.9	107.19	66.73
$Ag(CN)_2^{-}(aq)$	270.3	305.5	192.	.

	H_f° (kJ/mol)	G_f° (kJ/mol)	S° (J/K mol)	C_P° (J/K mol)
GOLD				
Au(c)	0.0	0.0	47.40	25.42
Ag(g)	366.1	326.3	180.50	20.79
Au^+(aq)	.	(163.)	.	.
Au^{3+}(aq)	.	(434.)	.	.
AuO_3^{3-}(aq)	.	−51.8	.	.
$HAuO_3^{2-}$(aq)	.	−142.2	.	.
$H_2AuO_3^-$(aq)	.	−218.3	.	.
$Au(OH)_3$(c)	−424.7	−316.92	189.5	.
AuF_3(c)	−363.6	.	.	.
AuCl(c)	−34.7	.	(100.4)	.
$AuCl_2^-$(aq)	.	−151.12	.	.
$AuCl_3$(c)	−117.6	.	(146.)	.
$AuCl_4^-$(aq)	−322.2	−235.14	266.9	.
$AuBr_4^-$(aq)	−191.6	−167.3	336.0	.
$Au(CN)_2^-$(aq)	242.3	285.8	172.	.
NICKEL				
Ni(c)	0.0	0.0	29.87	26.07
Ni(g)	429.7	384.5	182.19	23.59
Ni^{2+}(aq)	−54.0	−45.6	−128.9	.
NiO(c)	−239.7	−211.7	37.99	44.31
Ni_2O_3(c)	−489.5	.	.	.
$Ni(OH)_2$(c)	−529.7	−447.2	88.	.
$Ni(OH)_3$(c)	−669.	.	(81.6)	.
NiF_2(c)	−651.4	−604.1	73.60	64.06
$NiCl_2$(c)	−305.32	−259.32	97.65	71.67
NiS(c)	−82.0	−79.5	52.97	45.11
$NiSO_4$(c)	−872.91	−759.7	92.	138.
$NiSO_4 \cdot 6H_2O$(c, green)	−2682.82	−2224.61	334.47	327.86
$Ni(NO_3)_2$(c)	−415.1	.	.	.
$Ni(NH_3)_6^{2+}$(aq)	−630.1	−255.7	394.6	.
$Ni(CN)_4^{2-}$(aq)	367.8	472.1	218.	.
$Ni(C_5H_5)_2$(g)	333.1	434.43	.	.
$Ni(en)^{2+}$(aq)	−147.3	.	.	.
$Ni(en)_2^{2+}$(aq)	−240.2	.	.	.
$Ni(en)_3^{2+}$(aq)	−338.1	.	.	.
$Ni(en)_3Cl_2$(c)	−661.1	.	.	.
$Ni(en)_3Cl_2 \cdot 2H_2O$(c)	−1276.1	.	.	.

	$H_f°$ (kJ/mol)	$G_f°$ (kJ/mol)	$S°$ (J/K mol)	$C_P°$ (J/K mol)
COBALT				
Co(c, hexagonal)	0.0	0.0	30.04	24.81
Co(g)	424.7	380.3	179.51	23.02
Co^{2+}(aq)	−58.2	−54.4	−113.	.
Co^{3+}(aq)	92.	134.	−305.	.
CoO(c)	−237.94	−214.20	53.97	55.23
Co_3O_4(c)	−891.	−774.	102.5	123.4
$Co(OH)_2$(c, pink)	−539.7	−454.3	79.	.
$Co(OH)_3$(c)	−716.7	.	(83.7)	.
CoF_2(c)	−692.0	−647.2	81.96	68.78
CoF(c)	−790.36	−718.89	94.56	91.80
$CoCl_2$(c)	−312.5	−269.8	109.16	78.49
$CoCl_2 \cdot H_2O$(c)	−615.	.	.	.
$CoCl_4^{2-}$(aq)	.	.	.	.
CoS(c)	−82.8	.	(67.4)	.
$CoSO_4$(c)	−888.3	−782.53	118.0	103.2
$Co(NO_3)_2$(c)	−420.5	.	(192.)	.
$Co(NH_3)_4^{2+}$(aq)	−145.2	−92.4	13.	.
$Co(NH_3)_6^{3+}$(aq)	−584.9	−157.0	146.	.
$Co(NH_3)_5Cl^{2+}$(aq)	−628.0	−291.7	341.4	.
$Co(CN)_6^{3-}$(aq)	.	.	232.6	.
$Co(en)_3^{2+}$(aq)	−318.0	.	.	.
$Co(en)_3^{3+}$(aq)	−303.8	.	.	.
IRON				
Fe(c)	0.0	0.0	27.28	25.10
Fe(g)	416.3	370.7	180.49	25.68
Fe^{2+}(aq)	−89.1	−78.90	−137.7	.
Fe^{3+}(aq)	−48.5	−4.7	−315.9	.
Fe_2O_3(c, hematite)	−824.2	−742.2	87.40	103.85
Fe_3O_4(c, magnetite)	−1118.4	−1015.4	146.4	143.43
$Fe(OH)^+$(aq)	−290.8	−229.41	−142.	.
$Fe(OH)_2$(c)	−569.0	−486.5	88.	.
$Fe(OH)_2^+$(aq)	.	438.0	.	.
$Fe(OH)_3$(c)	−823.0	−696.5	106.7	.
FeF_3(c)	−1041.82	−972.29	98.32	91.00
$FeCl^{2+}$(aq)	−180.3	−143.9	−113.	.
$FeCl_3$(c)	−399.49	−334.00	142.3	96.65
$FeCl_3 \cdot 6H_2O$(c)	−2223.8	.	.	.
$FeBr^{2+}$(aq)	−144.8	−112.2	−138.	.
FeS(c)	−100.0	−100.4	60.29	50.54
FeS_2(c, pyrite)	−178.2	−166.9	52.93	62.17
$FeSO_4$(c)	−928.4	−820.8	107.5	100.58
$FeSO_4 \cdot 7H_2O$(c)	−3014.57	−2509.87	409.2	394.47

	H_f° (kJ/mol)	G_f° (kJ/mol)	S° (J/K mol)	C_p° (J/K mol)
$FeNO^{2+}(aq)$	−9.2	82.8	−213.	.
$Fe(NO_3)_3 \cdot 9H_2O(c)$	−3285.3	.	.	.
$FeSO_4 \cdot NH_3(c)$	−1060.2	.	.	.
$FeSO_4 \cdot 2NH_3(c)$	−1181.1	.	.	.
$FeSO_4 \cdot 6NH_3(c)$	−1587.8	.	.	.
$Fe_3C(c, \text{cementite})$	25.1	20.1	104.6	105.9
$Fe(CO)_5(l)$	−774.0	−705.3	338.1	240.6
$Fe(C_5H_5)_2(g)$	211.8	318.1	.	.
$Fe(phen)_3^{2+}(aq)$	.	.	.	.
$Fe(phen)_3^{3+}(aq)$	.	.	.	.
$Fe(CN)_6^{3-}(aq)$	561.9	729.4	270.3	.
$Fe(CN)_6^{4-}(aq)$	455.6	695.08	95.0	.
$Fe(SCN)^{2+}(aq)$	23.4	71.1	−130.	.
$Fe_2SiO4(c)$	−1479.9	−1379.0	145.2	132.88
$Ag_4Fe(CN)_6 \cdot H_2O(c)$	.	514.8	.	.

PALLADIUM

	H_f° (kJ/mol)	G_f° (kJ/mol)	S° (J/K mol)	C_p° (J/K mol)
$Pd(c)$	0.0	0.0	37.57	25.98
$Pd(g)$	378.2	339.7	167.05	20.86
$Pd^{2+}(aq)$	149.0	176.5	−184.	.
$PdO(g)$	348.9	325.9	218.	.
$PdF_4(c)$	.	.	.	.
$PdCl^+(aq)$	−38.	22.6	−117.	.
$PdCl_2(c)$	−198.7	.	.	.
$PdCl_4^{2-}(aq, 1M\ HCl)$	−550.2	−417.1	167.	.
$PdCl_6^{2-}(aq, 1M\ HCl)$	−598.	−430.0	272.	.

PLATINUM

	H_f° (kJ/mol)	G_f° (kJ/mol)	S° (J/K mol)	C_p° (J/K mol)
$Pt(c)$	0.0	0.0	41.63	25.86
$Pt(g)$	565.3	520.5	192.41	25.53
$Pt^{2+}(aq)$	.	254.8	.	.
$PtO_2(g)$	171.5	167.8	.	.
$Pt_3O_4(c)$	−163.	.	.	.
$Pt(OH)_2(c)$	−351.9	.	(111.)	.
$PtF_6(c)$	.	.	235.6	.
$PtCl_2(c)$	−123.4	.	(131.)	.
$PtCl_4^{2-}(aq)$	−499.2	−361.4	155.	.
$PtCl_6^{2-}(aq)$	−668.2	−482.7	219.7	.
$Pt(NH_3)_4^{2+}(aq)$	−361.9	−52.9	42.	.
$Pt(CN)_4^{2-}(aq)$	.	710.5	.	.

	$H_f°$ (kJ/mol)	$G_f°$ (kJ/mol)	$S°$ (J/K mol)	$C_P°$ (J/K mol)
MANGANESE				
Mn(c, alpha)	0.0	0.0	32.01	26.32
Mn(g)	280.7	238.5	173.70	20.79
Mn^{2+}(aq)	−220.75	−228.1	−73.6	50.
MnO(c)	−385.22	−362.90	59.71	45.44
MnO_2(c)	−520.03	−465.14	53.05	54.14
MnO_4^-(aq)	−541.4	−447.2	191.2	−82.0
MnO_4^{2-}(aq)	−653.	−500.87	59.	.
Mn_2O_3(c)	−959.0	−881.1	110.5	107.65
Mn_3O_4(c)	−1387.8	−1283.2	155.6	139.66
$Mn(OH)_2$(amorphous)	−695.4	−615.0	99.2	.
$Mn(OH)_3^-$(aq)	.	−744.2	.	.
MnF_2(c)	−854.4	.	92.26	66.78
$MnCl_2·H_2O$(c)	−789.9	−696.1	174.1	.
MnS(c, green)	−214.2	−218.4	78.2	49.96
MnS(amorphous, pink)	−213.8	.	.	49.96
$MnSO_4$(c)	−1065.25	−957.36	112.1	100.5
$Mn_2(CO)_{10}$(c)	−1677.8	.	.	.
$MnCO_3$(c)	−894.1	−816.7	85.8	81.50
$Mn(CN)_6^{4-}$(aq)	556.	.	.	.
$Mn(en)^{2+}$(aq)	−288.3	.	.	.
$Mn(en)_2^{2+}$(aq)	−357.3	.	.	.
$Mn(en)_3^{2+}$(aq)	−434.3	.	.	.
CHROMIUM				
Cr(c)	0.0	0.0	23.77	23.35
Cr(g)	396.6	351.8	174.50	20.79
Cr^{2+}(aq)	−143.5	.	.	.
Cr^{3+}(aq)	.	(−215.)	(−308.)	.
CrO_3(c)	−589.5	.	.	.
CrO_4^{2-}(aq)	−881.15	−727.75	50.21	.
Cr_2O_3(c)	−1139.7	−1058.1	81.12	118.74
$Cr_2O_7^{2-}$(aq)	−1490.3	−1301.1	261.9	.
$HCrO_4^-$(aq)	−878.2	−764.7	184.1	.
$Cr(OH)_3$(c)	−1064.0	.	(80.3)	.
CrF_2(c)	−778.	.	(82.0)	.
CrF_3(c)	−1159.	−1088.	93.89	78.74
$CrCl_2$(c)	−395.4	−356.0	115.31	71.17
$CrCl_3$(c)	−556.5	−486.1	123.0	91.80
$Cr(CO)_6$(c)	−1077.0	.	.	.
$Cr(C_6H_6)_2$(c)	150.	.	.	.
$PbCrO_4$(c)	−930.9	.	153.68	.
Ag_2CrO_4(c)	−731.74	−641.76	217.6	142.26

	$Hf°$ (kJ/mol)	$Gf°$ (kJ/mol)	$S°$ (J/K mol)	$Cp°$ (J/K mol)
MOLYBDENUM				
Mo(c)	0.0	0.0	28.66	24.06
Mo(g)	658.1	612.5	181.95	20.86
MoO_2(c)	−588.94	−533.01	46.28	55.98
MoO_3(c)	−745.09	−667.97	77.74	74.98
MoO_4^{2-}(aq)	−997.9	−836.3	27.2	.
MoF_6(l)	−1585.53	−1473.00	259.66	169.79
MoF_6(g)	−1557.66	−1472.20	350.52	120.58
$MoCl_3$(c)	−387.0	.	(138.)	.
$MoCl_4$(c)	−480.3	.	(187.)	.
$MoCl_5$(c)	−527.2	.	(222.)	.
$Mo(CO)_6$(c)	−982.8	−877.7	325.9	242.25
$PbMoO_4$(c)	−1051.9	−951.4	166.1	119.70
Ag_2MoO_4(c)	−840.6	−748.0	213.	.
TUNGSTEN(WOLFRAM)				
W(c)	0.0	0.0	32.64	24.27
W(g)	849.4	807.1	173.95	21.09
WO_2(c)	−589.69	−533.89	50.54	56.11
WO_3(c)	−842.87	−764.03	75.90	73.76
WO_4^{2-}(aq)	−1075.7	−914.3	40.7	.
WF_6(l)	−1747.7	−1631.37	251.5	.
WF_6(g)	−1721.7	−1632.1	341.06	119.03
WCl_6(c)	−602.5	.	(289.)	.
W_2C(c)	−26.4	.	.	.
$W(CO)_6$(c)	−953.5	.	.	.
VANADIUM				
V(c)	0.0	0.0	28.91	24.89
V(g)	515.21	754.43	182.23	26.01
V^{2+}(aq)	.	(−229.)	.	.
V^{3+}(aq)	.	(−254.)	.	.
VO^{2+}(aq)	−486.6	−446.4	−133.9	.
VO_2^+(aq)	−649.8	−587.0	−42.3	.
VO_3^-(aq)	−888.3	−783.6	50.	.
V_2O_3(c)	−1218.8	−1139.03	98.3	103.22
V_2O_4(c, alpha)	−1427.2	−1318.3	102.5	116.98
V_2O_5(c)	−1550.6	−1419.5	131.0	127.65
VF_5(l)	−1480.3	−1373.1	175.7	.
VCl_2(c)	−452.	−406.	97.1	72.22
VCl_3(c)	−580.7	−511.2	131.0	93.18
VCl_4(l)	−569.4	−403.7	255.	.
NH_4VO_3(c)	−1053.1	−888.1	140.6	129.33
$V(CO)_6$(g)	−987.	.	.	.

	$H_f°$ (kJ/mol)	$G_f°$ (kJ/mol)	$S°$ (J/K mol)	$C_P°$ (J/K mol)
TITANIUM				
Ti(c)	0.0	0.0	30.63	25.02
Ti(g)	469.9	425.1	180.30	24.43
TiO_2(c, rutile)	−944.7	−889.45	50.33	55.02
Ti_2O_3(c)	−1520.9	−1434.2	78.78	95.36
TiF_4(amorphous)	−1649.3	−1559.3	133.97	114.27
$TiCl_2$(c)	−513.8	−464.4	87.4	69.83
$TiCl_3$(c)	720.9	−653.5	139.7	97.15
$TiCl_4$(l)	−804.2	−737.2	252.34	145.18
EUROPIUM				
Eu(c)	0.0	0.0	77.78	27.66
Eu(g)	175.3	142.2	188.80	20.80
Eu^{2+}(aq)	−527.	−540.2	−8.	.
Eu^{3+}(aq)	−605.0	−574.1	−222.	8.
EuO(c)	−592.0	−556.9	63.	.
Eu_2O_3(c, monoclinic)	−1651.4	−1556.8	146.	122.2
$Eu(OH)_3$(c)	.	−1194.4	.	.
EuF(g)	−293.	.	.	.
EuF_3(c)	.	.	.	.
$EuCl^{2+}$(aq)	−772.4	−710.5	−151.	.
$EuCl_2^+$(aq)	.	−837.6	.	.
$EuCl_3$(c)	−936.0	.	.	.
$EuSO_4^+$(aq)	−1499.1	−1338.8	−84.	.
$Eu(SO_4)_2^-$(aq)	−2402.0	−2093.5	−8.	.
$Eu_2(SO_4)_3 \cdot 8H_2O$(c)	.	.	672.0	610.9
CERIUM				
Ce(c)	0.0	0.0	72.0	26.94
Ce(g)	423.	385.	191.77	23.08
Ce^{3+}(aq)	−696.2	−672.0	−205.	.
Ce^{4+}(aq)	−537.2	−503.8	−301.	.
CeO_2(c)	−1088.7	−1024.6	62.30	61.63
Ce_2O_3(c)	−1796.2	−1706.2	150.6	114.6
CeF_3(c)	.	.	115.1	93.3
$CeCl^{2+}$(aq)	−840.6	−798.7	−88.3	.
$CeCl_3$(c)	−1053.5	−977.8	151.	87.4
$CeSO_4^+$(aq)	−1590.8	−1436.3	−71.	.
$Ce(SO_4)_2^-$(aq)	−2493.2	−2190.6	8.	.
$Ce_2(SO_4)_3$(c)	−3954.3	.	.	.
CeN(g)	373.6	.	.	32.22

	$Hf°$ (kJ/mol)	$Gf°$ (kJ/mol)	$S°$ (J/K mol)	$C_P°$ (J/K mol)
LANTHANUM				
La(c)	0.0	0.0	56.9	27.11
La(g)	431.0	393.56	182.38	22.75
La^{3+}(aq)	−707.1	−683.7	−217.6	−13.
La_2O_3(c)	−1793.7	−1705.8	127.32	108.78
$LaF_3 \cdot H_2O$(c)	−1987.4	.	.	.
$LaCl_3$(c)	−1071.1	.	.	108.8
$LaCl_3 \cdot 7H_2O$(c)	−3178.6	−2712.9	462.8	431.0
$LaSO_4^+$(aq)	−1602.9	−1448.5	−84.	.
$La(SO_4)_2^-$(aq)	−2507.1	−2203.6	−13.	.
$La_2(SO_4)_3$(c)	−3941.3	.	.	280.
PLUTONIUM				
Pu(g)	.	.	.	.
Pu(c)	0.0	0.0	(50.6)	.
Pu^{3+}(aq)	−593.3	−587.9	−163.	.
Pu^{4+}(aq)	−540.2	−494.5	−364.	.
PuO_2(c)	−1050.	.	.	.
PuF_3(aq)	−1567.	.	.	.
$PuCl_3$(c)	−962.3	−895.	(159.)	.
URANIUM				
U(c)	0.0	0.0	50.21	27.66
U(g)	535.6	491.2	199.77	23.69
U^{3+}(aq)	−489.1	−475.4	−192.	.
U^{4+}(aq)	−591.2	−531.0	−410.	.
UO_2(c)	−1084.9	−1031.7	77.03	63.60
UO_2^{2+}(aq)	−1019.6	−953.5	−97.5	.
UO_3(c, gamma)	−1223.8	−1145.9	96.11	81.67
U_3O_8(c, alpha)	−3574.8	−3369.7	282.59	238.36
UF_3(c)	−1502.1	−1433.4	123.43	95.10
UF_4(c)	−1914.2	−1823.3	151.67	116.02
UF_5(c, alpha)	−2075.3	−1968.5	199.6	.
UF_6(c)	−2197.0	−2068.5	227.6	166.77
UCl_3(c)	−866.5	−799.1	159.0	102.5
UCl_4(c)	−1019.2	−930.0	197.1	122.01
UCl_5(c)	−1059.	−950.	242.7	.
UCl_6(c)	−1091.	−962.	285.8	175.7
$UO_2SO_4 \cdot 3H_2O$(c)	−2754.3	−2417.7	268.	282.8
$UO_2(NO_3)_2 \cdot 6H_2O$(c)	−3168.5	−2585.3	505.64	466.9
$UO_2(OAc)_2 \cdot 2H_2O$(c)	−2558.9	.	.	.

	H_f° (kJ/mol)	G_f° (kJ/mol)	S° (J/K mol)	C_P° (J/K mol)
THORIUM				
Th(c)	0.0	0.0	53.39	27.32
Th(g)	598.3	557.53	190.15	20.79
Th^{4+}(aq)	−769.0	−705.1	−422.6	·
ThO_2(c)	−1226.4	−1168.77	65.23	61.76
$Th(OH)_4$(c)	−1764.	−1586.	·	·
ThF_4(c)	−2091.6	−1997.0	142.05	110.54
$ThCl_4$(c)	−1186.6	−1094.5	190.4	·
$Th(SO_4)_2$(c)	−2542.6	−2310.3	159.0	·
$Th(NO_3)_4 \cdot 4H_2O$(c)	−2704.8	·	·	·
BERYLLIUM				
Be(c)	0.0	0.0	9.50	16.44
Be(g)	324.3	286.6	136.27	20.86
Be^{2+}(aq)	−382.8	−379.73	−129.7	·
BeO(c, alpha)	609.6	−580.03	14.14	25.62
BeF_2(c, quartz)	−1026.8	−979.4	53.35	51.84
$BeCl_2$(c, alpha)	−490.4	−445.6	82.68	64.85
$BeCl_2$(c, beta)	495.8	−448.9	75.81	62.43
MAGNESIUM				
Mg(c)	0.0	0.0	32.68	24.89
Mg(g)	147.70	113.10	148.65	20.79
Mg^{2+}(aq)	−466.85	−454.8	−138.1	·
MgO(c)	−601.70	−569.43	26.94	37.15
MgH_2(c)	−75.3	−35.9	31.09	35.35
$Mg(OH)_2$(c)	−924.54	−833.51	63.18	77.03
MgF_2(c)	−1123.4	−1070.2	57.24	61.59
$MgCl_2$(c)	−641.32	−591.79	89.62	71.38
$MgCl_2 \cdot 6H_2O$(c)	−2499.02	−2114.64	366.1	314.06
$Mg(ClO_4)_2$(c)	−568.90	·	·	·
$Mg(ClO_4)_2 \cdot 2H_2O$(c)	−1218.8	·	·	·
$MgSO_4$(c)	−1284.9	−1170.6	91.6	96.48
$MgSO_4 \cdot 7H_2O$(c)	−3388.71	−2871.5	372.	·
Mg_3N_2(c)	−460.7	·	·	·
$Mg(NO_3)_2$(c)	−790.65	−589.4	164.0	141.92
$MgCO_3$c)	−1095.8	−1012.1	65.7	75.52
$MgSiO_3$(c)	−1549.00	−1462.09	67.74	81.38
$MgNH_4PO_4 \cdot 6H_2O$(c)	−3681.9	·	·	·

	$Hf°$ (kJ/mol)	$Gf°$ (kJ/mol)	$S°$ (J/K mol)	$Cp°$ (J/K mol)
CALCIUM				
$Ca(c)$	0.0	0.0	41.42	25.31
$Ca(g)$	178.2	144.3	154.88	20.79
$Ca^{2+}(aq)$	−542.83	−553.58	−53.1	.
$CaO(c)$	−635.09	−604.03	39.75	42.80
$CaH_2(c)$	−186.2	−147.2	42.	.
$Ca(OH)_2(c)$	−986.09	−898.49	83.39	87.49
$CaF_2(c)$	−1219.6	−1167.3	68.87	67.03
$CaCl_2(c)$	−795.8	−748.1	104.6	72.59
$CaCl_2·2H_2O(c)$	−1402.9		.	.
$CaBr_2(c)$	−683.8	−663.6	130.	75.04
$CaI_2(c)$	−533.5	−528.9	142.	77.15
$CaSO_3(c)$	.	.	101.38	91.71
$CaSO_3·1/2H_2O(c)$	−1311.7	−1199.23	121.3	.
$CaSO_4(c, anhydrite)$	−1434.11	−1321.79	106.7	99.66
$CaSO_4·1/2H_2O(c, alpha)$	−1576.74	−1436.74	130.5	119.41
$CaSO_4·2H_2O(c)$	−2022.63	−1797.28	194.1	186.02
$Ca(NO_3)_2(c)$	−938.39	−743.07	193.3	149.37
$Ca_3(PO_4)_2(c, beta)$	−4120.8	−3884.7	236.0	227.82
$CaHPO_4(c)$	−1814.39	−1681.18	111.38	110.04
$CaHPO_4·2H_2O(c)$	−2403.6	−2154.8	189.5	197.1
$CaC_2(c)$	−59.8	−64.9	69.96	62.72
$CaCO_3(c, calcite)$	−1206.92	−1128.79	92.9	81.88
$CaCO_3(c, aragonite)$	−1207.13	−1127.75	88.7	81.25
$CaC_2O_4·H_2O(c)$	−1674.86	−1513.87	156.5	152.80
$Ca(OAc)_2(c)$	−1479.5	.	.	.
$Ca(OAc)_2·H_2O(c)$	−1772.3	.	.	.
$Ca(EDTA)^{2-}(aq)$	.	.	.	.
$CaSiO_3(c)$	−1634.94	−1549.66	81.92	85.27
STRONTIUM				
$Sr(c)$	0.0	0.0	52.3	26.4
$Sr(g)$	164.4	130.9	164.62	20.86
$Sr^{2+}(aq)$	−545.80	−559.48	32.6	.
$SrO(c)$	−592.0	−561.9	54.4	45.02
$Sr(OH)_2(c)$	−968.89	−881.10	97.07	74.89
$SrF_2(c)$	−1210.3	−1165.8	82.13	70.00
$SrCl_2(c)$	−828.9	−781.1	114.85	75.60
$SrBr_2(c)$	−717.6	−697.1	135.10	75.35
$SrI_2(c)$	−561.49	−557.70	159.12	77.95
$SrSO_4(c)$	−1453.1	−1340.9	117.	.
$Sr(NO_3)_2(c)$	−978.22	−780.02	194.56	149.91
$SrCO_3(c)$	−1220.1	−1140.1	97.1	81.42
$SrC_2O_4(c)$	−1370.7		.	.

	$H_f°$ (kJ/mol)	$G_f°$ (kJ/mol)	$S°$ (J/K mol)	$C_P°$ (J/K mol)
BARIUM				
Ba(c)	0.0	0.0	62.8	28.07
Ba(g)	180.	146.	170.24	20.86
Ba^{2+}(aq)	−537.64	−560.77	9.6	·
BaO(c)	−553.5	−525.1	72.42	47.78
BaO_2(c)	−634.3	(−568.2)	·	66.9
$Ba(OH)_2$(c)	−944.7	·	·	·
$Ba(OH)_2 \cdot 8H_2O$(c)	−3342.2	−2792.8	427.	·
BaF_2(c)	−1207.1	−1156.8	96.36	71.21
$BaCl_2$(c)	−858.6	−810.4	123.68	75.14
$BaCl_2.H_2O$(c)	−1160.6	−1055.63	166.9	·
$BaCl_2 \cdot 2H_2O$(c)	−1460.13	−1296.32	202.9	161.96
$BaSO_3$(c)	−1179.5	·	·	·
$BaSO_4$(c)	−1473.2	−1362.2	132.2	101.75
$Ba(NO_3)_2$(c)	−992.07	−796.72	214.	151.4
$BaCO_3$(c)	−1216.3	−1137.6	112.1	85.35
BaC_2O_4(c)	−1368.6	·	·	·
$BaCrO_4$(c)	−1446.0	−1345.22	158.6	·
LITHIUM				
Li(c)	0.0	0.0	29.12	24.77
Li(g)	159.37	126.66	138.77	20.86
Li^+(aq)	−278.49	−293.31	13.4	68.6
Li_2(g)	215.9	174.4	196.94	36.10
Li_2O(c)	−597.94	−561.18	37.57	54.10
LiH(c)	−90.54	−68.35	20.01	27.87
LiH(g)	139.2	116.47	170.90	29.73
LiOH(c)	−484.93	−438.95	42.80	49.66
$LiOH \cdot H_2O$(c)	−788.01	−680.95	71.21	79.50
LiF(c)	−615.97	−587.71	35.65	41.59
LiCl(c)	−408.61	−384.37	59.33	47.99
LiBr(c)	−351.21	−342.00	74.27	48.92
LiI(c)	−270.41	−270.29	86.78	51.04
Li_2SO_4(c)	−1436.49	−1321.70	115.1	117.57
Li_2CO_3(c)	−1215.9	−1132.06	90.37	99.12
$LiBH_4$(c)	−190.8	−125.0	75.86	82.55
$LiAlH_4$(c)	−116.3	−44.7	78.74	83.18

	$Hf°$ (kJ/mol)	$Gf°$ (kJ/mol)	$S°$ (J/K mol)	$Cp°$ (J/K mol)
SODIUM				
Na(c)	0.0	0.0	51.21	28.24
Na(g)	107.32	79.76	153.71	20.79
Na^+(aq)	−240.12	−261.90	59.0	46.4
Na_2(g)	142.05	103.94	230.23	37.57
NaO_2(c)	−260.2	−218.4	115.9	72.13
Na_2O(c)	−414.22	−375.46	75.06	69.12
Na_2O_2(c)	−510.87	−447.67	95.0	89.24
NaH(c)	−56.28	−33.46	40.02	36.40
NaH(g)	130.25	108.85	188.38	30.29
NaOH(c)	−425.61	−379.49	64.45	59.54
$NaOH·H_2O$(c)	−734.54	−629.34	99.50	90.17
NaF(c)	−573.65	−543.49	51.46	46.86
NaCl(c)	−411.15	−384.38	72.13	50.50
$NaClO_4$(c)	−383.30	−254.85	142.3	111.
NaBr(c)	361.06	−348.98	86.82	51.38
NaI(c)	−287.78	−286.06	98.53	52.09
Na_2S(c)	−364.8	−349.8	83.7	79.45
Na_2SO_3(c)	−1100.8	−1012.5	145.94	120.25
Na_2SO_4(c)	−1387.08	−1270.16	149.58	128.20
$Na_2SO_4·10H_2O$(c)	−4327.26	−3646.85	592.0	587.4
$Na_2S_2O_3$(c)	−1123.0	−1028.0	155.	.
$NaHSO_3$(c)	.	.	.	.
$NaHSO_4$(c)	−1125.5	−992.8	113.0	.
NaN_3(c)	21.71	93.81	96.86	76.61
$NaNO_2$(c)	−358.65	−284.55	103.8	.
$NaNO_3$(c)	−467.85	−367.00	116.52	92.88
$NaNH_2$(c)	−123.8	−64.0	76.90	66.15
$NaH_2PO_4·H_2O$(c)	−1833.0	.	.	.
$Na_2HPO_4·7H_2O$(c)	−3821.7	−3279.8	434.59	.
Na_3PO_4(c)	−1917.40	−1788.80	173.80	153.47
Na_2CO_3(c)	−1130.68	−1044.44	134.98	112.30
$Na_2CO_3·H_2O$(c)	−1431.26	−1285.31	168.11	145.60
$Na_2C_2O_4$(c)	−1318.4	.	(155.)	412.
$NaHCO_3$(c)	−950.81	−851.0	101.7	87.61
$NaOAc·3H_2O$(c)	−1603.3	−1328.6	243.	.
$Na_2EDTA·2H_2O$(c)	.	.	.	.
NaCN(c)	−87.49	−76.43	115.60	70.37
Na_2SiO_3(c)	−1554.90	−1462.80	113.85	111.9
Na_2SiF_6(c)	−2909.6	−2754.2	207.1	187.07
$NaBH_4$(c)	−188.61	−123.86	101.29	86.78

	$H_f°$ (kJ/mol)	$G_f°$ (kJ/mol)	$S°$ (J/K mol)	$C_P°$ (J/K mol)
POTASSIUM				
K(c)	0.0	0.0	64.18	29.58
K(g)	89.24	60.59	160.34	20.79
K^+(g)	514.00	480.95	154.58	20.79
K^+(aq)	−252.38	−283.27	102.5	21.8
K_2(g)	123.7	87.5	149.73	37.89
KO_2(c)	−284.93	−239.4	116.7	77.53
K_2O(c)	−363.17	−322.09	94.1	83.68
K_2O_2(c)	−494.1	−425.1	102.1	115.
KH(g)	130.	113.	192.41	31.05
KOH(c)	−424.76	−379.08	788.9	64.9
KF(c)	−567.27	−537.75	66.57	49.04
$KF·2H_2O$(c)	−1163.62	−1021.49	155.2	·
KHF_2(c, alpha)	−927.68	−859.68	104.27	76.94
KCl(c)	−436.75	−409.14	82.59	51.30
KCl(g)	−214.14	−233.0	239.10	36.48
$KClO_3$(c)	−397.73	−296.25	143.1	100.25
$KClO_4$(c)	−432.75	−303.9	151.0	112.38
KBr(c)	−393.80	−380.66	95.90	52.30
$KBrO_3$(c)	−360.24	−271.16	149.16	105.19
KI(c)	−327.90	−324.89	106.32	52.93
KI_3(c)	−328.0	−308.	·	·
KIO_3(c)	−501.37	−418.35	151.46	106.48
K_2SO_4(c)	−1437.79	−1321.37	175.56	131.46
$K_2S_2O_8$(c)	−1916.1	−1697.3	278.7	213.09
KNO_3(c)	−494.63	−394.86	133.05	96.40
KH_2PO_4(c)	−1568.33	−1415.85	134.85	116.57
K_2CO_3(c)	−1151.02	−1063.5	155.52	114.43
$K_2C_2O_4$(c)	−1346.8	−1241.	·	·
$KHCO_3$(c)	−963.2	−863.5	115.5	·
KCN(c)	−113.0	−101.86	128.49	66.27
KSCN(c)	−200.16	−178.31	124.26	88.53
$KAl(SO_4)_2$(c)	−2470.2	−2240.0	204.6	192.97
$KAl(SO_4)_2·12H_2O$(c)	−6061.8	−5141.0	687.4	651.03
$K_3Fe(CN)_6$(c)	−249.8	−129.6	426.06	·
$K_4Fe(CN)_6$(c)	−594.1	−453.0	418.8	332.21
$K_4Fe(CN)_6·3H_2O$(c)	−1466.5	−1168.8	593.7	482.42
K_2PtCl_4(c)	−1054.4	·	·	180.3
$KMnO_4$(c)	−837.2	−737.6	171.71	117.57
K_2CrO_4(c)	−1403.7	−1295.7	200.12	145.98
$KCr(SO_4)_2·12H_2O$(c)	−5777.3	−4870.	·	·

	$H_f°$ (kJ/mol)	$G_f°$ (kJ/mol)	$S°$ (J/K·mol)	$C_P°$ (J/K mol)
RUBIDIUM				
Rb(c)	0.0	0.0	76.78	31.06
Rb(g)	80.88	53.06	169.09	20.79
Rb$^+$(aq)	−251.17	−284.98	121.50	.
Rb$_2$O(c)	−339.	−291.	.	.
RbOH(c)	−418.19	−364.	.	.
RbF(c)	−557.7	.	(114.)	.
RbCl(c)	−435.35	−407.80	95.90	52.38
RbBr(c)	−394.59	−381.79	109.96	52.84
RbI(c)	−333.80	−328.86	118.41	53.18
Rb$_2$SO$_4$(c)	−1435.61	−1316.89	197.44	134.06
RbNO$_3$(c)	−495.05	−395.78	147.3	102.1
CESIUM				
Cs(c)	0.0	0.0	85.23	32.17
Cs(g)	76.07	49.12	175.60	20.79
Cs(l)	2.08	0.02	92.07	32.44
Cs$^+$(aq)	−258.28	−292.02	133.05	−10.5
Cs$_2$O(c)	−345.77	−308.14	146.86	75.98
CsOH(c)	−417.73	−370.72	98.74	67.87
CsF(c)	−553.5	−525.5	92.80	51.09
CsCl(c)	−443.04	−414.53	101.17	52.47
CsBr(c)	−405.81	−391.41	113.05	52.93
CsI(c)	−346.60	−340.58	123.05	52.80
Cs$_2$SO$_4$(c)	−1443.02	−1323.58	211.92	134.89
CsNO$_3$(c)	−505.97	−406.54	155.2	.
CsAl(SO$_4$)$_2$·12H$_2$O(c)	−6094.8	−5167.4	686.09	614.6

INDEX

Putnam, were almost alone, attending the Public Declamations. —
A dirty little Scoundrel from the
Junior-Class had parodied, and altered,
into a very insulting piece, against
the Medical Students; one of Peter
Pindar's Blackguard Poems. — He ascend-
ed the Stage, turned himself towards,
and directly addressed us. The Language was too abusive, and indecent,
to have been uttered, in a Brothel;
and yet Doctor John Smith, the Pro-
fessor of Languages, and an Ordained
Clergyman, sat very composedly, and
listened to it. He even approved it
when he had finished. I afterwards
found, that he looked to see who
was present, when the Speaker
begun; and discovering but one or two,